Classic Acoustic Playlist 2

Published 2004

Griffin House, 161 Hammersmith Road, London, W6 8BS, England

Editorial and production by Artemis Music Limited
www.artemismusic.com

How to use this book

All the songs in this book have been carefully arranged to sound great on the acoustic guitar. They are in the same keys as the original recordings, and where possible authentic chord voicings have been used, except where an alternative voicing more accurately reflects the overall tonality.

Where a capo was used on the original track, it is indicated at the top of the song under the chord boxes. If you don't have a capo, you can still play the song, but it won't sound in the same key as the original. Where a song is played in an altered tuning, that is also indicated at the top of the song.

Understanding chord boxes

Chord boxes show the neck of your guitar as if viewed head on – the vertical lines represent the strings (low E to high E, from left to right), and the horizontal lines represent the frets.

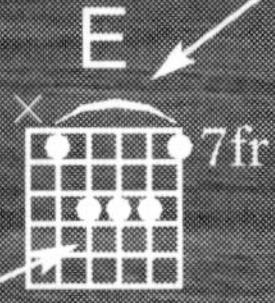

An x above a string means 'don't play this string'.

A o above a string means 'play this open string'.

The black dots show you where to put your fingers.

E

7fr

A curved line joining two dots on the fretboard represents a 'barre'. This means that you flatten one of your fretting fingers (usually the first) so that you hold down all the strings between the two dots, at the fret marked.

A fret marking at the side of the chord box shows you where chords that are played higher up the neck are located.

Tuning your guitar

The best way to tune your guitar is to use an electronic tuner. Alternatively, you can use relative tuning – this will ensure that your guitar is in tune with itself, but won't guarantee that you will be in tune with the original track (or any other musicians).

How to use relative tuning

Fret the low E string at the 5th fret and pluck – compare this with the sound of the open A string. The two notes should be in tune – if not, adjust the tuning of the A string until the two notes match.

Repeat this process for the other strings according to this diagram:

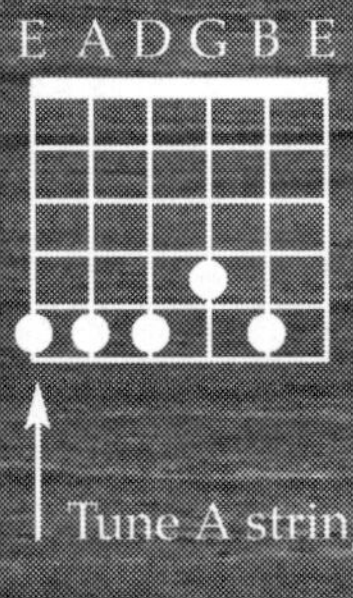

E A D G B E

Tune A string to this note.

Note that the B string should match the note at the 4th fret of the G string, whereas all the other strings match the note at the 5th fret of the string below.

As a final check, ensure that the bottom E string and top E string are in tune with each other.

Contents

All Or Nothing

Words and Music by
STEPHEN MARRIOTT AND RONNIE LANE

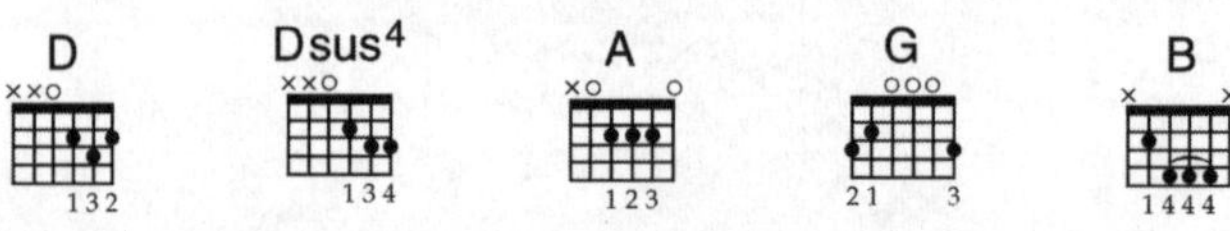

♩ = 112

Intro

```
    D        Dsus4  D    D        Dsus4  D
4/4 ||: /    /    /    /  | /    /    /    /  :||
```

Verse 1

```
A                               D
        I thought you'd listen to my    reasoning
A                           D                        A
        But now I see you don't____ hear a thing.
G                               D
        Trying to make you see
A
        How it's got to be.
G  A   D
Yes it's  alright.
```

Chorus

```
                        B
All or nothing, yeah, yeah,

All or nothing
G
        All or nothing for me.
```

```
Link        D       Dsus4  D    D      Dsus4  D
            | (me) /   /      /   | /   /   /      /   |
             D      Dsus4  D    D      Dsus4  D
            | /   /   /      /   | /   /   /      /   ||


Verse 2     A                                        D
                 Things could work out just like I          want them to, yeah,
            A                                  D                              A
                 If I could have the other          half of you, yeah.
            G
                 You know I would
                 D      A
            Ha! Yeah,     if I only could
            G   A
            Yes it's


Chorus 2    D                          B
            Yeah, all or nothing, oh, yeah,
                                                G
            All or nothing – you hear my children saying

            All or nothing for me.


Link 2      D       Dsus4  D    D      Dsus4  D
            | (me) /   /      /   | /   /   /      /   |
             D      Dsus4  D    D      Dsus4  D
            | /   /   /      /   | /   /   /      /   ||


Verse 3   ||: A                                          D          :|| D  A
                 Ba ba ba ba-da                    ba ba ba-da ba.
            G                                         D
                 I ain't telling you no lies, girl.
            A
                 So don't you sit there and cry, yeah, yeah.
```

Chorus 3 D B
All or nothing, my-my________ yeah,
G
All or nothing, oh,_______________ yeah,

All or nothing.
A
You got to, got to, got to keep on trying, yeah!

Chorus 4 D
All or nothing,
B
All or nothing,
G
Got to keep on working out for me, baby,
A
All or nothing for me, for me, for me,

Come on, children, yeah!

Chorus 5 D B
(with vocal ad lib.) All or nothing, yeah, yeah,

All or nothing
G
All or nothing for me.

Coda
D Dsus^4 D D Dsus^4 D
| (me) / / / | / / / / |
D Dsus^4 D D
| / / / / | / ||

All The Young Dudes

Words and Music by
DAVID BOWIE

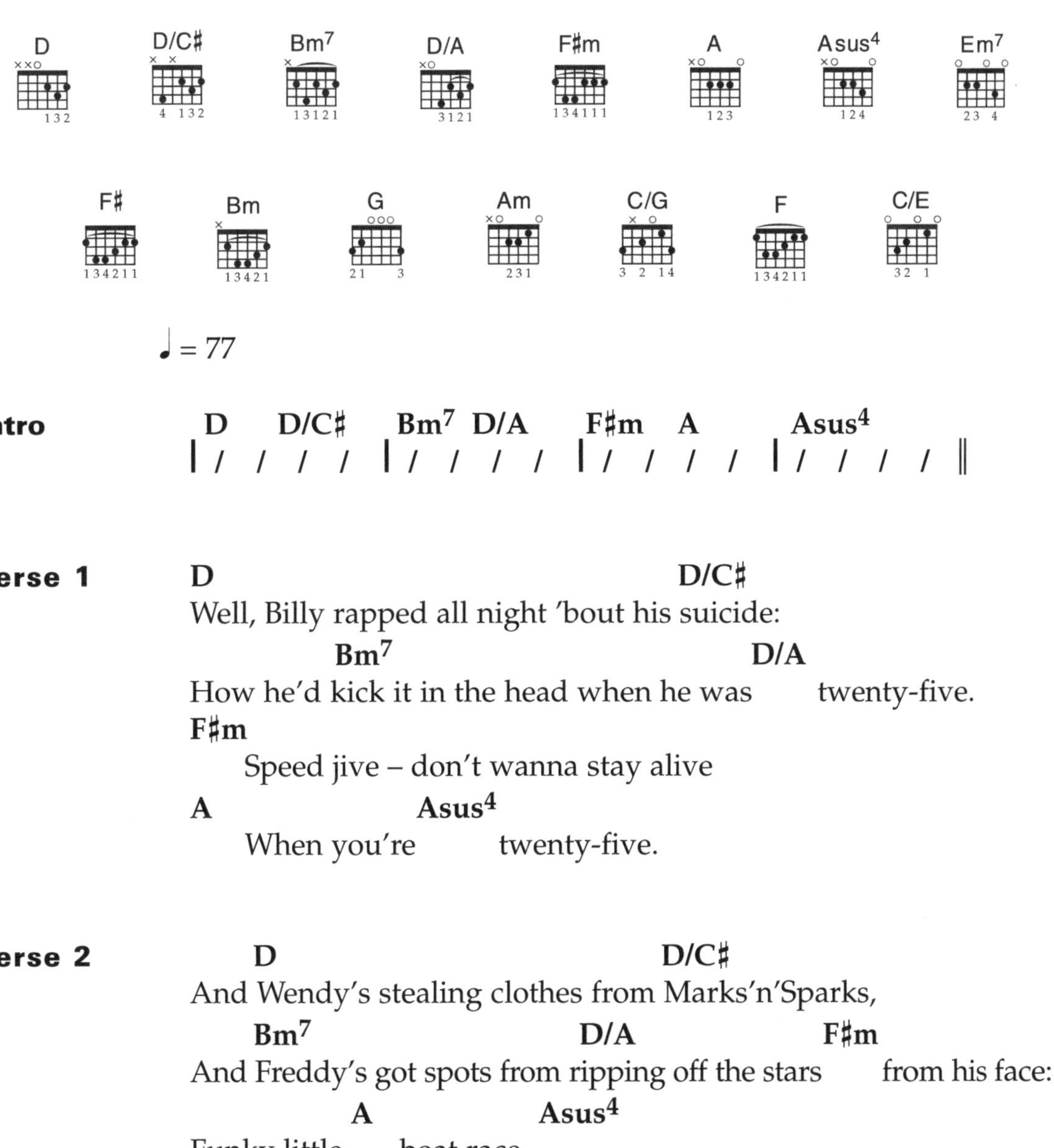

♩ = 77

Intro

D D/C♯ | Bm7 D/A | F♯m A | Asus4 ‖
| / / / / | / / / / | / / / / | / / / / ‖

Verse 1

D D/C♯
Well, Billy rapped all night 'bout his suicide:
Bm7 D/A
How he'd kick it in the head when he was twenty-five.
F♯m
Speed jive – don't wanna stay alive
A Asus4
When you're twenty-five.

Verse 2

D D/C♯
And Wendy's stealing clothes from Marks'n'Sparks,
Bm7 D/A F♯m
And Freddy's got spots from ripping off the stars from his face:
A Asus4
Funky little boat race.

Prechorus

Em^7
The television man is crazy,
F♯ Bm
Saying we're juvenile delinquent wrecks.
G D A Asus^4
Oh man, I need T.V. when I got T. Rex._______

Oh brother, you guessed – I'm a dude, dad.

Chorus

D D/C♯ Bm^7
All the young dudes____ (hey, dudes!)
D/A Am
Carry the news.____ (where are ya?)
C/G F C/E G C A
Boogaloo dudes____ (stand up, c'mon!) carry the news.____
D D/C♯ Bm^7
All the young dudes____ (I wanna hear you)
D/A Am
Carry the news.____ (I wanna see you)
C/G F
Boogaloo dudes____ (and I want to talk to you)
C/E G C A
Carry the news.___
(All of you… now).

Verse 3

D D/C♯
Now Jimmy's looking sweet 'cause he dresses like a queen,
Bm^7 D/A
But he can kick like a mule – it's a real mean team –
F♯m A Asus^4
But we can love, oh yes, we can love.

Verse 4

D D/C♯
And my brother's back at home with his Beatles and his Stones,
Bm^7 D/A
We never got it off on that revolution stuff:
F♯m A Asus^4
What a drag – too many snags.

Prechorus 2

```
                Em7
Well, I've drunk a lot of wine and I'm feeling fine,
         F♯                   Bm
Gonna race some cat to bed.
Bm7  G                      D
Oh, is there concrete all around
                  A          Asus4
Or is it in my      head?_____   Yeah, I'm a dude, yeah.
```

Chorus 2

```
     D    D/C♯             Bm7
||:    All the young dudes____  (hey, dudes!)
     D/A             Am
     Carry the news.____  (where are ya?)
     C/G               F                  C/E        G    C    A
     Boogaloo dudes____  (stand up!)  carry the news.____
     D    D/C♯             Bm7
       All the young dudes____  (I wanna hear ya)
     D/A             Am
     Carry the news.____  (I wanna see you)
     C/G               F
     Boogaloo dudes____  (and I want to relate to you)
     C/E          G   C    A
     Carry the news.___          :||  repeat Chorus to fade, vocal ad lib.
```

Babe I'm Gonna Leave You

Words and Music by
JIMMY PAGE, ROBERT PLANT AND ANNE BREDON

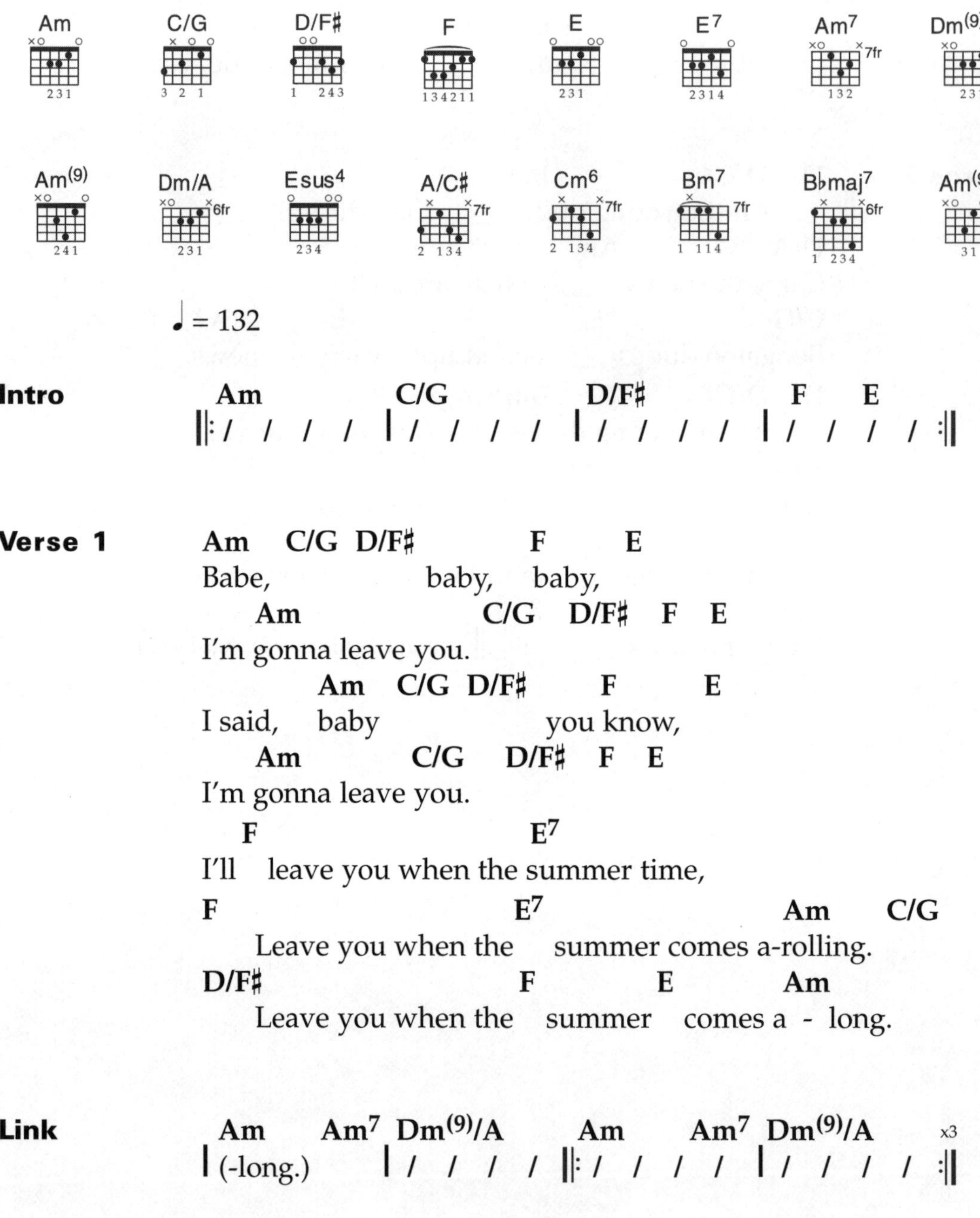

Verse 2

Am C/G D/F♯ F
Babe, babe, babe, babe, babe, babe, ba - by,
E Am C/G D/F♯ F
Baby, I don't wanna leave you, I ain't joking, woman,
E Am C/G D/F♯ F E
I've got to ramble, oh yeah.
Am C/G D/F♯ F E F E^7
Baby, baby, I have really really got to ramble.
F E^7 Am C/G
I can hear it calling me the way it used to do.
D/F♯ F E Am
I can hear it calling me back home.

Link 2

Am Am^7 Dm$^{(9)}$/A Am Am^7 Dm$^{(9)}$/A x3
| (home.) | / / / / ||: / / / / | / / / / :||

Am$^{(9)}$ Am^7 Dm/A x4
||: / / / / | / / / / :||

Chorus

Am C/G D/F♯
Babe, oh!
F E Am C/G D/F♯
Babe, I'm gonna leave you.
F E Am C/G D/F♯ F
Oh__ ba - - - by, you know
E Am C/G D/F♯
I've really got to leave you.
F E F E
Oh I can hear it calling me,
F E Am
I said, don't you hear it calling me the way it used to.

Link 3

Am Am^7 Dm$^{(9)}$/A Am Am^7 Dm$^{(9)}$/A x3
| (used to.) | / / / / ||: / / / / | / / / / :||

Guitar solo

Am C/G D/F♯ F E
||: / / / / | / / / / | / / / / | / / / / :||

Verse 3

Am C/G D/F♯
I know, I know, I know
F E Am C/G D/F♯
I'm never, never, never, never, gonna leave you babe,
F E
But I gotta go away from this place.
Am C/G D/F♯ F
I gotta quit you, yeah.
E Am C/G D/F♯ F E
Oh, baby, baby, baby, baby,
Am C/G D/F♯ F E
Baby, baby, baby, oh.___
Am C/G D/F♯ F E
Don't you hear it calling me.

Verse 4

Am C/G D/F♯ F E Am
Oh, woman, woman,
C/G D/F♯ F E
I know, I know,
Am C/G D/F♯
Feels good to have you back again and I know that one day baby
F E Am C/G
It's gonna really grow, yes it is.
D/F♯ F E Am
We're gonna go walking through in the park every day,
C/G D/F♯ F E
Come what may, everyday,
Am C/G D/F♯ F
My-my, my-my, my-my,
E Am C/G D/F♯ F E
I'm gonna leave you, go away.________

Guitar solo 2

Am C/G D/F♯ F E
| / / / / | / / / / | / / / / | / / / / ‖

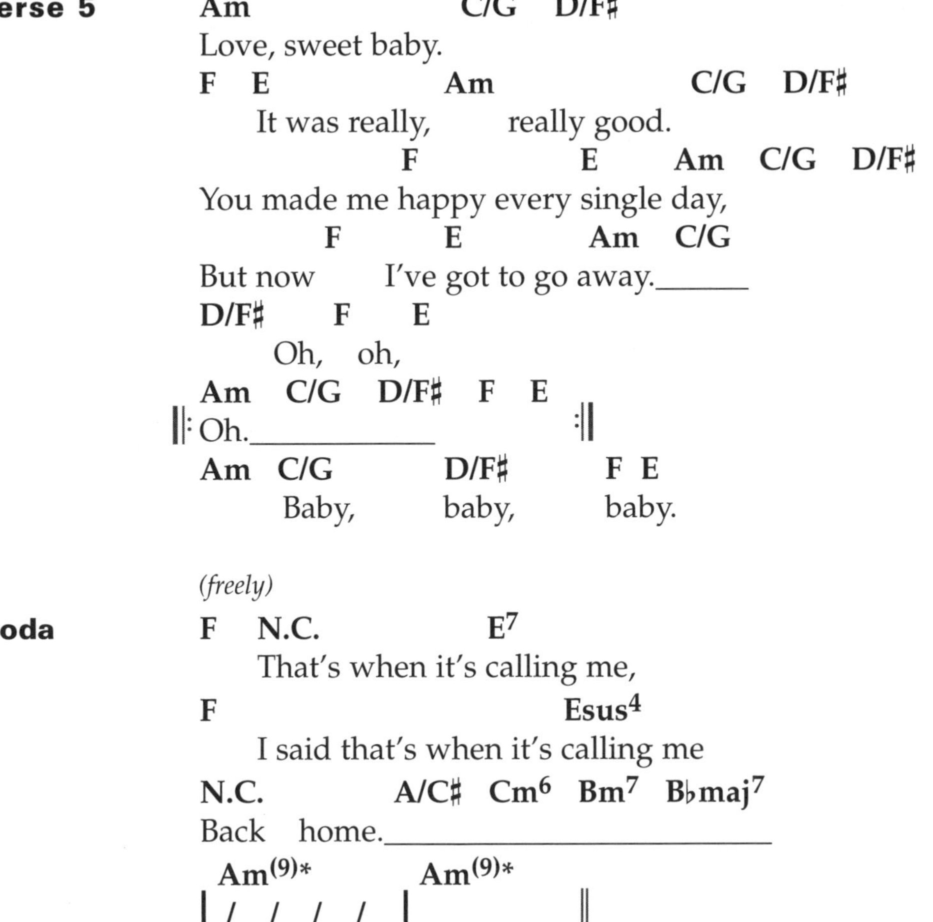

Verse 5

Am C/G D/F♯
Love, sweet baby.
F E Am C/G D/F♯
It was really, really good.
F E Am C/G D/F♯
You made me happy every single day,
F E Am C/G
But now I've got to go away.______
D/F♯ F E
Oh, oh,
Am C/G D/F♯ F E
‖: Oh.___________ :‖
Am C/G D/F♯ F E
Baby, baby, baby.

(freely)

Coda

F N.C. E^7
That's when it's calling me,
F Esus^4
I said that's when it's calling me
N.C. A/C♯ Cm^6 Bm^7 B♭maj^7
Back home.________________________
Am$^{(9)}$* Am$^{(9)}$*
| / / / / | ‖

Birdhouse In Your Soul

Words and Music by
JOHN FLANSBURGH AND JOHN LINNELL

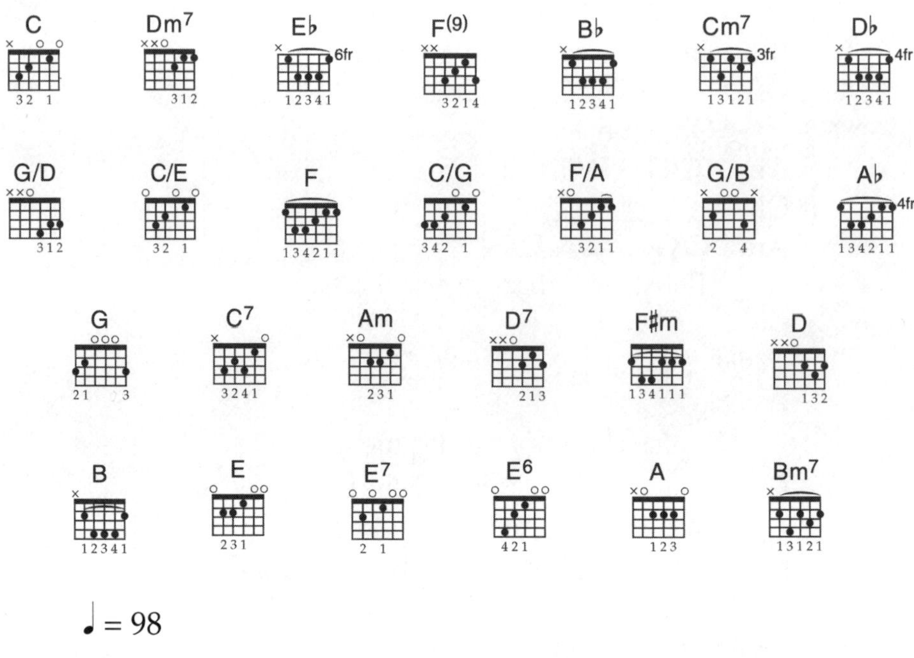

♩ = 98

Verse 1

4/4 **C** **Dm7** **E♭**
I'm your only friend, I'm not your only friend
F(9) **B♭**
But I'm a little glowing friend,
Cm7 **D♭** **G/D** **N.C.**
But really I'm not actually your friend but I am…

Chorus

C **C/E** **F**
Blue canary in the outlet by the light switch
C/G **F/A** **G/B**
Who watches over you?
C **G/B** **F/A** **F** **E♭**
Make a little birdhouse in your soul.

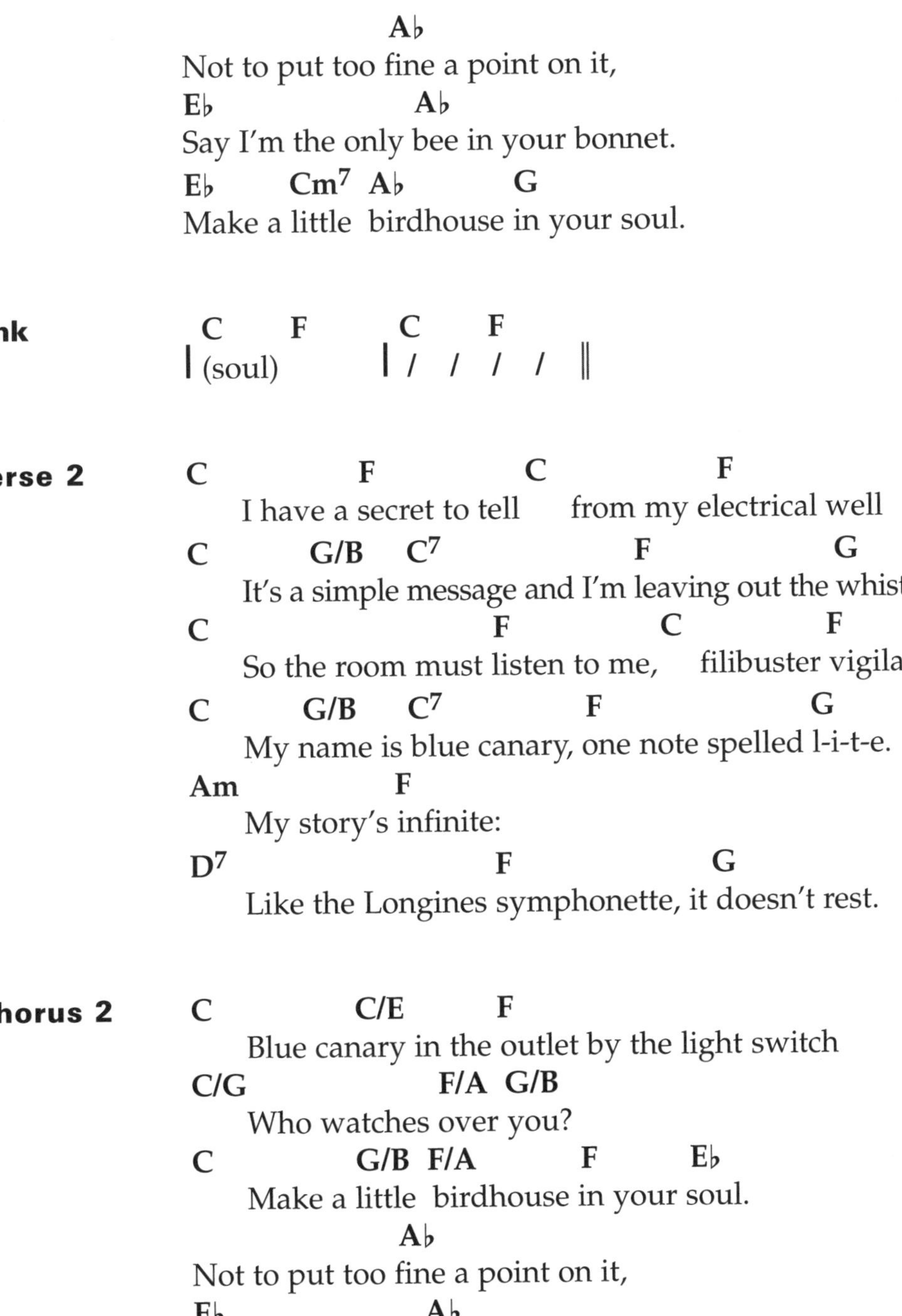

A♭
Not to put too fine a point on it,
E♭ A♭
Say I'm the only bee in your bonnet.
E♭ Cm^7 A♭ G
Make a little birdhouse in your soul.

Link

C F C F
| (soul) | / / / / ||

Verse 2

C F C F
I have a secret to tell from my electrical well
C G/B C^7 F G
It's a simple message and I'm leaving out the whistles and bells.
C F C F
So the room must listen to me, filibuster vigilantly,
C G/B C^7 F G
My name is blue canary, one note spelled l-i-t-e.
Am F
My story's infinite:
D^7 F G
Like the Longines symphonette, it doesn't rest.

Chorus 2

C C/E F
Blue canary in the outlet by the light switch
C/G F/A G/B
Who watches over you?
C G/B F/A F E♭
Make a little birdhouse in your soul.
A♭
Not to put too fine a point on it,
E♭ A♭
Say I'm the only bee in your bonnet.
E♭ Cm^7 A♭ G
Make a little birdhouse in your soul.

Link 2

C F C F
| (soul) | / / / / ||

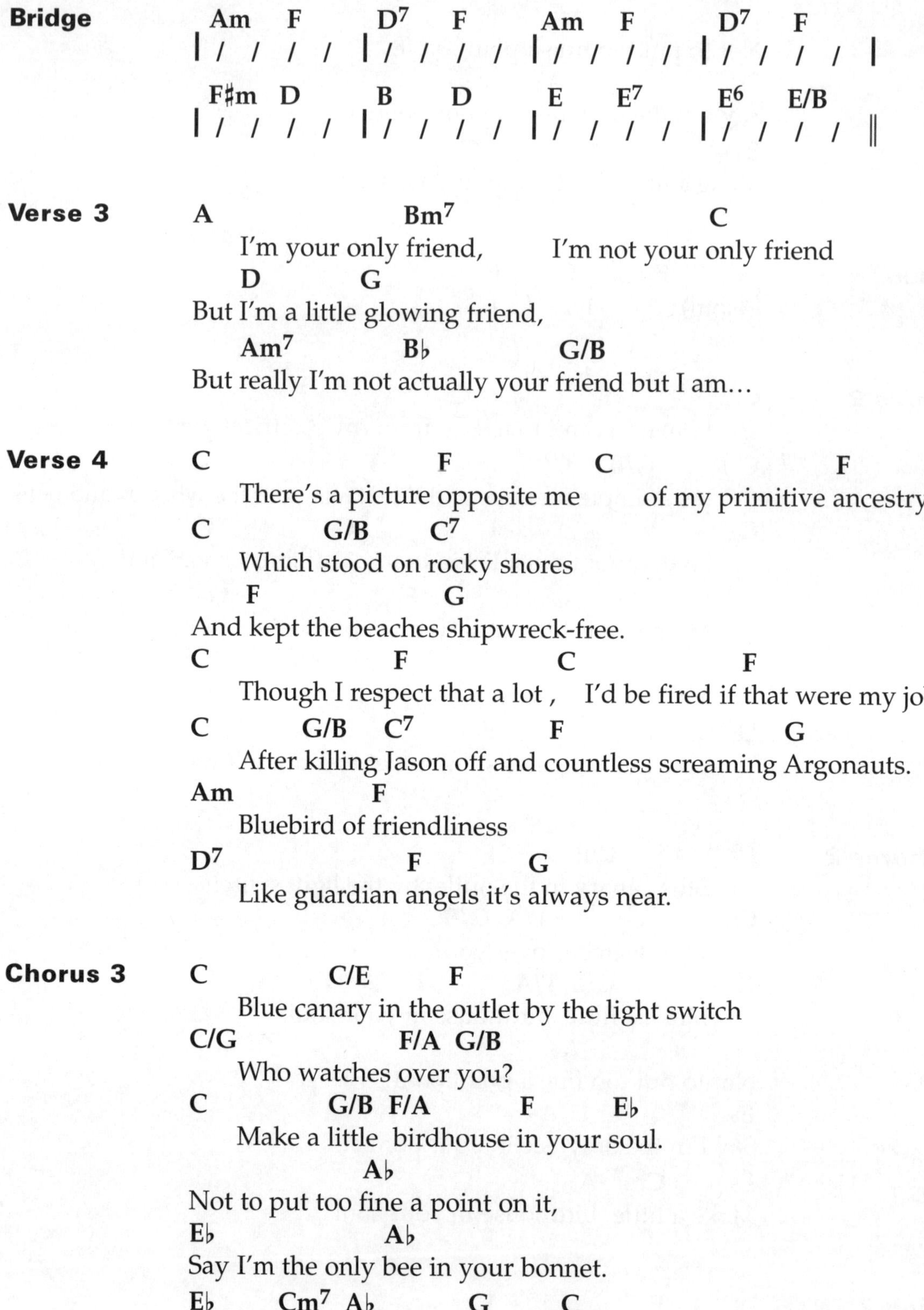

Bridge

```
 Am    F       D7    F       Am    F       D7    F
| / / / / / | / / / / / | / / / / / | / / / / / |
 F♯m   D       B     D       E     E7      E6    E/B
| / / / / / | / / / / / | / / / / / | / / / / / ||
```

Verse 3

```
A                 Bm7                        C
      I'm your only friend,      I'm not your only friend
      D          G
But I'm a little glowing friend,
      Am7             B♭             G/B
But really I'm not actually your friend but I am…
```

Verse 4

```
C                     F               C                F
      There's a picture opposite me       of my primitive ancestry
C          G/B      C7
      Which stood on rocky shores
      F                  G
And kept the beaches shipwreck-free.
C                  F                C                 F
      Though I respect that a lot ,   I'd be fired if that were my job,
C          G/B    C7              F                     G
      After killing Jason off and countless screaming Argonauts.
Am                F
      Bluebird of friendliness
D7                  F          G
      Like guardian angels it's always near.
```

Chorus 3

```
C            C/E        F
      Blue canary in the outlet by the light switch
C/G                 F/A  G/B
      Who watches over you?
C            G/B  F/A          F          E♭
      Make a little  birdhouse in your soul.
                   A♭
Not to put too fine a point on it,
E♭                 A♭
Say I'm the only bee in your bonnet.
E♭        Cm7  A♭          G         C
Make a little  birdhouse in your soul.
```

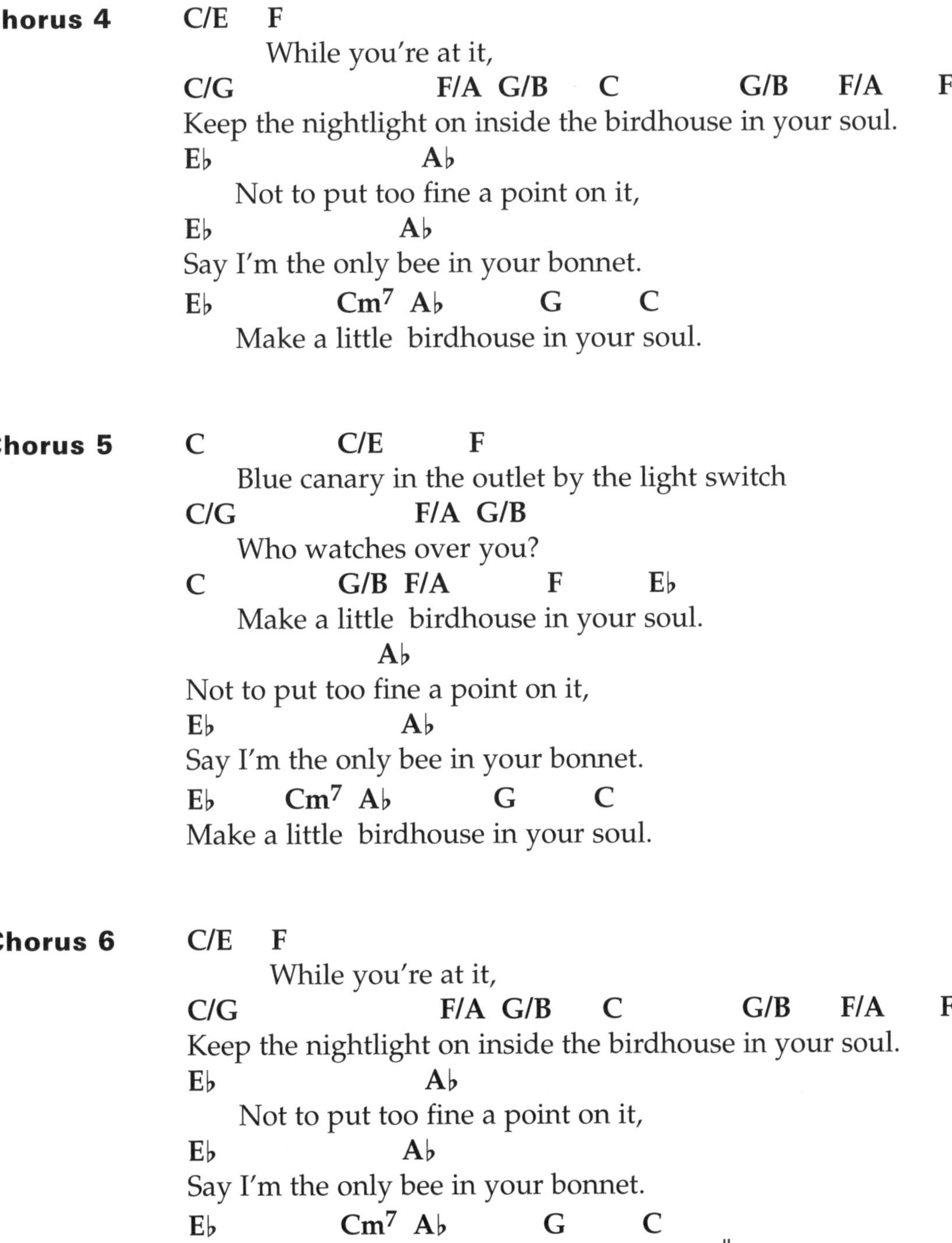

```
Chorus 4    C/E    F
                   While you're at it,
            C/G                     F/A  G/B     C             G/B     F/A     F
            Keep the nightlight on inside the birdhouse in your soul.
            E♭                    A♭
                 Not to put too fine a point on it,
            E♭                  A♭
            Say I'm the only bee in your bonnet.
            E♭             Cm7  A♭          G        C
                 Make a little  birdhouse in your soul.

Chorus 5    C              C/E          F
                 Blue canary in the outlet by the light switch
            C/G                   F/A  G/B
                 Who watches over you?
            C              G/B  F/A          F         E♭
                 Make a little  birdhouse in your soul.
                              A♭
            Not to put too fine a point on it,
            E♭                  A♭
            Say I'm the only bee in your bonnet.
            E♭        Cm7  A♭          G        C
            Make a little  birdhouse in your soul.

Chorus 6    C/E    F
                   While you're at it,
            C/G                     F/A  G/B     C             G/B     F/A     F
            Keep the nightlight on inside the birdhouse in your soul.
            E♭                    A♭
                 Not to put too fine a point on it,
            E♭                  A♭
            Say I'm the only bee in your bonnet.
            E♭             Cm7  A♭          G        C
                 Make a little  birdhouse in your soul. ||
```

Broken Arrow

Words and Music by
ROBBIE ROBERTSON

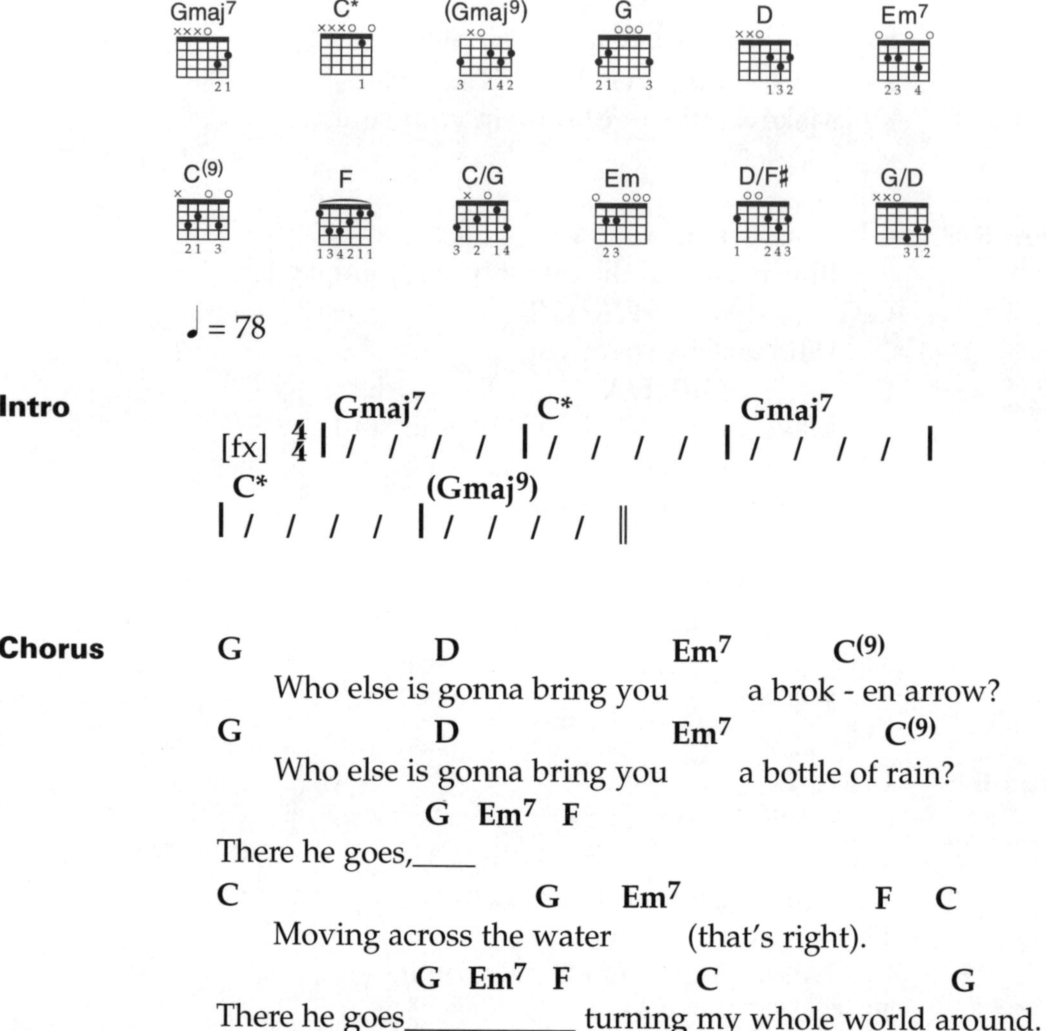

♩ = 78

Intro

```
                Gmaj7              C*                  Gmaj7
[fx] 4/4 | /  /  /  /  | /  /  /  /  | /  /  /  /  |
  C*                (Gmaj9)
| /  /  /  /  | /  /  /  /  ||
```

Chorus

```
G                   D                    Em7          C(9)
     Who else is gonna bring you     a brok - en arrow?
G                   D                    Em7              C(9)
     Who else is gonna bring you     a bottle of rain?
                    G   Em7  F
There he goes,____
C                             G      Em7                    F    C
     Moving across the water       (that's right).
                   G   Em7  F            C                   G
There he goes___________ turning my whole world around.
```

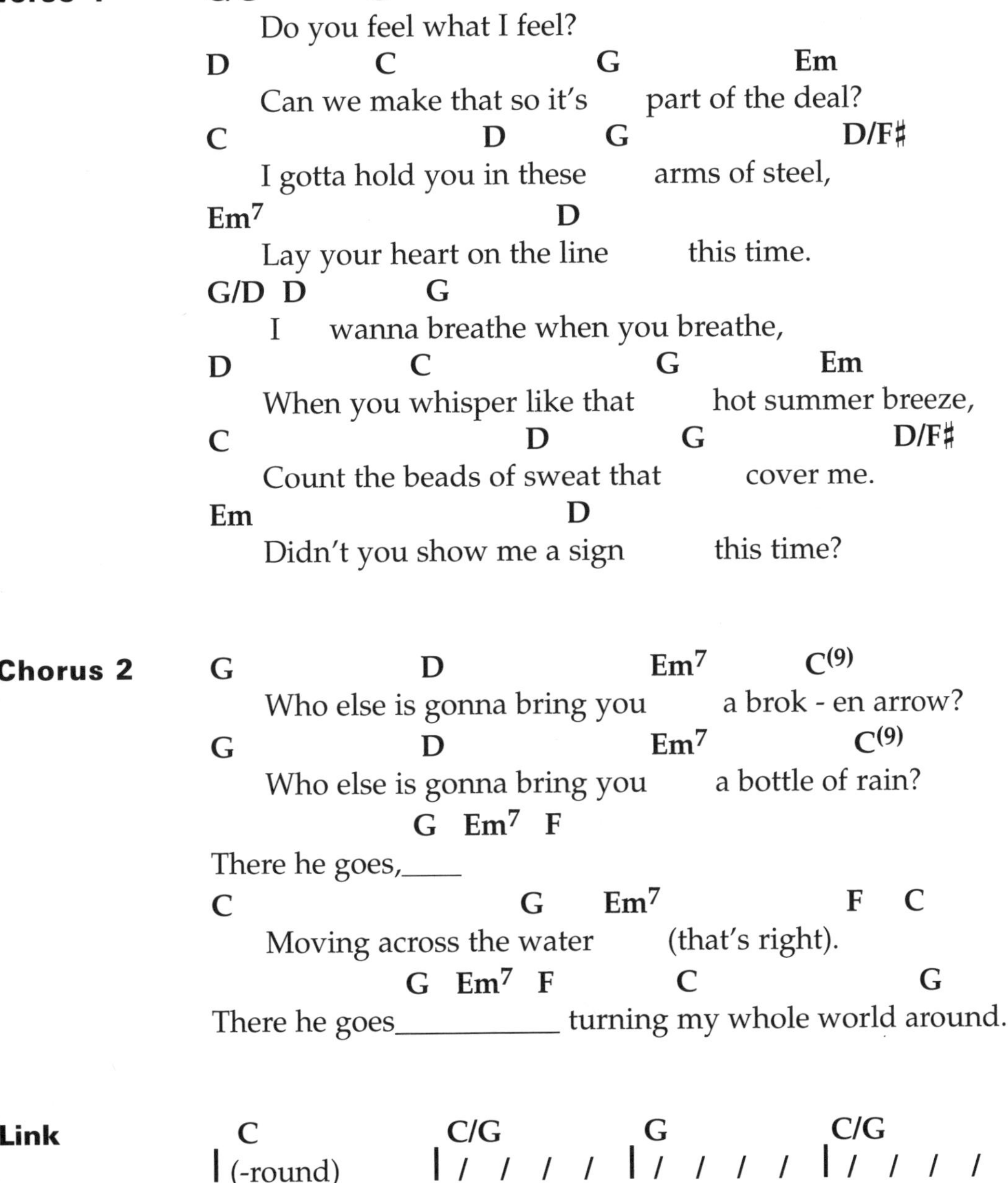

Verse 1

C/G G
Do you feel what I feel?
D C G Em
Can we make that so it's part of the deal?
C D G D/F♯
I gotta hold you in these arms of steel,
Em7 D
Lay your heart on the line this time.
G/D D G
I wanna breathe when you breathe,
D C G Em
When you whisper like that hot summer breeze,
C D G D/F♯
Count the beads of sweat that cover me.
Em D
Didn't you show me a sign this time?

Chorus 2

G D Em7 C(9)
Who else is gonna bring you a brok - en arrow?
G D Em7 C(9)
Who else is gonna bring you a bottle of rain?
G Em7 F
There he goes,____
C G Em7 F C
Moving across the water (that's right).
G Em7 F C G
There he goes__________ turning my whole world around.

Link

C	C/G	G	C/G	
(-round)	/ / / /	/ / / /	/ / / /	‖

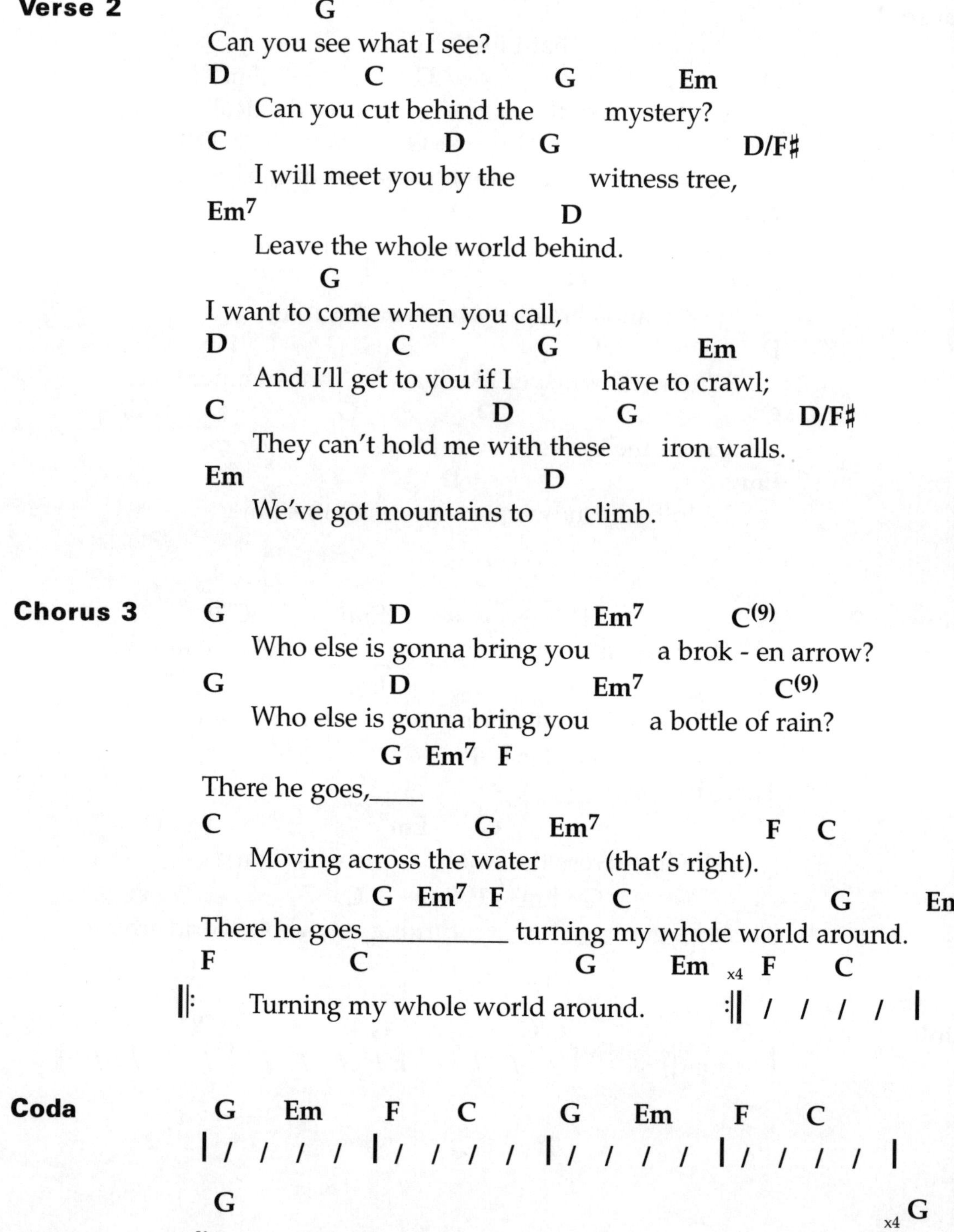
Verse 2
G
Can you see what I see?
D C G Em
Can you cut behind the mystery?
C D G D/F♯
I will meet you by the witness tree,
Em7 D
Leave the whole world behind.
G
I want to come when you call,
D C G Em
And I'll get to you if I have to crawl;
C D G D/F♯
They can't hold me with these iron walls.
Em D
We've got mountains to climb.
Chorus 3
G D Em7 C(9)
Who else is gonna bring you a brok - en arrow?
G D Em7 C(9)
Who else is gonna bring you a bottle of rain?
G Em7 F
There he goes,____
C G Em7 F C
Moving across the water (that's right).
G Em7 F C G Em
There he goes____________ turning my whole world around.
F C G Em x4 F C
Turning my whole world around.
Coda
G Em F C G Em F C
G x4 G

Come On Eileen

Words and Music by
KEVIN ROWLAND, JAMES PATERSON AND KEVIN ADAMS

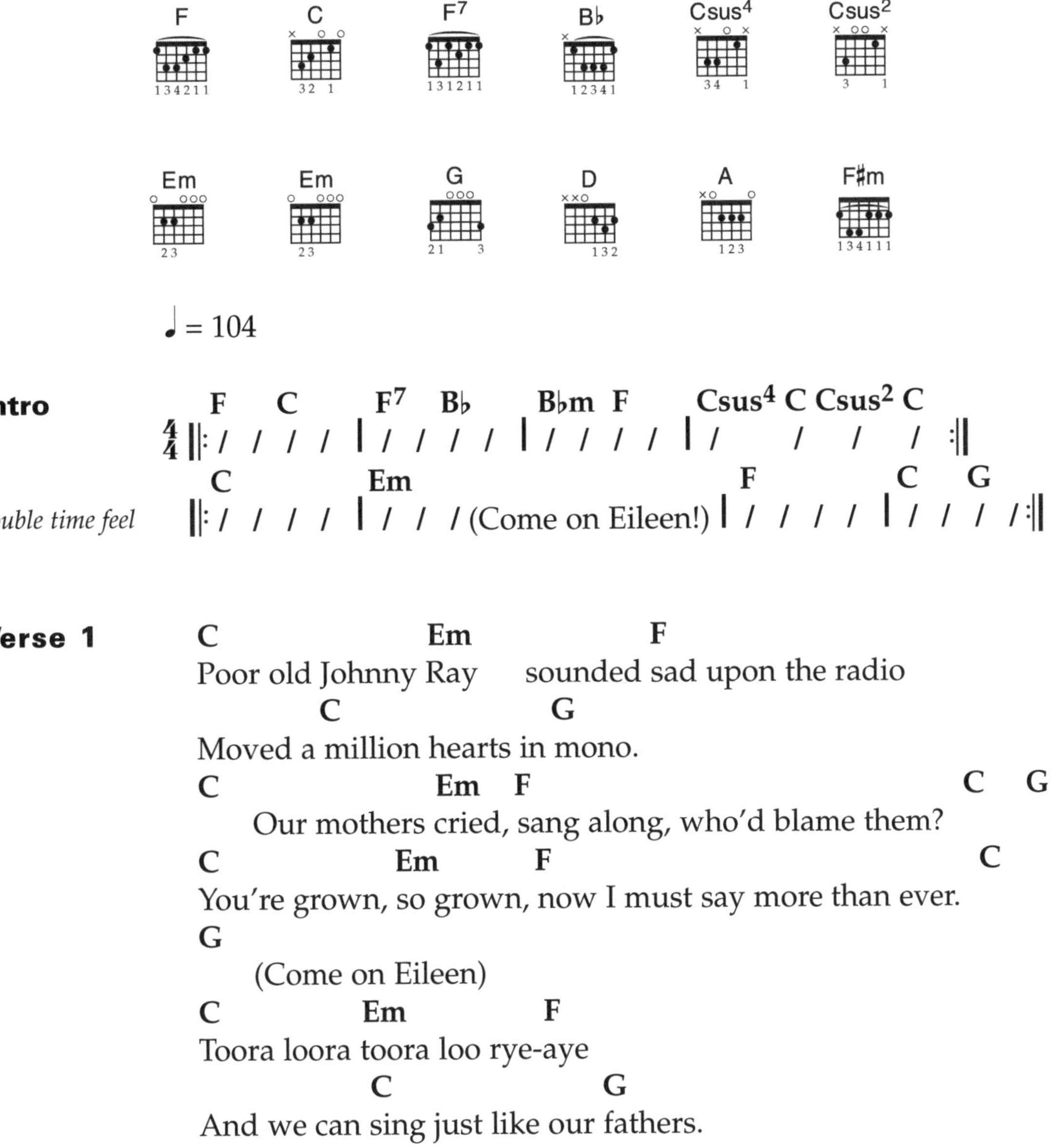

♩ = 104

Intro

F C | F7 B♭ | B♭m F | Csus4 C Csus2 C

4/4 ‖: / / / / | / / / / | / / / / | / / / / :‖

C | Em | F | C G

Double time feel ‖: / / / / | / / / / (Come on Eileen!) | / / / / | / / / / :‖

Verse 1

C Em F
Poor old Johnny Ray sounded sad upon the radio
C G
Moved a million hearts in mono.
C Em F C G
Our mothers cried, sang along, who'd blame them?
C Em F C
You're grown, so grown, now I must say more than ever.
G
(Come on Eileen)
C Em F
Toora loora toora loo rye-aye
C G
And we can sing just like our fathers.

```
Chorus           D                       A
half time feel   Come on Eileen, oh I swear (what he means)
                        Em                  G   A
                 At this moment, you mean everything.
                      D                  A
                 With you in that dress my thoughts, I confess,
                         Em             G    A
                 Verge on dirty, ah come on Eileen.


Link               A
                 | / / / / | / / / / ||
                   C          Em                        F            C    G
double time feel | / / / / | / / / (Come on Eileen!) | / / / / | / / / / |


Verse 2          C                  Em        F
                 These people 'round here: beaten-down eyes

                 Sunk in smoke-dried faces,
                     C                  G
                 So resigned to what their fate is.
                     C                  Em
                 But not us (no, never), no not us (no, never):
                 F                           C    G
                 We are far too young and clever,          remember!
                 C           Em          F
                 Toora loora toora loo rye-aye.
                           C             G
                 Eileen, I'll hum this tune forever.
```

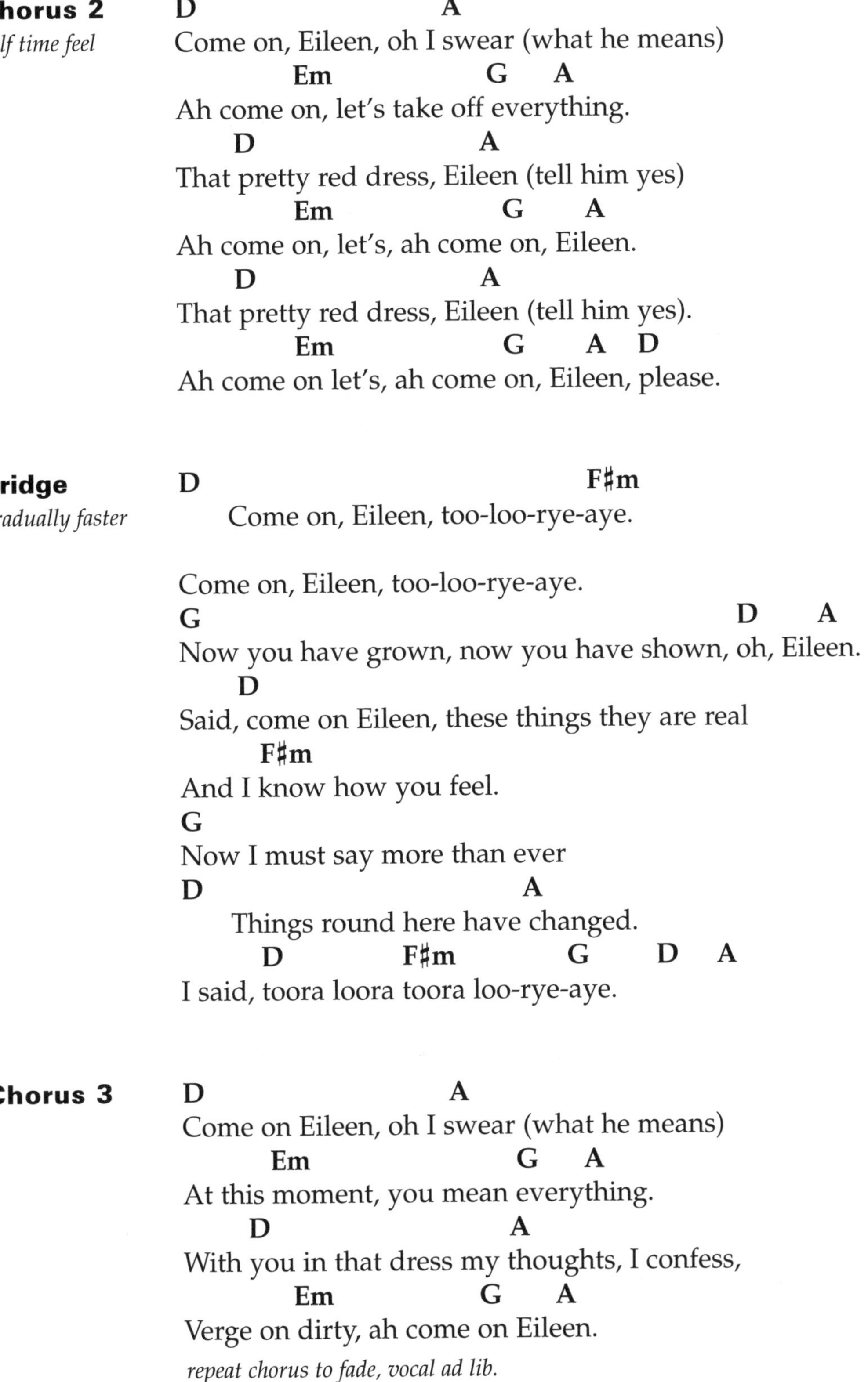

Chorus 2
half time feel

D A
Come on, Eileen, oh I swear (what he means)
Em G A
Ah come on, let's take off everything.
D A
That pretty red dress, Eileen (tell him yes)
Em G A
Ah come on, let's, ah come on, Eileen.
D A
That pretty red dress, Eileen (tell him yes).
Em G A D
Ah come on let's, ah come on, Eileen, please.

Bridge
gradually faster

D F♯m
Come on, Eileen, too-loo-rye-aye.

Come on, Eileen, too-loo-rye-aye.
G D A
Now you have grown, now you have shown, oh, Eileen.
D
Said, come on Eileen, these things they are real
F♯m
And I know how you feel.
G
Now I must say more than ever
D A
Things round here have changed.
D F♯m G D A
I said, toora loora toora loo-rye-aye.

Chorus 3

D A
Come on Eileen, oh I swear (what he means)
Em G A
At this moment, you mean everything.
D A
With you in that dress my thoughts, I confess,
Em G A
Verge on dirty, ah come on Eileen.
repeat chorus to fade, vocal ad lib.

Cat's In The Cradle

Words and Music by
HARRY CHAPIN AND SANDY CHAPIN

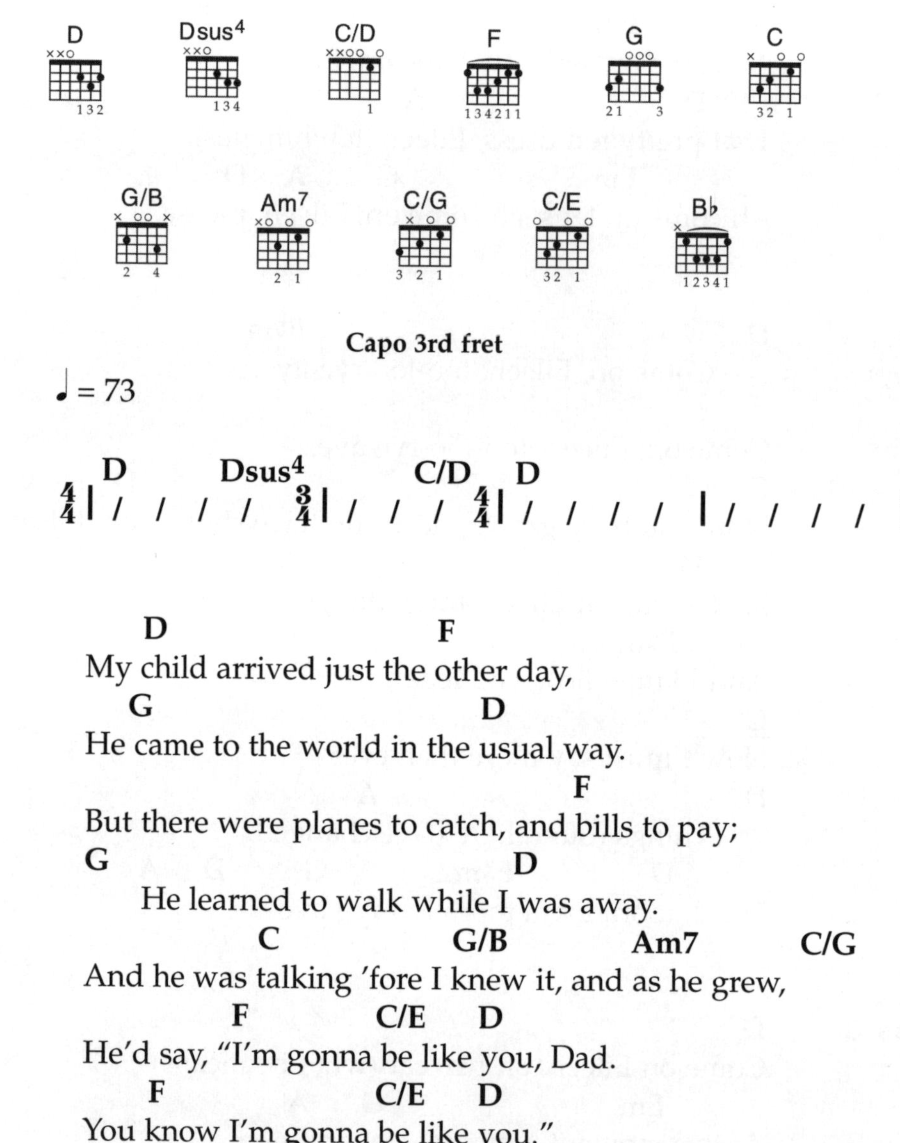

Capo 3rd fret

♩ = 73

Intro

D	Dsus4	C/D	D	
4/4 / / / /	3/4 / / /	4/4 / / / /	/ / / / ‖	

Verse 1

D F
My child arrived just the other day,
G D
He came to the world in the usual way.
F
But there were planes to catch, and bills to pay;
G D
He learned to walk while I was away.
C G/B Am7 C/G
And he was talking 'fore I knew it, and as he grew,
F C/E D
He'd say, "I'm gonna be like you, Dad.
F C/E D
You know I'm gonna be like you."

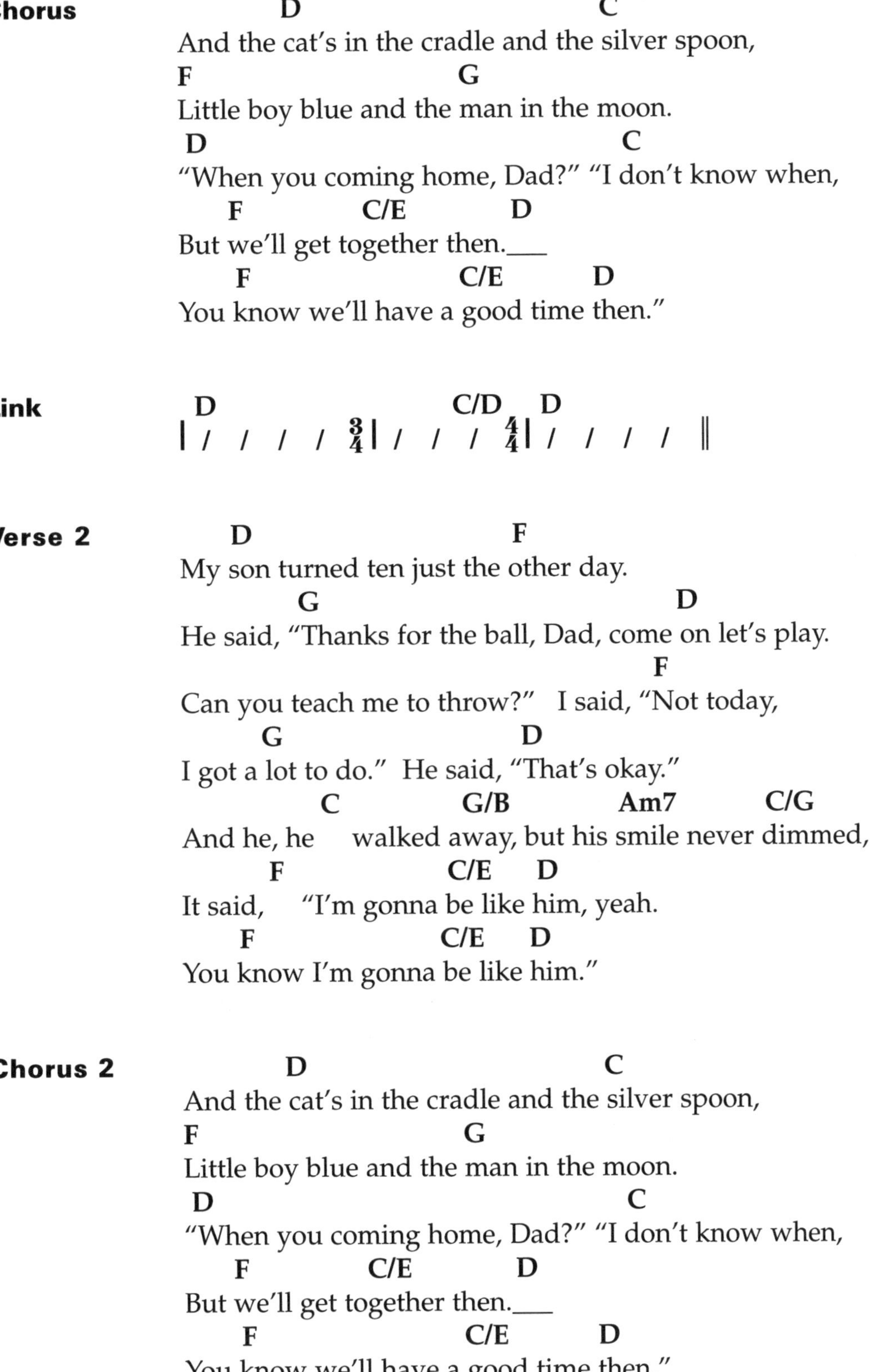

Chorus

D C
And the cat's in the cradle and the silver spoon,
F G
Little boy blue and the man in the moon.
D C
"When you coming home, Dad?" "I don't know when,
F C/E D
But we'll get together then.___
F C/E D
You know we'll have a good time then."

Link

D C/D D
| / / / / $\frac{3}{4}$ | / / / $\frac{4}{4}$ | / / / / ||

Verse 2

D F
My son turned ten just the other day.
G D
He said, "Thanks for the ball, Dad, come on let's play.
F
Can you teach me to throw?" I said, "Not today,
G D
I got a lot to do." He said, "That's okay."
C G/B Am7 C/G
And he, he walked away, but his smile never dimmed,
F C/E D
It said, "I'm gonna be like him, yeah.
F C/E D
You know I'm gonna be like him."

Chorus 2

D C
And the cat's in the cradle and the silver spoon,
F G
Little boy blue and the man in the moon.
D C
"When you coming home, Dad?" "I don't know when,
F C/E D
But we'll get together then.___
F C/E D
You know we'll have a good time then."

Link

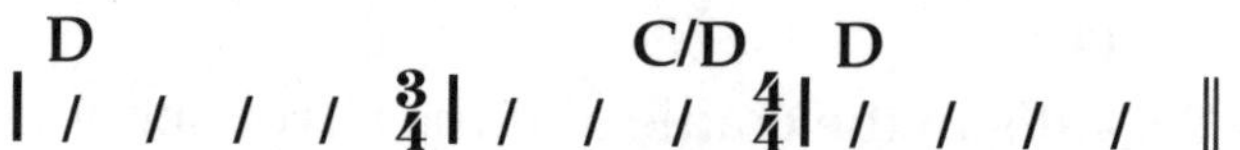

Verse 3

D F
Well, he came from college just the other day,
G D
So much like a man I just had to say
F
"Son, I'm proud of you. Can you sit for a while?"
G D
He shook his head, and he said with a smile,
C G/B Am7 C/G
"What I'd really like, Dad, is to borrow the car keys.
F C/E D
See you later. Can I have them please?"

Chorus 3

D C
And the cat's in the cradle and the silver spoon,
F G
Little boy blue and the man in the moon.
D C
"When you coming home, son?" "I don't know when,
F C/E D
But we'll get together then.___
F C/E D
You know we'll have a good time then."

Link

B♭ C Am7 D B♭ C Am7
| / / / / | / / / / | / / / / |

D
| / / / / | / / / / ||

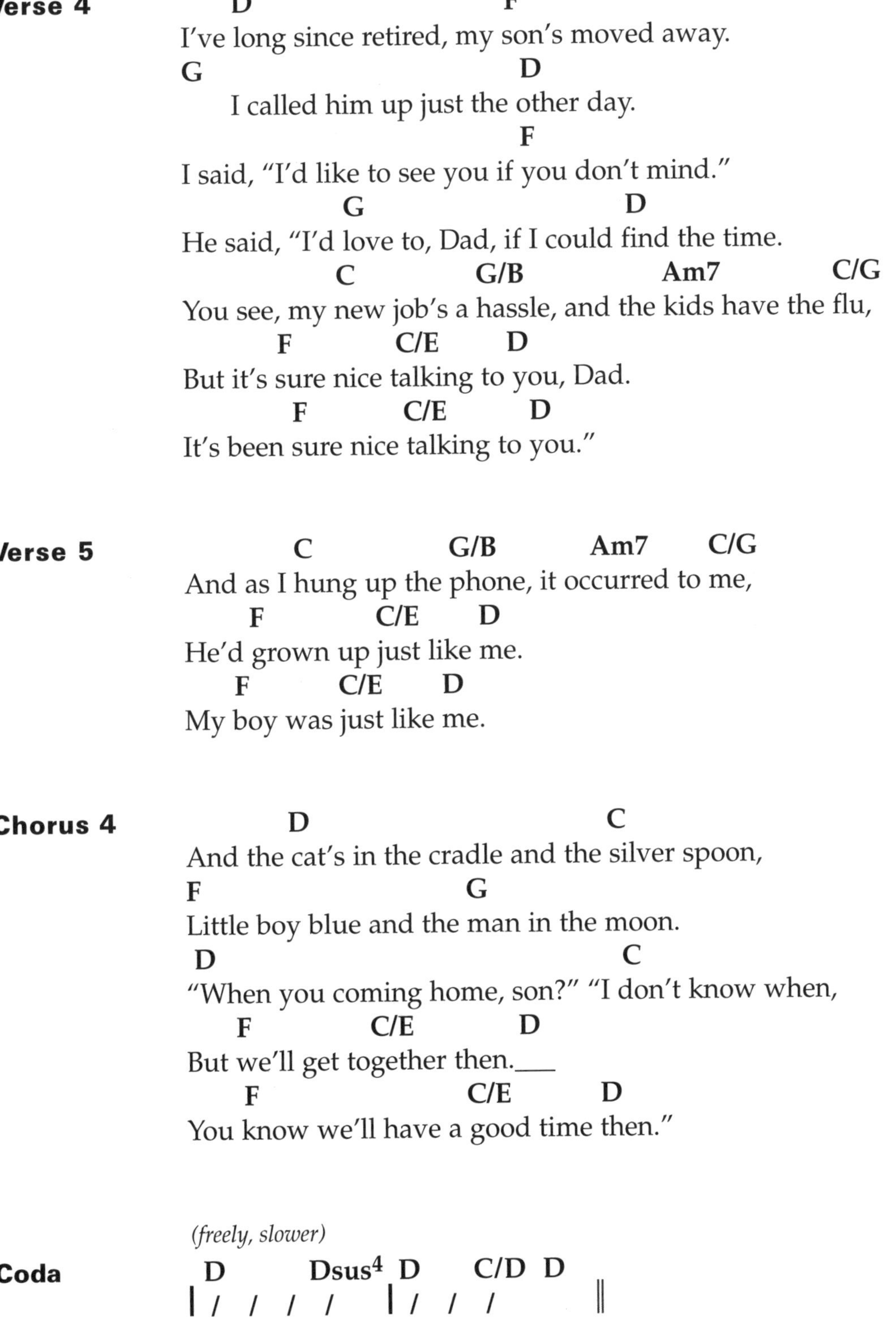

Verse 4

D F
I've long since retired, my son's moved away.
G D
I called him up just the other day.
F
I said, "I'd like to see you if you don't mind."
G D
He said, "I'd love to, Dad, if I could find the time.
C G/B Am7 C/G
You see, my new job's a hassle, and the kids have the flu,
F C/E D
But it's sure nice talking to you, Dad.
F C/E D
It's been sure nice talking to you."

Verse 5

C G/B Am7 C/G
And as I hung up the phone, it occurred to me,
F C/E D
He'd grown up just like me.
F C/E D
My boy was just like me.

Chorus 4

D C
And the cat's in the cradle and the silver spoon,
F G
Little boy blue and the man in the moon.
D C
"When you coming home, son?" "I don't know when,
F C/E D
But we'll get together then.___
F C/E D
You know we'll have a good time then."

(freely, slower)

Coda

D Dsus4 D C/D D
| / / / / | / / / ||

Chestnut Mare

Words and Music by
ROGER McGUINN AND JACQUES LEVY

D D/C♯ Bm Bm/A G D/F♯
A Em D7 C G6 Asus2

Intro 4/4

```
D     D/C♯        Bm  Bm/A G          D/F♯           A
   Al - ways alone,          never          with a herd;
D         D/C♯            Bm         Bm/A
   Prettiest     mare   I've     ever seen,
G                    D/F♯            A
   You'll have to         take my word.
```

♩ = 114

Chorus

```
G        D/F♯          Em         A          D       D/C♯  Bm    A
   I'm      going to catch that horse if I    can,_____
G              D/F♯  Em     A           D       D/C♯  Bm    A
   And       when I do I'll give her my    brand._____
```

Verse 1

```
D                             D/C♯
   Well I was up on             Stony Ridge
Bm        A
   After this chestnut mare,
G  D/F♯                                   Em     A
             I'd been chasing her for weeks.
D              D/C♯
   Oh      I'd catch a little glimpse of her
       Bm                   A
Every once in a while,
             G           D/F♯        A
Taking her meal  or bathing,            fine lady.
```

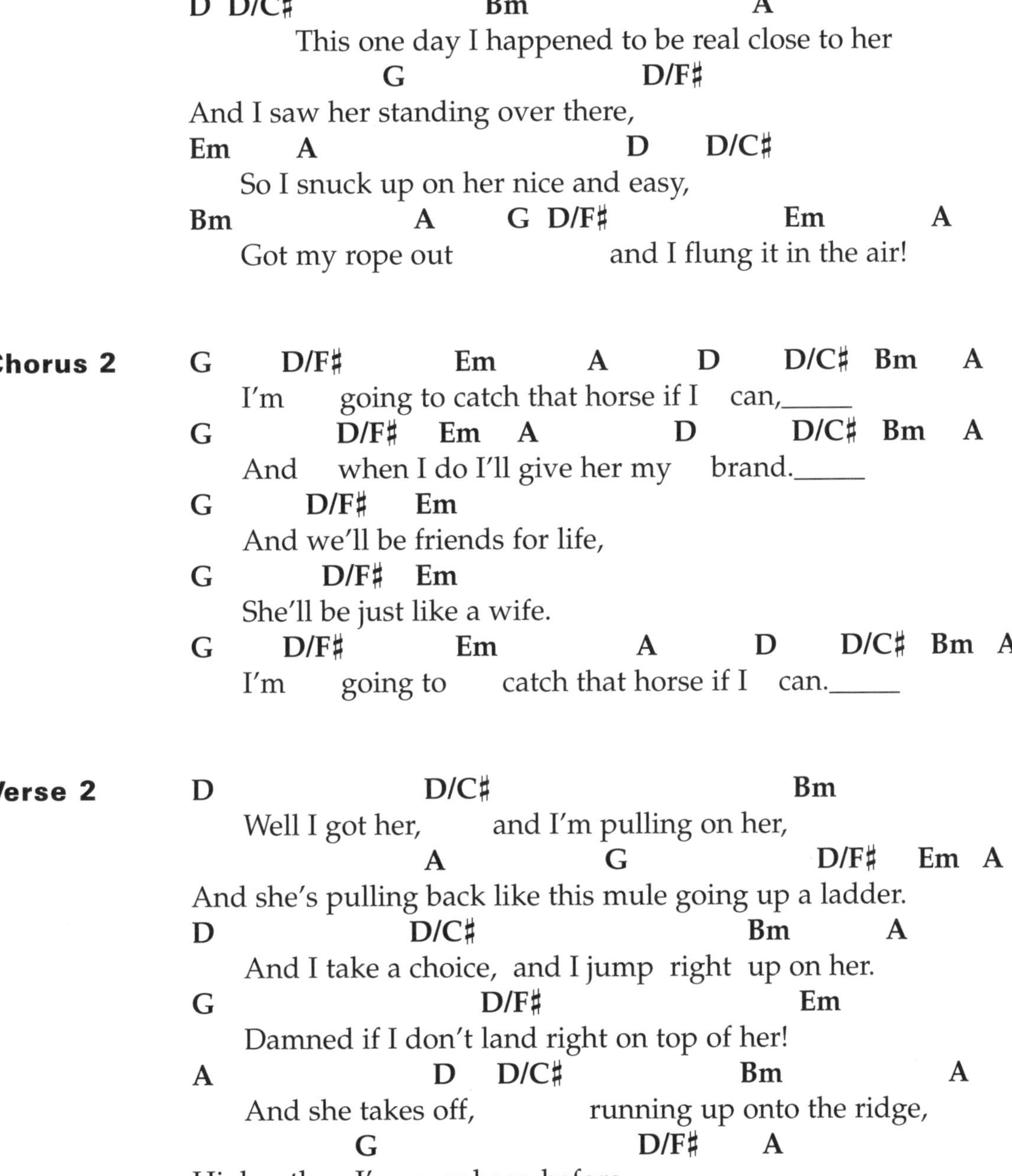

D D/C♯ Bm A
This one day I happened to be real close to her
G D/F♯
And I saw her standing over there,
Em A D D/C♯
So I snuck up on her nice and easy,
Bm A G D/F♯ Em A
Got my rope out and I flung it in the air!

Chorus 2

G D/F♯ Em A D D/C♯ Bm A
I'm going to catch that horse if I can,_____
G D/F♯ Em A D D/C♯ Bm A
And when I do I'll give her my brand._____
G D/F♯ Em
And we'll be friends for life,
G D/F♯ Em
She'll be just like a wife.
G D/F♯ Em A D D/C♯ Bm A
I'm going to catch that horse if I can._____

Verse 2

D D/C♯ Bm
Well I got her, and I'm pulling on her,
A G D/F♯ Em A
And she's pulling back like this mule going up a ladder.
D D/C♯ Bm A
And I take a choice, and I jump right up on her.
G D/F♯ Em
Damned if I don't land right on top of her!
A D D/C♯ Bm A
And she takes off, running up onto the ridge,
G D/F♯ A
Higher than I've ever been before.

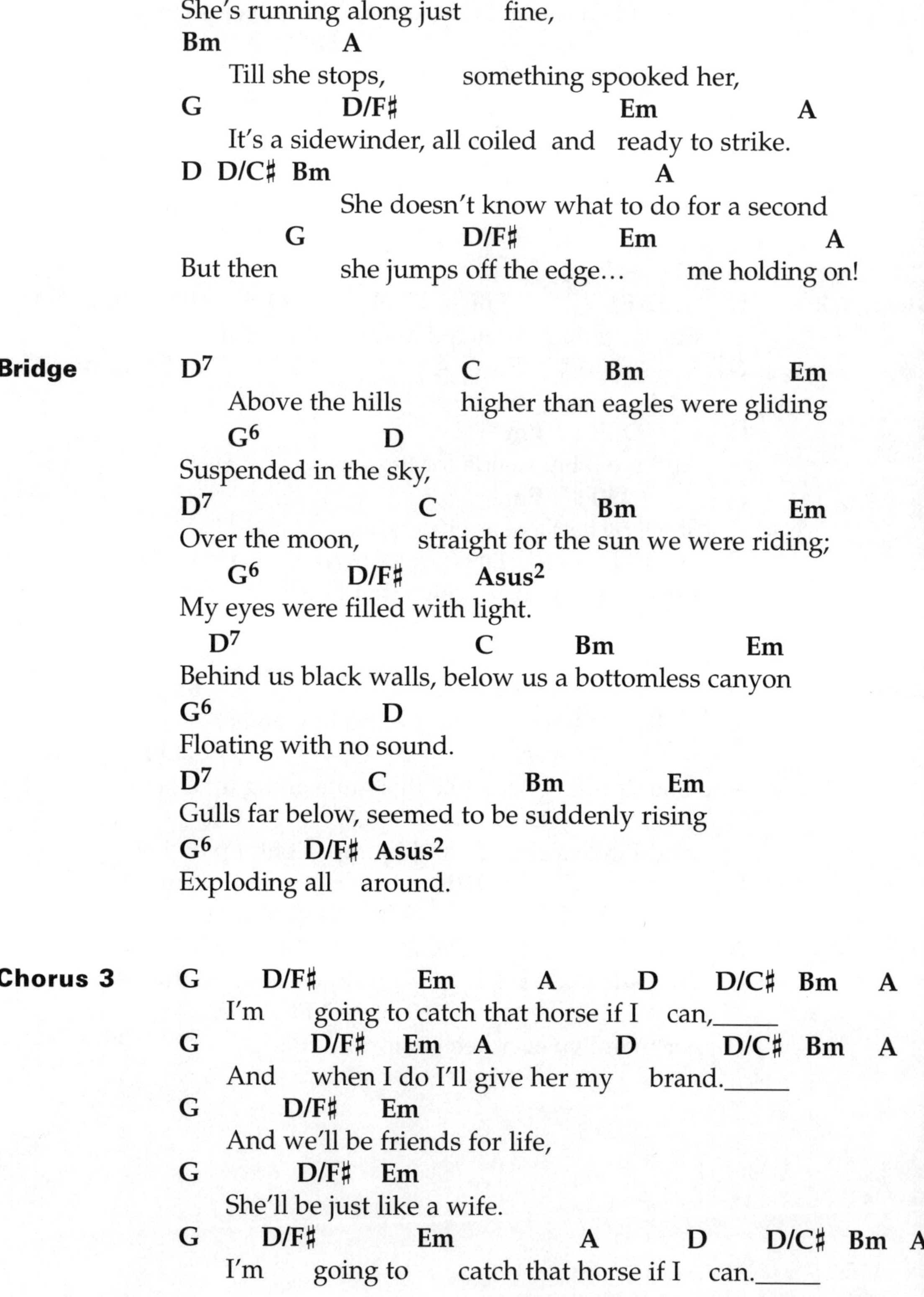

```
                          D         D/C♯
She's running along just     fine,
Bm             A
     Till she stops,        something spooked her,
G              D/F♯                        Em              A
     It's a sidewinder, all coiled  and   ready to strike.
D  D/C♯  Bm                                  A
             She doesn't know what to do for a second
          G              D/F♯              Em                   A
But then       she jumps off the edge...        me holding on!
```

Bridge

```
D⁷                        C             Bm            Em
     Above the hills        higher than eagles were gliding
     G⁶              D
Suspended in the sky,
D⁷                    C                 Bm                Em
Over the moon,        straight for the sun we were riding;
     G⁶          D/F♯        Asus²
My eyes were filled with light.
   D⁷                            C           Bm             Em
Behind us black walls, below us a bottomless canyon
G⁶                   D
Floating with no sound.
D⁷                  C              Bm          Em
Gulls far below, seemed to be suddenly rising
G⁶          D/F♯  Asus²
Exploding all    around.
```

Chorus 3

```
G        D/F♯          Em          A          D        D/C♯  Bm    A
     I'm        going to catch that horse if I     can,_____
G              D/F♯   Em    A                D        D/C♯  Bm    A
     And       when I do I'll give her my      brand._____
G         D/F♯      Em
     And we'll be friends for life,
G          D/F♯   Em
     She'll be just like a wife.
G        D/F♯          Em              A           D        D/C♯  Bm  A
     I'm        going to       catch that horse if I    can._____
```

Verse 3

```
D                   D/C#     Bm                   A
     And we were falling        down this crevice,
G                          D/F#   Em   A
     About a mile down, I'd say,
                  D                  D/C#
I look down and I see this red thing below us
Bm                    A
     Coming up real fast
               G              D/F#                Em
And it's our reflection in this          little pool of water
               A          D           D/C#
About six  feet wide and one foot deep.
Bm                    A          G           D/F#
     And we're falling down right through it,
        Em                     A
And we hit and we splashed it dry.
D                  D/C#          Bm                 A
     That's when I lost my hold          and she got away.
G                        D/F#     Em               A
     But I'm gonna try to get her again some day.
```

Chorus 4

```
G       D/F#          Em        A        D      D/C#  Bm    A
     I'm      going to catch that horse if I   can,_____
G          D/F#   Em   A            D       D/C#  Bm    A
     And      when I do I'll give her my    brand._____
G       D/F#    Em
     And we'll be friends for life,
G          D/F#  Em
     She'll be just like a wife.
G       D/F#    Em       A
     I'm going to catch that horse,
G       D/F#          Em        A
     I'm      going to catch that horse,
G       D/F#    Em       A        D       D/C#  Bm      A
     I'm going to catch that horse if I    can.______________
G  D/F#        Em        A       G     D/F#   Em   A    D
     I'm going to catch that horse if I can._______________  ||
```

Comfortably Numb

Words and Music by
GEORGE ROGER WATERS AND DAVID GILMOUR

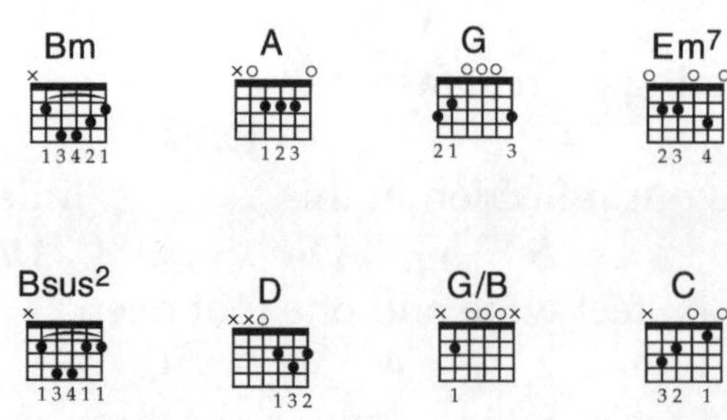

♩ = 62

Intro **Bm**
4/4 | / / / / | / / / / |

Verse 1

```
Bm                          A
Hello – is there anybody in there?
                  G         Em7
Just nod if you can hear me.
Bsus2
Is there anyone at home?
Bm                           A
Come on now, I hear you're feeling down,
     G                Em7
Well I can ease your pain, get you
Bsus2
On your feet again.
Bm                           A
Relax – I need some information first,
G                  Em7          Bsus2
Just the basic facts  –  can you show me where it hurts?
```

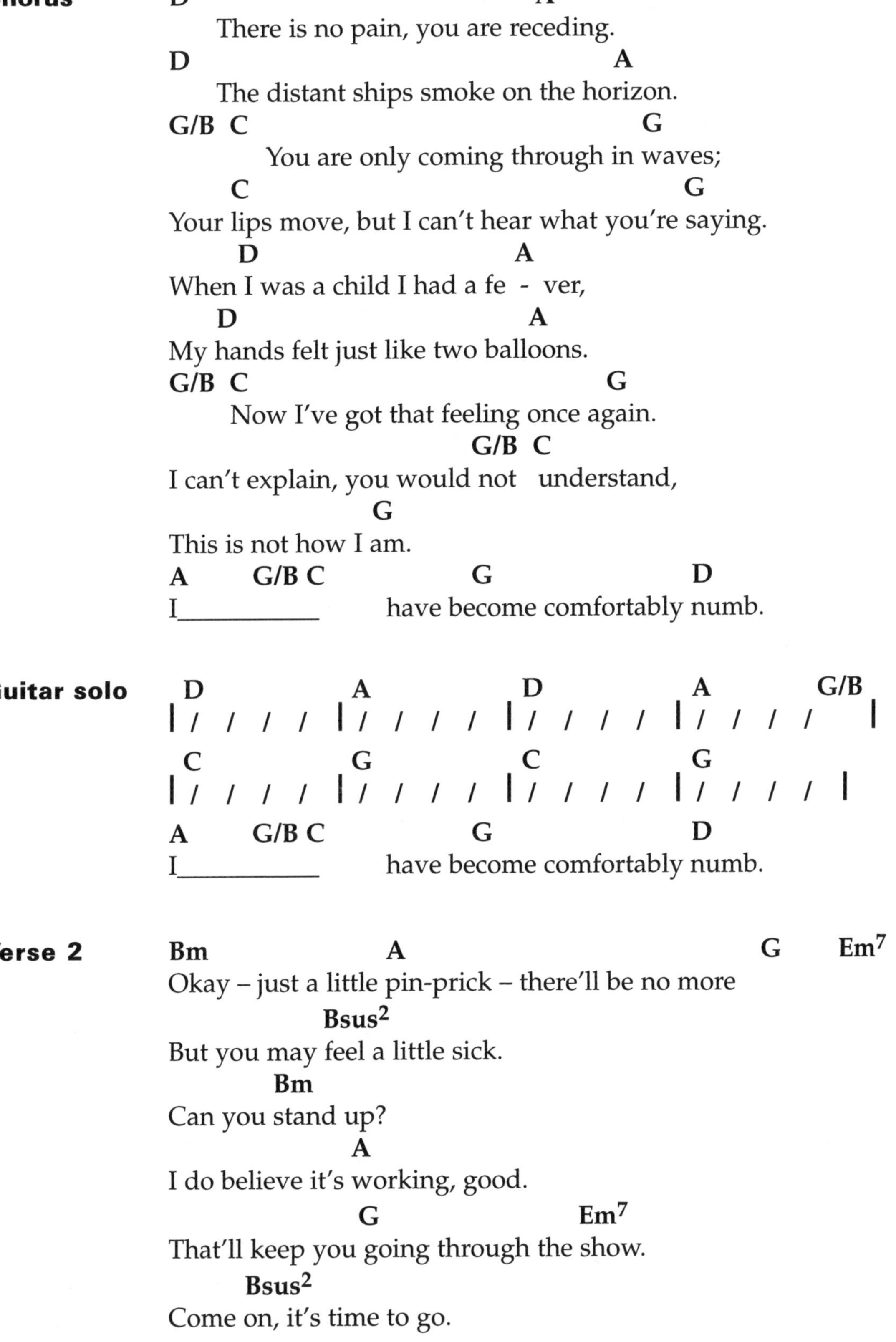
Chorus
D A
There is no pain, you are receding.
D A
The distant ships smoke on the horizon.
G/B C G
You are only coming through in waves;
C G
Your lips move, but I can't hear what you're saying.
D A
When I was a child I had a fe - ver,
D A
My hands felt just like two balloons.
G/B C G
Now I've got that feeling once again.
G/B C
I can't explain, you would not understand,
G
This is not how I am.
A G/B C G D
I__________ have become comfortably numb.
Guitar solo
D A D A G/B
| / / / / | / / / / | / / / / | / / / / |
C G C G
| / / / / | / / / / | / / / / | / / / / |
A G/B C G D
I__________ have become comfortably numb.
Verse 2
Bm A G Em7
Okay – just a little pin-prick – there'll be no more
Bsus2
But you may feel a little sick.
Bm
Can you stand up?
A
I do believe it's working, good.
G Em7
That'll keep you going through the show.
Bsus2
Come on, it's time to go.

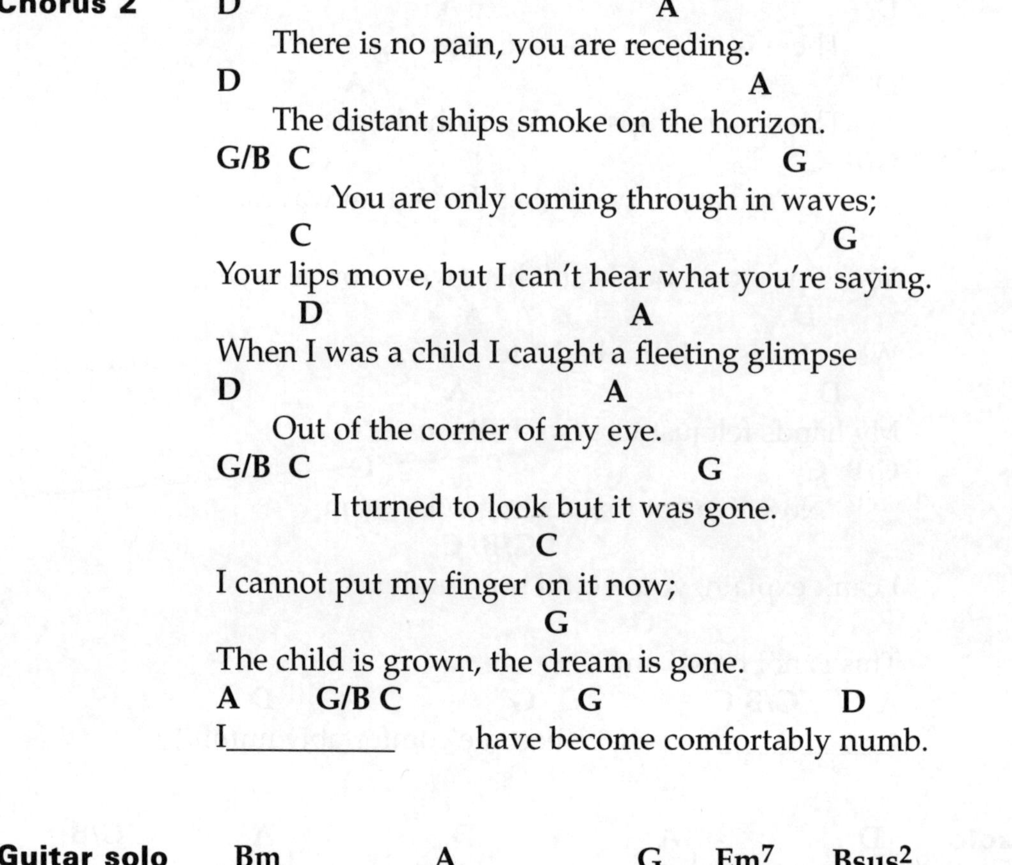

Chorus 2

```
D                                  A
    There is no pain, you are receding.
D                                       A
    The distant ships smoke on the horizon.
G/B  C                                  G
         You are only coming through in waves;
     C                                    G
Your lips move, but I can't hear what you're saying.
     D                            A
When I was a child I caught a fleeting glimpse
D                             A
    Out of the corner of my eye.
G/B  C                          G
         I turned to look but it was gone.
                          C
I cannot put my finger on it now;
                          G
The child is grown, the dream is gone.
A         G/B C             G             D
I_____________ have become comfortably numb.
```

Guitar solo

```
 Bm              A                G       Em⁷      Bsus²
‖: /  /  /  /  | /  /  /  /  | /  /  /  /  | /  /  /  / :‖
```

repeat ad lib. to fade

Debora

Words and Music by
MARC BOLAN

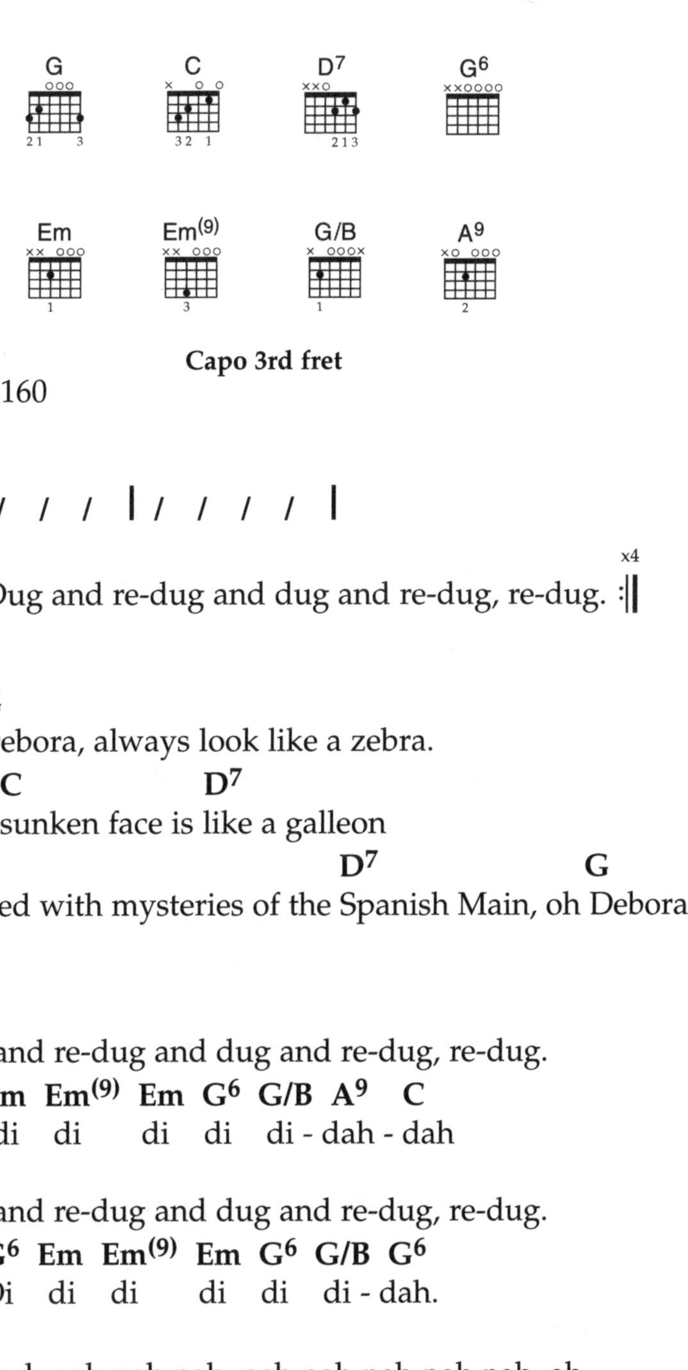

Capo 3rd fret

♩ = 145-160

Intro

G
| / / / / | / / / / |

G
||: Dug and re-dug and dug and re-dug, re-dug. :|| x4

Verse 1

G
Oh Debora, always look like a zebra.
C D7
Your sunken face is like a galleon
C D7 G
Clawed with mysteries of the Spanish Main, oh Debora.

Chorus

G
Dug and re-dug and dug and re-dug, re-dug.
G6 Em Em(9) Em G6 G/B A9 C
Di di di di di di - dah - dah

Dug and re-dug and dug and re-dug, re-dug.
G G6 Em Em(9) Em G6 G/B G6
Di di di di di di - dah.
A9
Nah nah nah nah nah, nah nah nah nah nah, ah.

Link

G
||: Dug and re-dug and dug and re-dug, re-dug. :||

Verse 2

G
Oh Debora, always dress like a conjuror.
C D^7
It's fine to see your young face hiding
C D^7 G
'Neath the stallion that I'm riding, Debora.

Chorus 2

G^6 Em Em$^{(9)}$ Em G^6 G/B A^9
Di di di di di di - dah.
C
Dug and re-dug and dug and re-dug, re-dug.
G G^6 Em Em$^{(9)}$ Em G^6 G/B A^9
Di di di di di di - dah.

||: Nah nah nah nah nah, nah nah nah nah nah. :||

Oh Debora, oh Debora.

Chorus 3

G G^6 Em Em$^{(9)}$ Em G^6 G/B A^9
Di di di di di di - dah.
C
Dug and re-dug and dug and re-dug, re-dug.
G G^6 Em Em$^{(9)}$ Em G^6 G/B G^6
Di di di di di di - dah.
A^9 G
Nah nah nah nah nah, nah nah nah nah nah, shhh…

Link

G x4
||: Dug and re-dug and dug and re-dug, re-dug. :||

Verse 3

G
Oh Debora, you look like a stallion.

Oh Debora, you look like a stallion.
C D^7
Your sunken face is like a galleon
C D^7 G
Clawed with mysteries of the Spanish Main, oh Debora.

Chorus 4

G^6 Em $Em^{(9)}$ Em G^6 G/B A^9
||: Di di di di di di - dah.
C
Dug and re-dug and dug and re-dug, re-dug. :||
C
Oh.________________
A^9
||: Nah nah nah nah nah, nah nah nah nah nah. :||

Oh Debora, oh Debora.

Chorus 5

G G^6 Em $Em^{(9)}$ Em G^6 G/B A^9
Di di di di di di - dah.
C
Dug and re-dug and dug and re-dug, re-dug.
G G^6 Em $Em^{(9)}$ Em G^6 G/B G^6
Di di di di di di di - dah.
A^9
Nah nah nah nah nah, nah nah nah nah nah.
G
Shhhh…

Don't Get Me Wrong

Words and Music by
CHRISSIE HYNDE

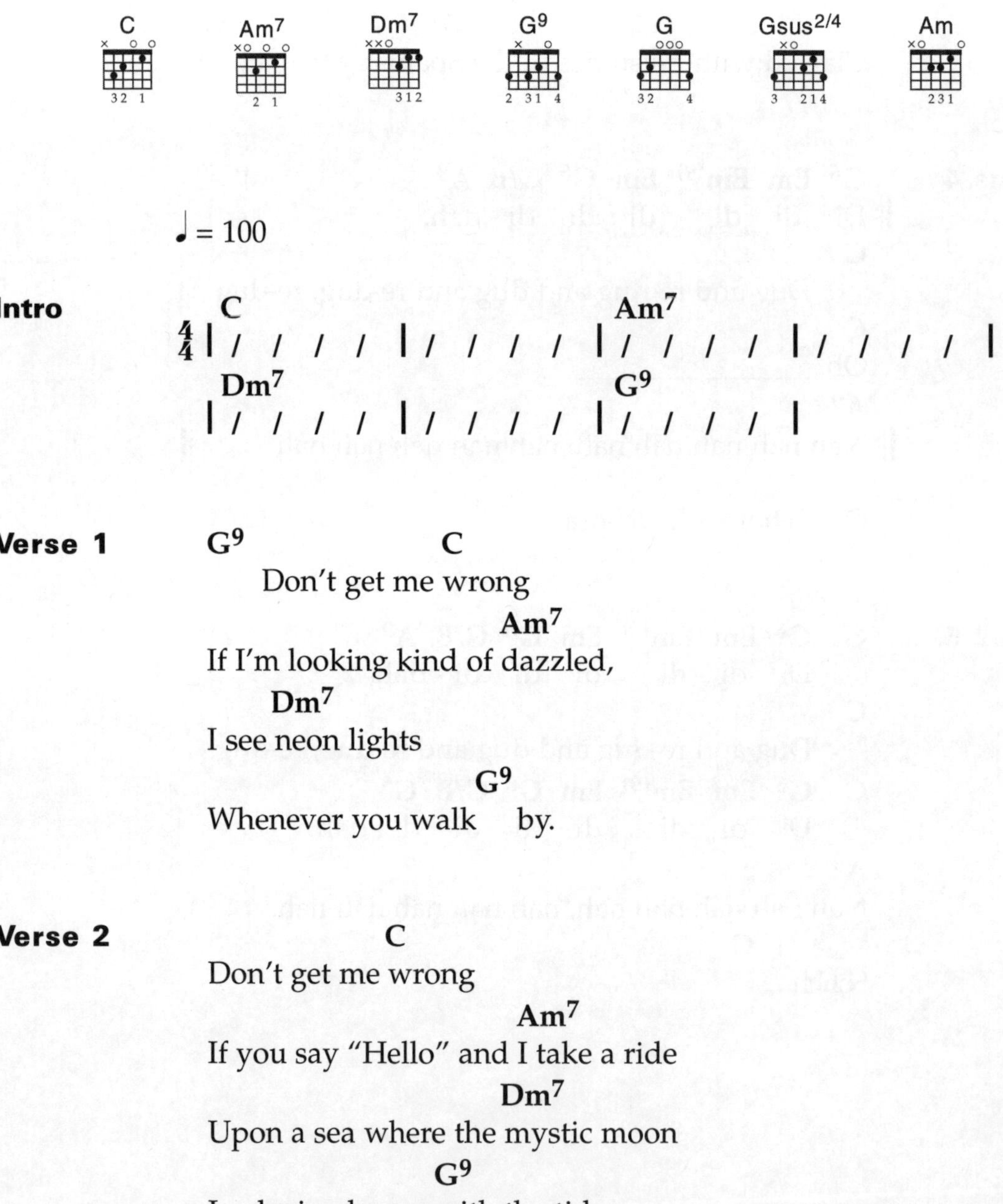

♩ = 100

Intro

```
    C                     Am7
4/4 | / / / / | / / / / | / / / / | / / / / |
    Dm7                   G9
    | / / / / | / / / / | / / / / |
```

Verse 1

G9 C
Don't get me wrong
Am7
If I'm looking kind of dazzled,
Dm7
I see neon lights
G9
Whenever you walk by.

Verse 2

C
Don't get me wrong
Am7
If you say "Hello" and I take a ride
Dm7
Upon a sea where the mystic moon
G9
Is playing havoc with the tide.

Don't get me wrong.

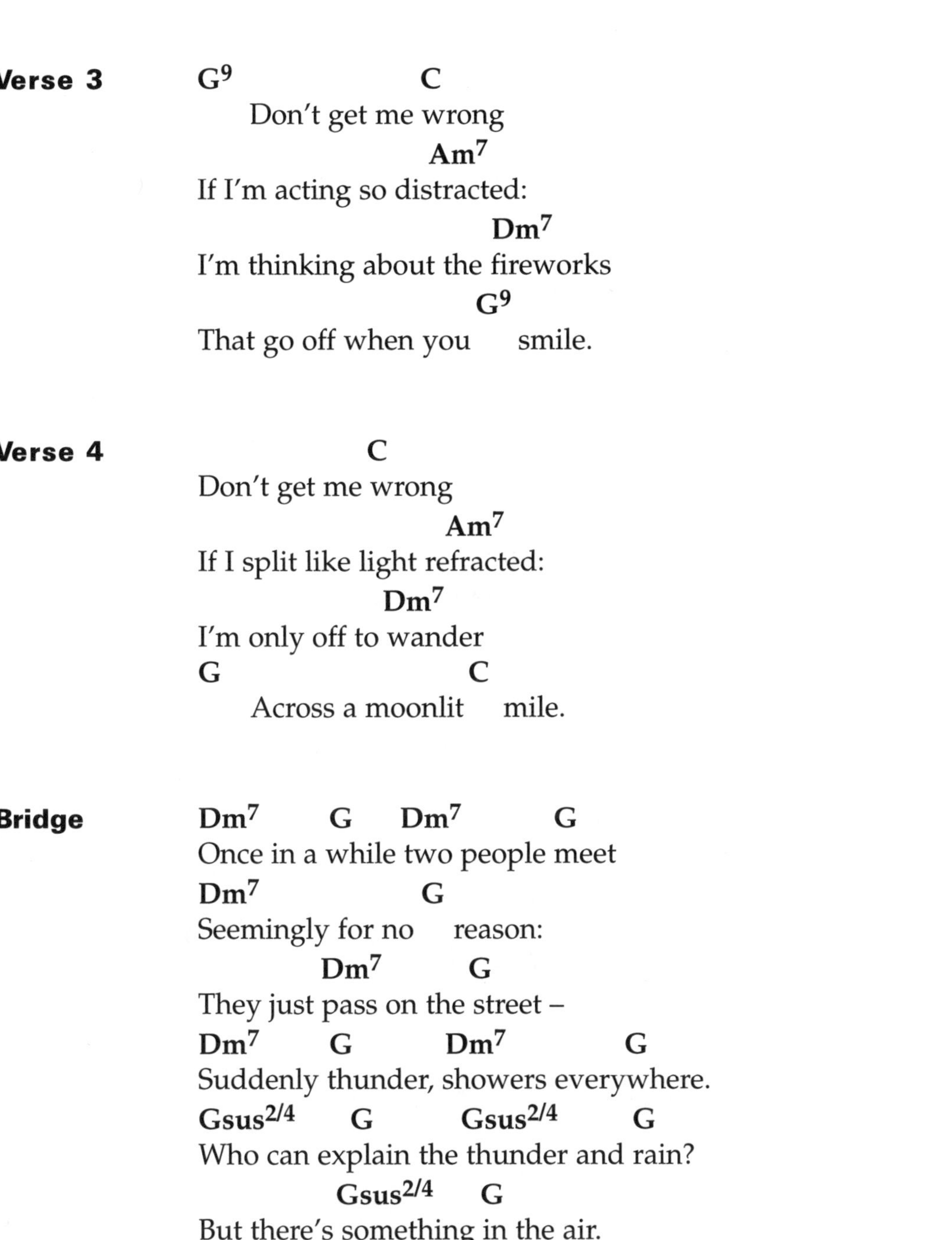

Link

C　　　　　　　　　　　　　　Am⁷
| (wrong.) / / / / | / / / / | / / / / | / / / / |
Dm⁷　　　　　　　　　　G⁹
| / / / / | / / / / | / / / / |

Verse 3

G⁹　　　　　C
Don't get me wrong
　　　　　　Am⁷
If I'm acting so distracted:
　　　　　　　　　Dm⁷
I'm thinking about the fireworks
　　　　　　　　G⁹
That go off when you smile.

Verse 4

　　　　　C
Don't get me wrong
　　　　　　　Am⁷
If I split like light refracted:
　　　　　Dm⁷
I'm only off to wander
G　　　　　　　C
Across a moonlit mile.

Bridge

Dm⁷　G　Dm⁷　G
Once in a while two people meet
Dm⁷　　　G
Seemingly for no reason:
　　　Dm⁷　G
They just pass on the street –
Dm⁷　G　　Dm⁷　　G
Suddenly thunder, showers everywhere.
Gsus2/4　G　　Gsus2/4　G
Who can explain the thunder and rain?
　　　Gsus2/4　G
But there's something in the air.

Guitar solo

```
 C                       Am7
‖: / / / / | / / / / | / / / / | / / / / |
                       ┌1                  ┌2
 Dm7                     G9                  G9
| / / / / | / / / / | / / / / | / / / / :‖ / / / / |
```

Verse 5

```
G9                C
      Don't get me wrong
                          Am7
If I come and go like fashion:
                       Dm7
I might be great tomorrow
                        G9
But hopeless yesterday.
```

Verse 6

```
                  C
Don't get me wrong
                            Am7
If I fall in the mode of passion:
                      Dm7
It might be unbelievable
G                  Am
      But let's not say "so long".
                         Dm7
It might just be fantastic.
G                Am
      Don't get me wrong.
 Am                      Am
| / / / / | / / / / | /   ‖
```

Find The River

Words and Music by
MICHAEL MILLS, PETER BUCK AND MICHAEL STIPE

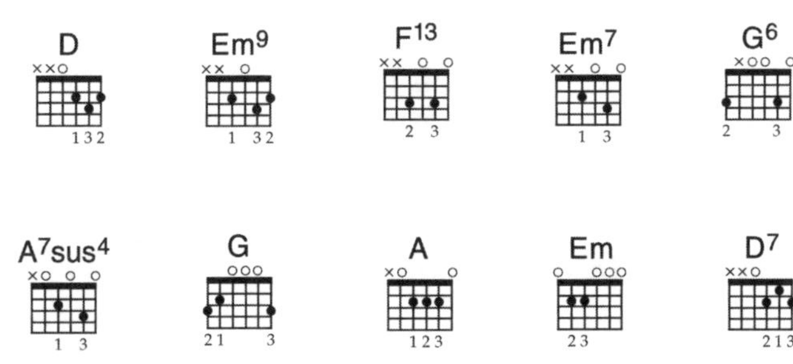

♩ = 71

Intro

```
   D           Em9         D           Em9
4/4 | / / / /  | / / / /  | / / / /  | / / / / |
   D     F13   Em7  G6     D     F13   A7sus4
    | / / / /  | / / / /  | / / / /  | / / / / |
```

Verse 1

```
D                F13
Hey now, little speedy-head,
   Em7                G6
The read on the speedmeter says
   D             F13               A7sus4
You have to go to task in the city
     D                    F13
Where people drown and people serve.
Em7                G6
Don't be shy,  your just dessert
  D        F13          A7sus4
Is only just light years to go.
```

Chorus

G A
Me, my thoughts are flower-strewn,
D Em
Ocean storm, bayberry moon,
G A D D^7
I have got to leave to find my way.
G A
Watch the road and memorize
D Em
This life that passed before my eyes
G A
And nothing is going my way.___

Link

D F^{13} Em^7 G^6 D F^{13} A^7sus^4
| / / / / | / / / / | / / / / | / / / / |

Verse 2

D F^{13}
The ocean is the river's goal,
Em^7 G^6
A need to leave the water knows
D F^{13} A^7sus^4
We're closer now than light years to go.

Chorus 2

G A
I have got to find the river.
D Em
Bergamot and vetiver
G A D D^7
Run through my head and fall away.
G A
Leave the road and memorize
D Em
This life that passed before my eyes
G A
And nothing is going my way.___

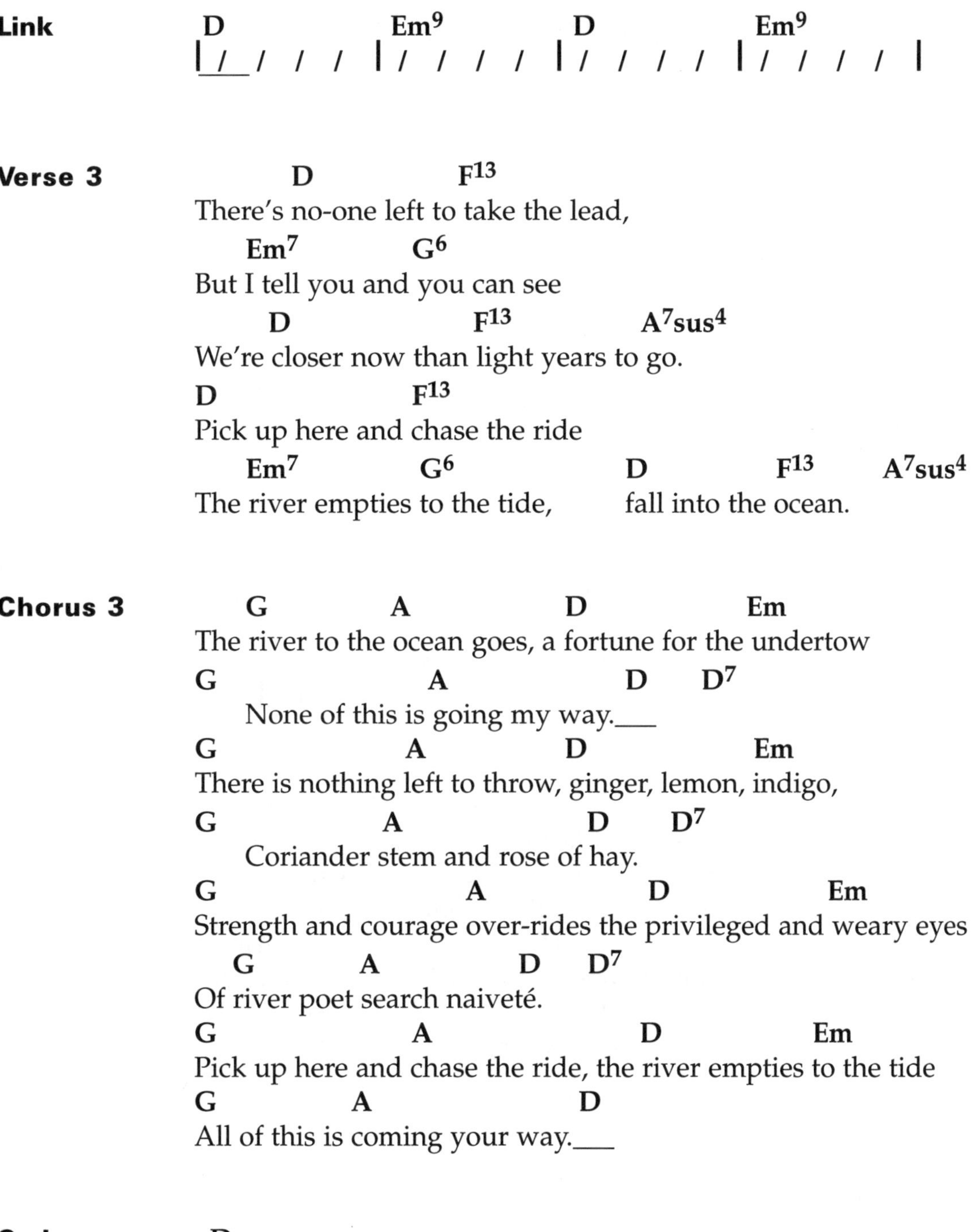

Link

D Em^9 D Em^9

| / / / / | / / / / | / / / / | / / / / |

Verse 3

D F^{13}
There's no-one left to take the lead,
Em^7 G^6
But I tell you and you can see
D F^{13} A^{7}sus^4
We're closer now than light years to go.
D F^{13}
Pick up here and chase the ride
Em^7 G^6 D F^{13} A^{7}sus^4
The river empties to the tide, fall into the ocean.

Chorus 3

G A D Em
The river to the ocean goes, a fortune for the undertow
G A D D^7
None of this is going my way.___
G A D Em
There is nothing left to throw, ginger, lemon, indigo,
G A D D^7
Coriander stem and rose of hay.
G A D Em
Strength and courage over-rides the privileged and weary eyes
G A D D^7
Of river poet search naiveté.
G A D Em
Pick up here and chase the ride, the river empties to the tide
G A D
All of this is coming your way.___

Coda

D

| / / / / | / / / / | / / / / *(fade)*

Echo Beach

Words and Music by
MARK GANE

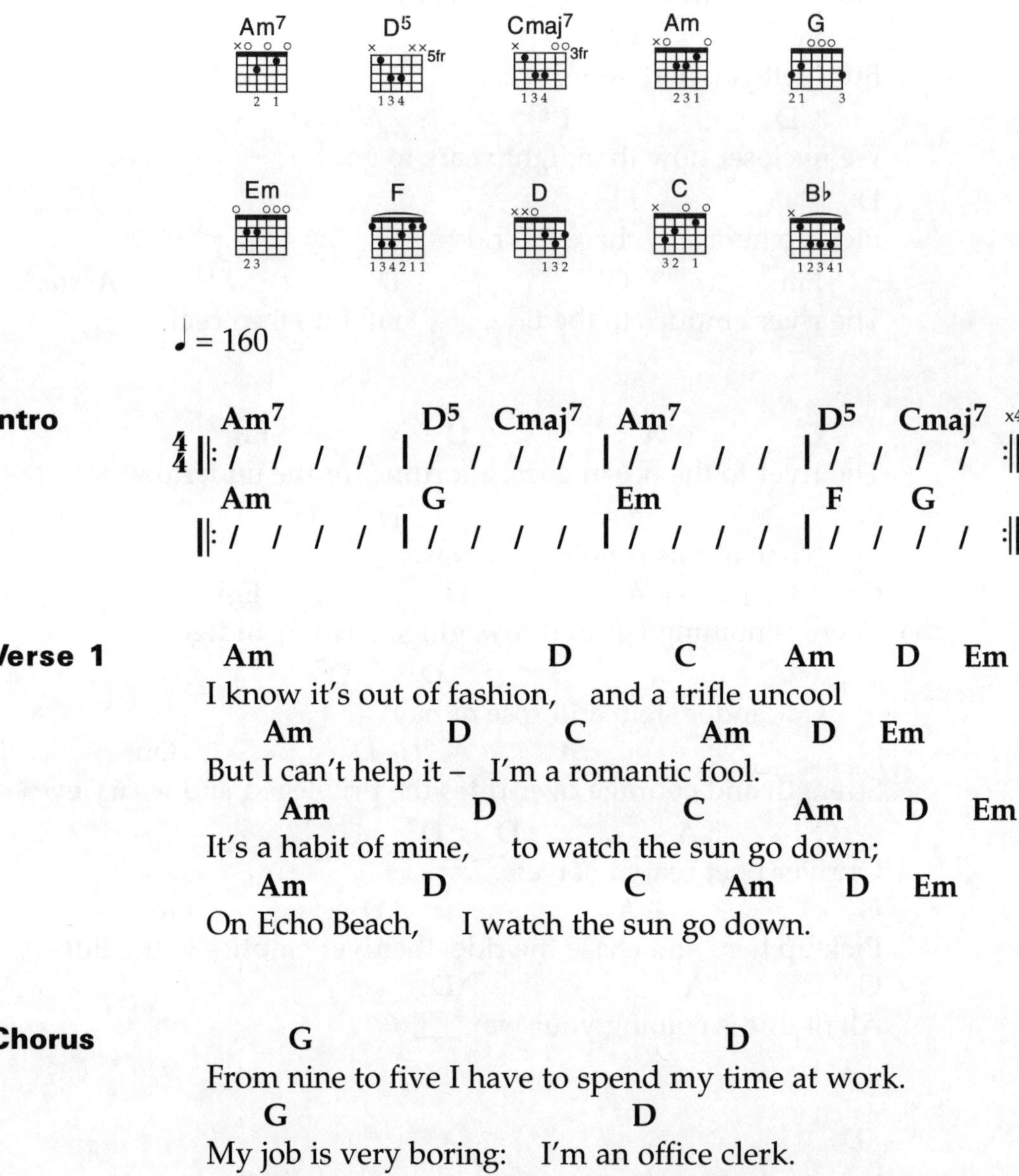

♩ = 160

Intro

Am7 D5 Cmaj7 Am7 D5 Cmaj7 x4
4/4 ‖: / / / / | / / / / | / / / / | / / / / :‖

Am G Em F G
‖: / / / / | / / / / | / / / / | / / / / :‖

Verse 1

Am D C Am D Em
I know it's out of fashion, and a trifle uncool
Am D C Am D Em
But I can't help it – I'm a romantic fool.
Am D C Am D Em
It's a habit of mine, to watch the sun go down;
Am D C Am D Em
On Echo Beach, I watch the sun go down.

Chorus

G D
From nine to five I have to spend my time at work.
G D
My job is very boring: I'm an office clerk.
Am Em
The only thing that helps me pass the time away
Am Em
Is knowing I'll be back at Echo Beach some day.

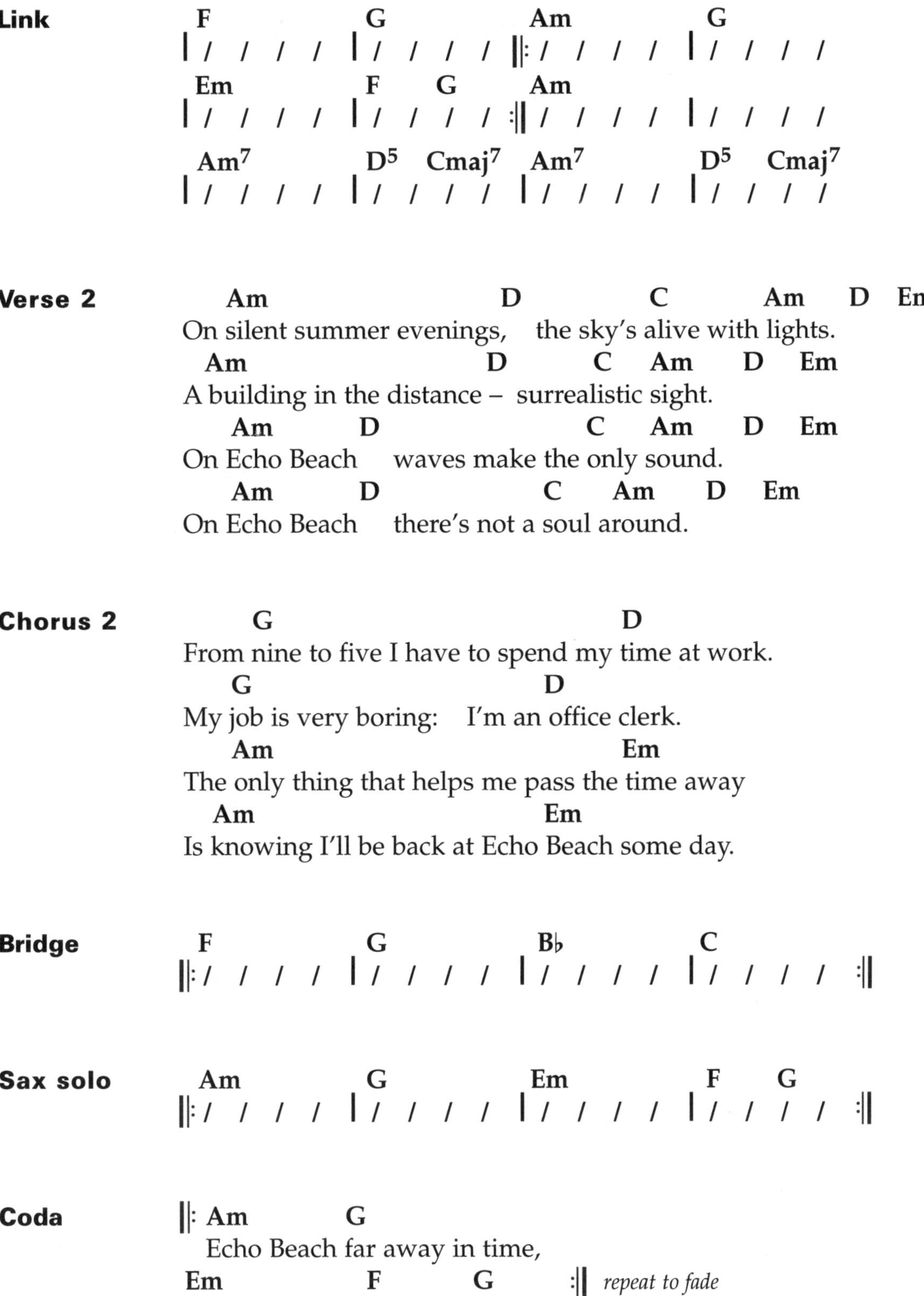

Link

F G Am G

Em F G Am

Am^7 D^5 Cmaj^7 Am^7 D^5 Cmaj^7

Verse 2

Am D C Am D Em
On silent summer evenings, the sky's alive with lights.
Am D C Am D Em
A building in the distance – surrealistic sight.
Am D C Am D Em
On Echo Beach waves make the only sound.
Am D C Am D Em
On Echo Beach there's not a soul around.

Chorus 2

G D
From nine to five I have to spend my time at work.
G D
My job is very boring: I'm an office clerk.
Am Em
The only thing that helps me pass the time away
Am Em
Is knowing I'll be back at Echo Beach some day.

Bridge

F G B♭ C

Sax solo

Am G Em F G

Coda

Am G
Echo Beach far away in time,
Em F G *repeat to fade*
Echo Beach far away in time.

Fire And Rain

Words and Music by
JAMES TAYLOR

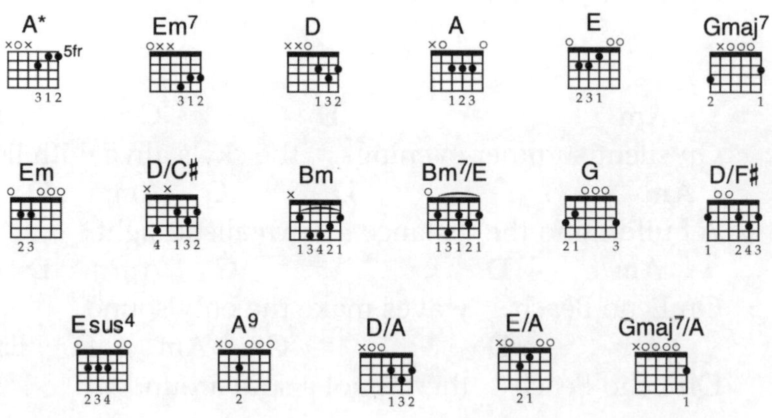

Capo 3rd fret

♩ = 74

Intro

A* Em7 D A E Gmaj7
4/4 | / / / / | / / / / | / / / / | / / / / ||

Verse 1

A Em D A
Just yesterday morning they let me know you were gone___
E Gmaj7
Suzanne, the plans they made put an end to you.
A Em D A
I walked out this morning and I wrote down this song,___
E Gmaj7
I just can't remember who to send it to.

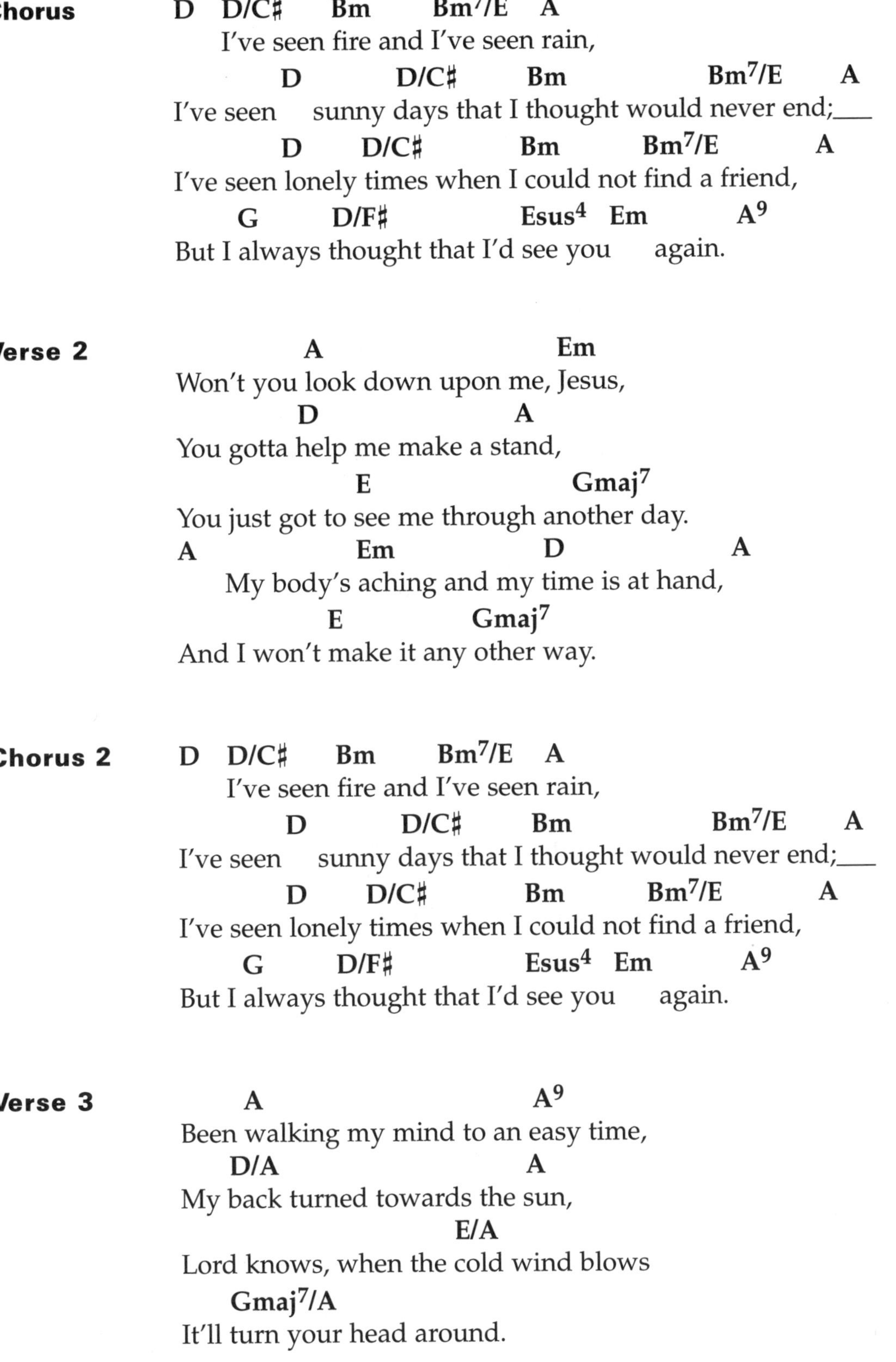

Chorus

D D/C♯ Bm Bm^{7}/E A
I've seen fire and I've seen rain,
D D/C♯ Bm Bm^{7}/E A
I've seen sunny days that I thought would never end;___
D D/C♯ Bm Bm^{7}/E A
I've seen lonely times when I could not find a friend,
G D/F♯ Esus^{4} Em A^{9}
But I always thought that I'd see you again.

Verse 2

A Em
Won't you look down upon me, Jesus,
D A
You gotta help me make a stand,
E Gmaj^{7}
You just got to see me through another day.
A Em D A
My body's aching and my time is at hand,
E Gmaj^{7}
And I won't make it any other way.

Chorus 2

D D/C♯ Bm Bm^{7}/E A
I've seen fire and I've seen rain,
D D/C♯ Bm Bm^{7}/E A
I've seen sunny days that I thought would never end;___
D D/C♯ Bm Bm^{7}/E A
I've seen lonely times when I could not find a friend,
G D/F♯ Esus^{4} Em A^{9}
But I always thought that I'd see you again.

Verse 3

A A^{9}
Been walking my mind to an easy time,
D/A A
My back turned towards the sun,
E/A
Lord knows, when the cold wind blows
Gmaj^{7}/A
It'll turn your head around.

A A9
Well there's hours of time on the telephone line
D/A A
To talk about things to come,____
E/A Gmaj7/A
Sweet dreams and flying machines in pieces on the ground.

Chorus 3

D D/C♯ Bm Bm7/E A
I've seen fire and I've seen rain,
D D/C♯ Bm Bm7/E A
I've seen sunny days that I thought would never end;___
D D/C♯ Bm Bm7/E A
I've seen lonely times when I could not find a friend,
G D/F♯ Esus4 Em
But I always thought that I'd see you, baby,
A9
One more time again, now.

Coda

Thought I'd see you one more time again

There's just a few things coming my way

This time around, now

Thought I'd see you, thought I'd see you,

Fire and rain, now. ‖

Fisherman's Blues

Words and Music by
MICHAEL SCOTT

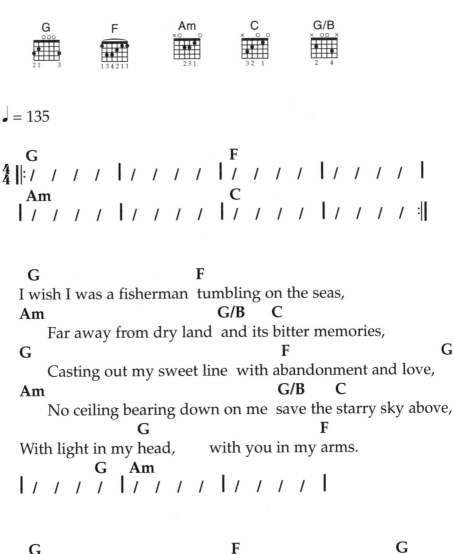

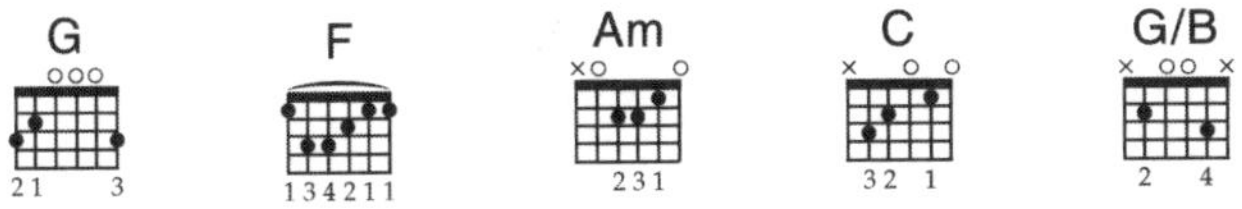

G F Am C G/B

♩ = 135

Intro

4/4 ‖: G / / / / | / / / / | F / / / / | / / / / |
| Am / / / / | / / / / | C / / / / | / / / / :‖

Verse 1

G F
I wish I was a fisherman tumbling on the seas,
Am G/B C
Far away from dry land and its bitter memories,
G F G
Casting out my sweet line with abandonment and love,
Am G/B C
No ceiling bearing down on me save the starry sky above,
G F
With light in my head, with you in my arms.
| / / / G / | Am / / / / | / / / / |

Link

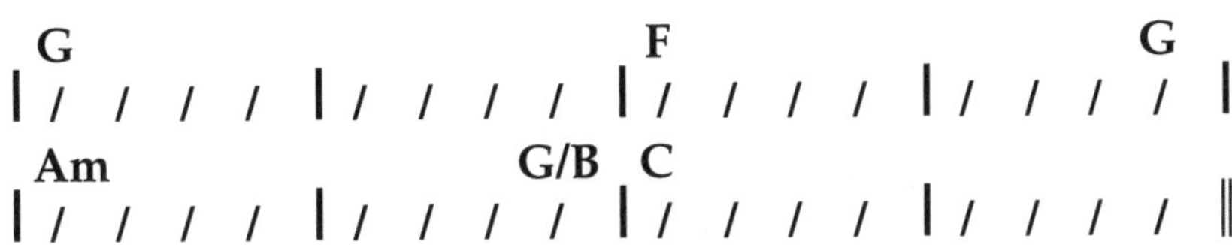

Verse 2

```
   G                                F
I wish I was the brakeman  on a hurtling fevered train
G              Am
     Crashing        head-long into the heartland
G/B   C
Like a cannon in the rain,
             G
With the feeling of the sleepers
            F                      G
And the burning of the coal,
Am                                    G/B   C
Counting the towns flashing by  and a night that's full of soul,
                    G                          F
With light in my head,       with you in my arms.
              G    Am
| / / / / | / / / / | / / / / |
```

Link 2

```
   G                          F                       G
||: / / / / | / / / / | / / / / | / / / / |
   Am                   G/B  C
| / / / / | / / / / | / / / / | / / / / :||
```

Verse 3

```
           G                          F
And I know I will be loosened  from bonds that hold me fast
       G     Am                               G/B
And if the chains are all hung around me
C
     Will fall away at last.
                G                              F
And on that   grand and fateful day  I will take thee in my hand,
 G   Am                         G/B  C
I will    ride on a train,    I will  be the fisherman
                   G                    F                   G   Am
With light in my head,  you in my arms,     whoo-oo-oo!
                  C
| / / / / | / / / / | / / / / ||
```

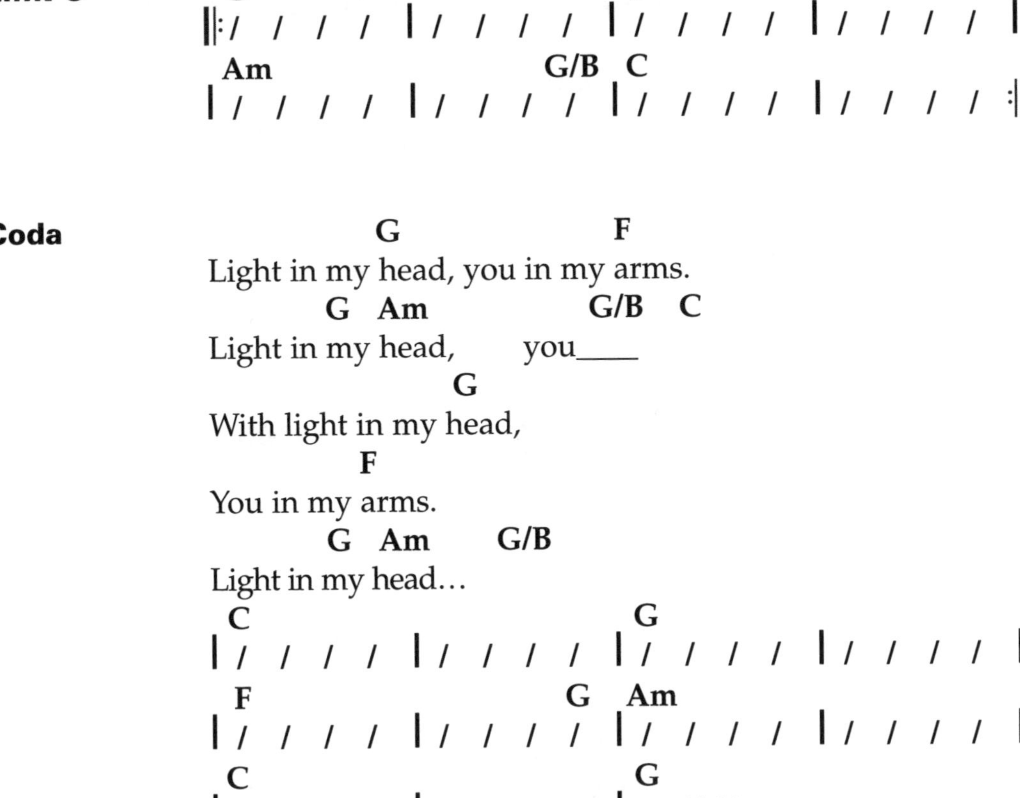
Link 3
G F G
Am G/B C
Coda
G F
Light in my head, you in my arms.
G Am G/B C
Light in my head, you____
G
With light in my head,
F
You in my arms.
G Am G/B
Light in my head…
C G
F G Am
C G
(fade)

Four Seasons In One Day

Words and Music by
NEIL FINN AND TIM FINN

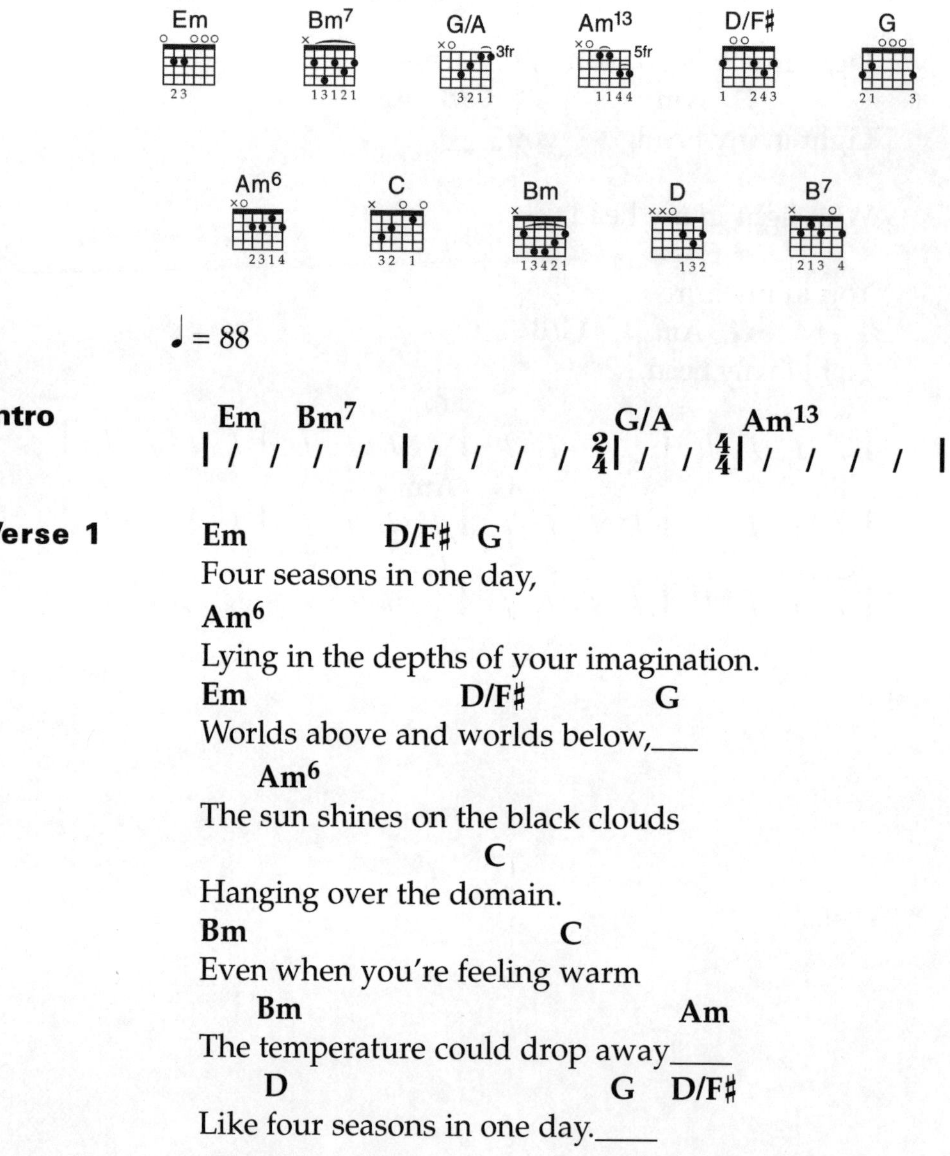

♩ = 88

Intro

Em Bm7 | / / / / | / / / / | 2/4 G/A / / | 4/4 Am13 / / / / |

Verse 1

Em **D/F♯** **G**
Four seasons in one day,
Am6
Lying in the depths of your imagination.
Em **D/F♯** **G**
Worlds above and worlds below,___
Am6
The sun shines on the black clouds
C
Hanging over the domain.
Bm **C**
Even when you're feeling warm
Bm **Am**
The temperature could drop away____
D **G** **D/F♯**
Like four seasons in one day.____

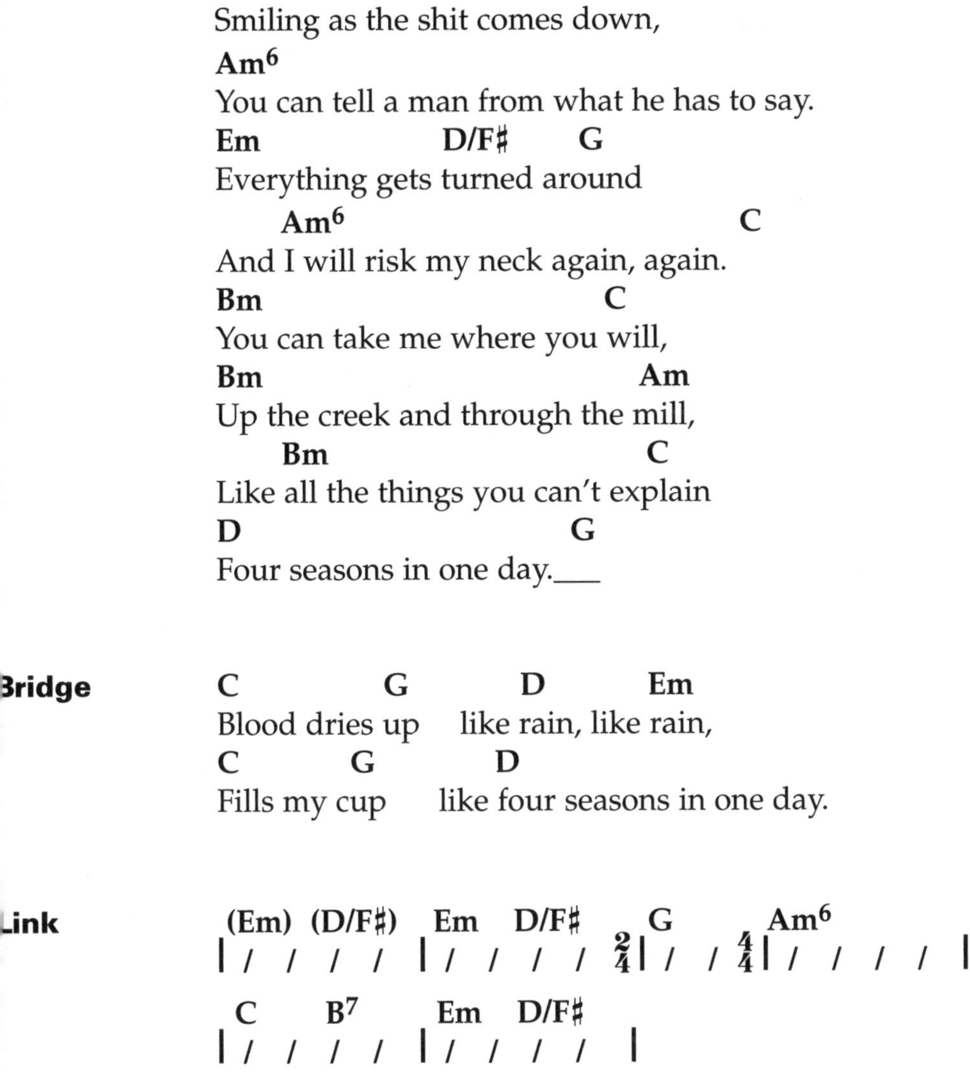

Verse 2

```
Em              D/F♯          G
Smiling as the shit comes down,
Am^6
You can tell a man from what he has to say.
Em                D/F♯      G
Everything gets turned around
     Am^6                             C
And I will risk my neck again, again.
Bm                          C
You can take me where you will,
Bm                            Am
Up the creek and through the mill,
     Bm                         C
Like all the things you can't explain
D                          G
Four seasons in one day.___
```

Bridge

```
C            G          D         Em
Blood dries up    like rain, like rain,
C          G          D
Fills my cup    like four seasons in one day.
```

Link

```
 (Em)  (D/F♯)    Em    D/F♯      G        Am^6
| / / / / | / / / / 2/4| / / 4/4| / / / / |

 C     B^7       Em    D/F♯
| / / / / | / / / / |
```

Verse 3

```
G   Am6
      Doesn't pay to make predictions
Em              D/F♯     G
Sleeping on an unmade bed,
Am6
Finding out wherever there is comfort
         C
There is    pain
Bm                 C
Only one step away,
     D                            G
Like four seasons in one day.___
```

Bridge 2

```
C          G          D          Em
Blood dries up    like rain, like rain,
C        G         D                N.C.
Fills my cup    like four seasons in one day.   ‖
```

Goin' Up The Country

Words and Music by
ALAN WILSON

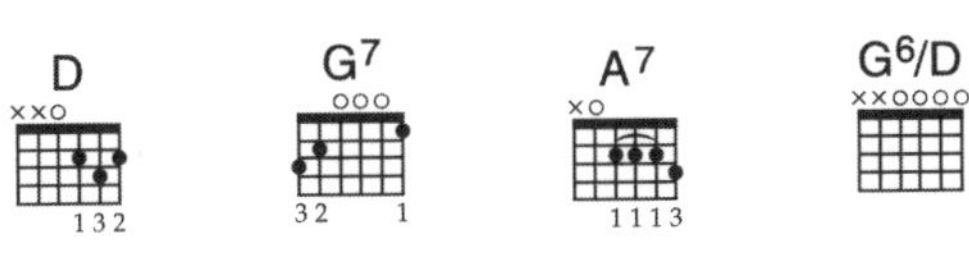

Capo 8th fret

♩ = 75

Intro

```
    D
4/4 | / / / / | / / / / | / / / / | / / / / |
    G7                  D
    | / / / / | / / / / | / / / / | / / / / |
    A7                  D
    | / / / / | / / / / | / / / / | / / / / ||
```

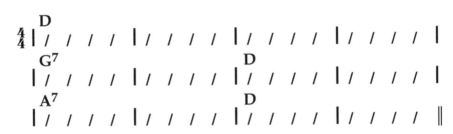

Verse 1

```
     D
I'm going up the country – baby, don't you want to go?
          G7                                      D
I'm going up the country – baby, don't you want to go?
          A7                                  D
I'm going to some place where I've never been before.
```

Verse 2

```
     D
I'm going, I'm going where the water tastes like wine,
   G7                             D
I'm going where the water tastes like wine,
      A7                                  D
We can jump in the water, stay drunk all the time.
```

Instrumental

D
| / / / / | / / / / | / / / / | / / / / |

G^7 D
| / / / / | / / / / | / / / / | / / / / |

A^7 D
| / / / / | / / / / | / / / / | / / / / ||

Verse 3

D
I'm going to leave the city, got to get away,

G^7 D
I'm going to leave the city, got to get away,

A^7 D
All this fussing and fighting, man, you know I sure can't stay.

Verse 4

D
Now baby pack your leaving trunk,

You know we've got to leave today.

Just exactly where we're going I cannot say,

G^7 D
But we might even leave the USA

A^7 D
'Cause there's a brand new game I want to play.

Instrumental

D
| / / / / | / / / / | / / / / | / / / / |

G^7 D
| / / / / | / / / / | / / / / | / / / / |

A^7 D
| / / / / | / / / / | / / / / | / / / / ||

Bridge

G^7
There's no use in you running
D
Or screaming and crying
A^7
'Cause you've got a home
D
As long as I've got mine.

Instrumental

| G^7 / / / / | / / / / | D / / / / | / / / / |
| A^7 / / / / | / / / / |

Coda

D / A /	/ / D / G^6/D /
D / / / /	/ / / /	/ / / /	/ / / /
G^7 / / / /	/ / / /	D / / / /	/ / / /
A^7 / / / /	/ / / /	D / / G^6/D / /	D /	

Fun, Fun, Fun

Words and Music by
BRIAN WILSON AND MIKE LOVE

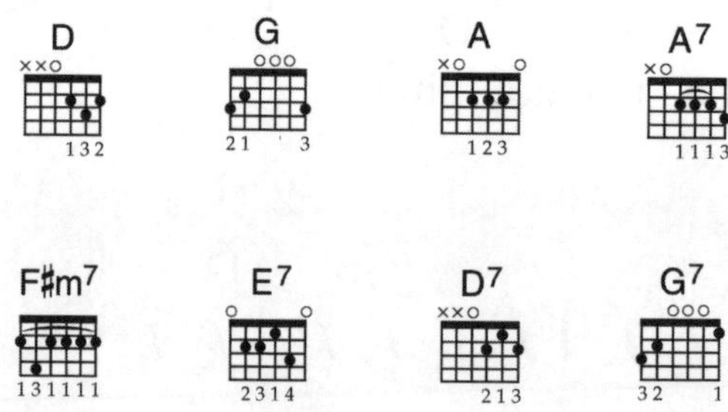

Capo 1st fret

♩ = 155

Intro

```
     (D)
4/4 | / / / / | / / / / | / / / / | / / / / |
     G                   D
    | / / / / | / / / / | / / / / | / / / / |
     A         G         D         A7
    | / / / / | / / / / | / / / / | / / / / ||
```

Verse 1

```
            D
Well,  she got her Daddy's car
                                          G
And she cruised through the hamburger stand, now;
           D
Seems she forgot all about the library
                    A
Like she told her old man, now.
           D
And with the radio blasting
                             G
Goes cruising just as fast as she can, now,
```

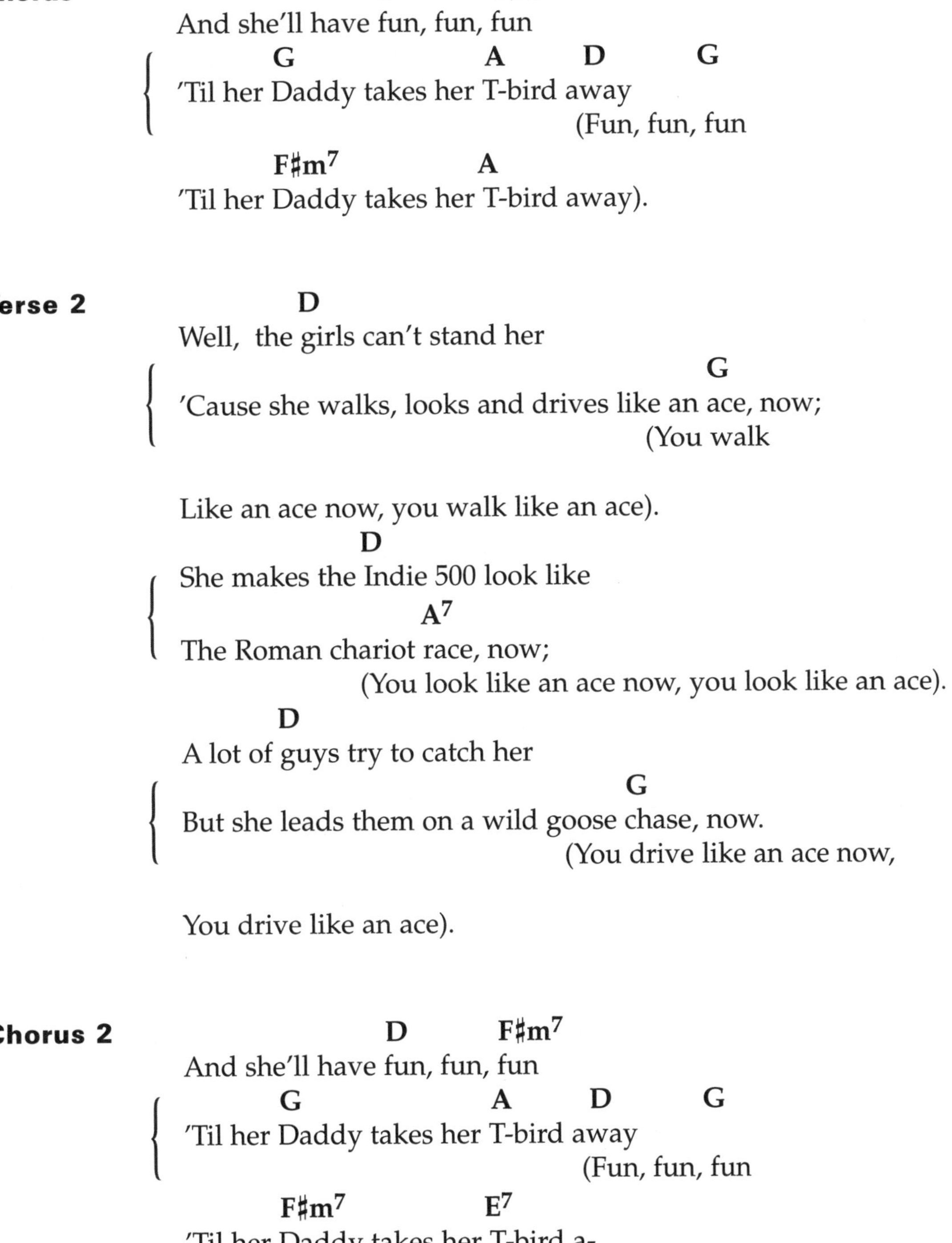

Chorus

D F♯m7
And she'll have fun, fun, fun
G A D G
'Til her Daddy takes her T-bird away
(Fun, fun, fun
F♯m7 A
'Til her Daddy takes her T-bird away).

Verse 2

D
Well, the girls can't stand her
G
'Cause she walks, looks and drives like an ace, now;
(You walk
Like an ace now, you walk like an ace).
D
She makes the Indie 500 look like
A7
The Roman chariot race, now;
(You look like an ace now, you look like an ace).
D
A lot of guys try to catch her
G
But she leads them on a wild goose chase, now.
(You drive like an ace now,
You drive like an ace).

Chorus 2

D F♯m7
And she'll have fun, fun, fun
G A D G
'Til her Daddy takes her T-bird away
(Fun, fun, fun
F♯m7 E7
'Til her Daddy takes her T-bird a-

Organ/ Guitar solo

A^7 (-way.)	/ / / /	D^7 / / / /	/ / / /
A^7 / / / /	/ / / /	E^7 / / / /	A / / / / ‖

Verse 3

D
Well, you knew all along

G
That your Dad was getting wise to you now,
(You shouldn't have lied now,

You shouldn't have lied).

D
And since he took your set of keys

A^7
You've been thinking that your fun is all through now.
(You shouldn't have lied now,

You shouldn't have lied).

D
But you can come along with me

G
'Cause we got a lot of things to do now,
(You shouldn't have lied now,

You shouldn't have lied).

Chorus 3

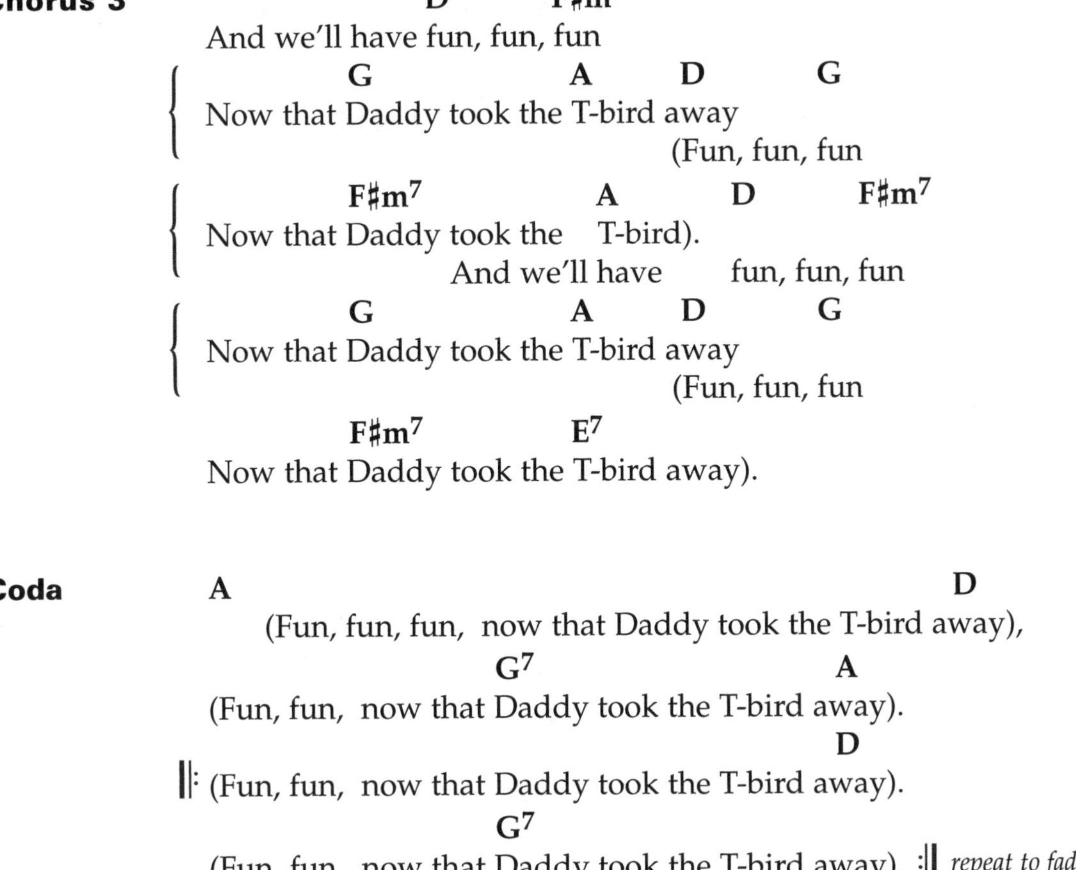

D F♯m⁷
And we'll have fun, fun, fun

G A D G
Now that Daddy took the T-bird away
(Fun, fun, fun

F♯m⁷ A D F♯m⁷
Now that Daddy took the T-bird).
And we'll have fun, fun, fun

G A D G
Now that Daddy took the T-bird away
(Fun, fun, fun

F♯m⁷ E⁷
Now that Daddy took the T-bird away).

Coda

A D
(Fun, fun, fun, now that Daddy took the T-bird away),

G⁷ A
(Fun, fun, now that Daddy took the T-bird away).

D
𝄆 (Fun, fun, now that Daddy took the T-bird away).

G⁷
(Fun, fun, now that Daddy took the T-bird away). 𝄇 *repeat to fade*

Go Your Own Way

Words and Music by
LINDSEY BUCKINGHAM

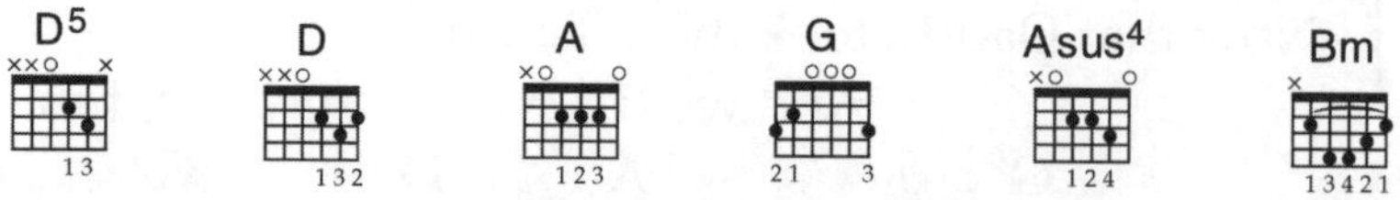

D^5 D A G Asus^4 Bm

Capo 3rd fret

♩ = 134

Intro
D^5
4/4 | / / / / | / / / / |

Verse 1
D A
Loving you isn't the right thing to do;
G D
How can I ever change things that I feel?____
A Asus^4
If I could, maybe I'd give you my world.
G D
How can I, when you won't take it from me?____

Chorus
Bm G A Bm
You can go your own way,____ (go your own way),____
G A
You can call it ano - ther lonely day.
Bm G A
You can go your own way,____ (go your own way).

Verse 2
D Asus^4
Tell me why everything turned around.
G D
Packing up, shacking up is all you wanna do.____

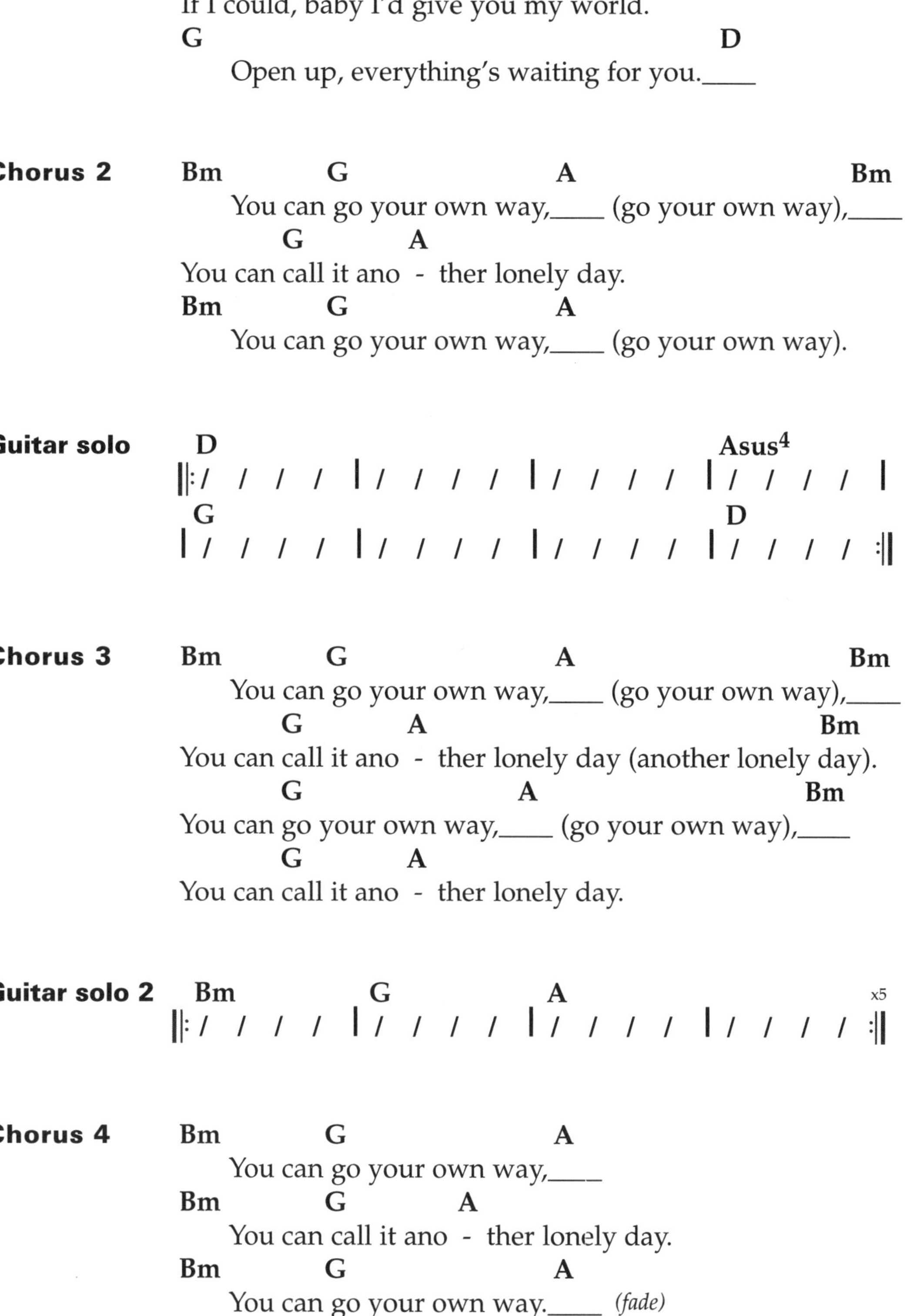

A Asus^4
If I could, baby I'd give you my world.
G D
Open up, everything's waiting for you.____

Chorus 2

Bm G A Bm
You can go your own way,____ (go your own way),____
G A
You can call it ano - ther lonely day.
Bm G A
You can go your own way,____ (go your own way).

Guitar solo

D Asus^4
𝄆 / / / / | / / / / | / / / / | / / / / |
G D
| / / / / | / / / / | / / / / | / / / / 𝄇

Chorus 3

Bm G A Bm
You can go your own way,____ (go your own way),____
G A Bm
You can call it ano - ther lonely day (another lonely day).
G A Bm
You can go your own way,____ (go your own way),____
G A
You can call it ano - ther lonely day.

Guitar solo 2

Bm G A x5
𝄆 / / / / | / / / / | / / / / | / / / / 𝄇

Chorus 4

Bm G A
You can go your own way,____
Bm G A
You can call it ano - ther lonely day.
Bm G A
You can go your own way.____ *(fade)*

Heroes

Words and Music by
DAVID BOWIE AND BRIAN ENO

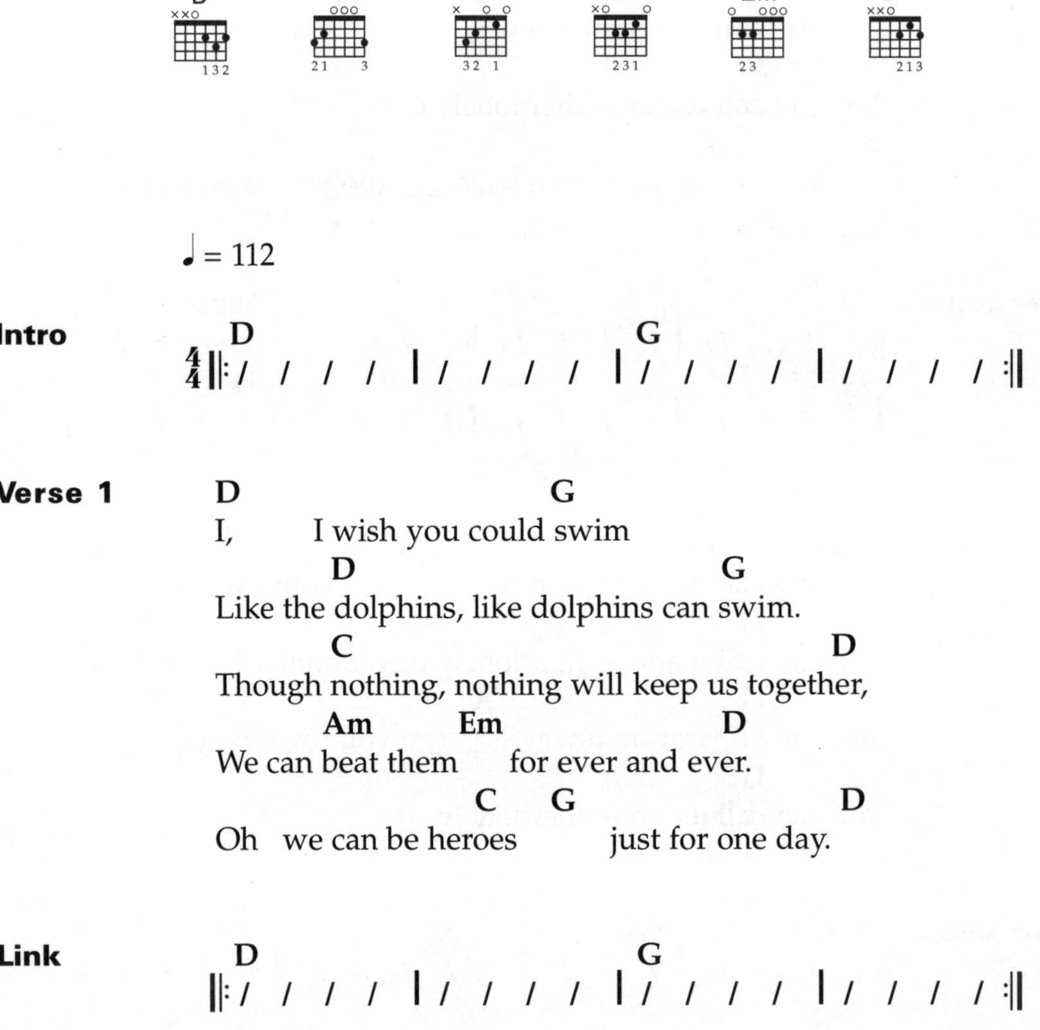

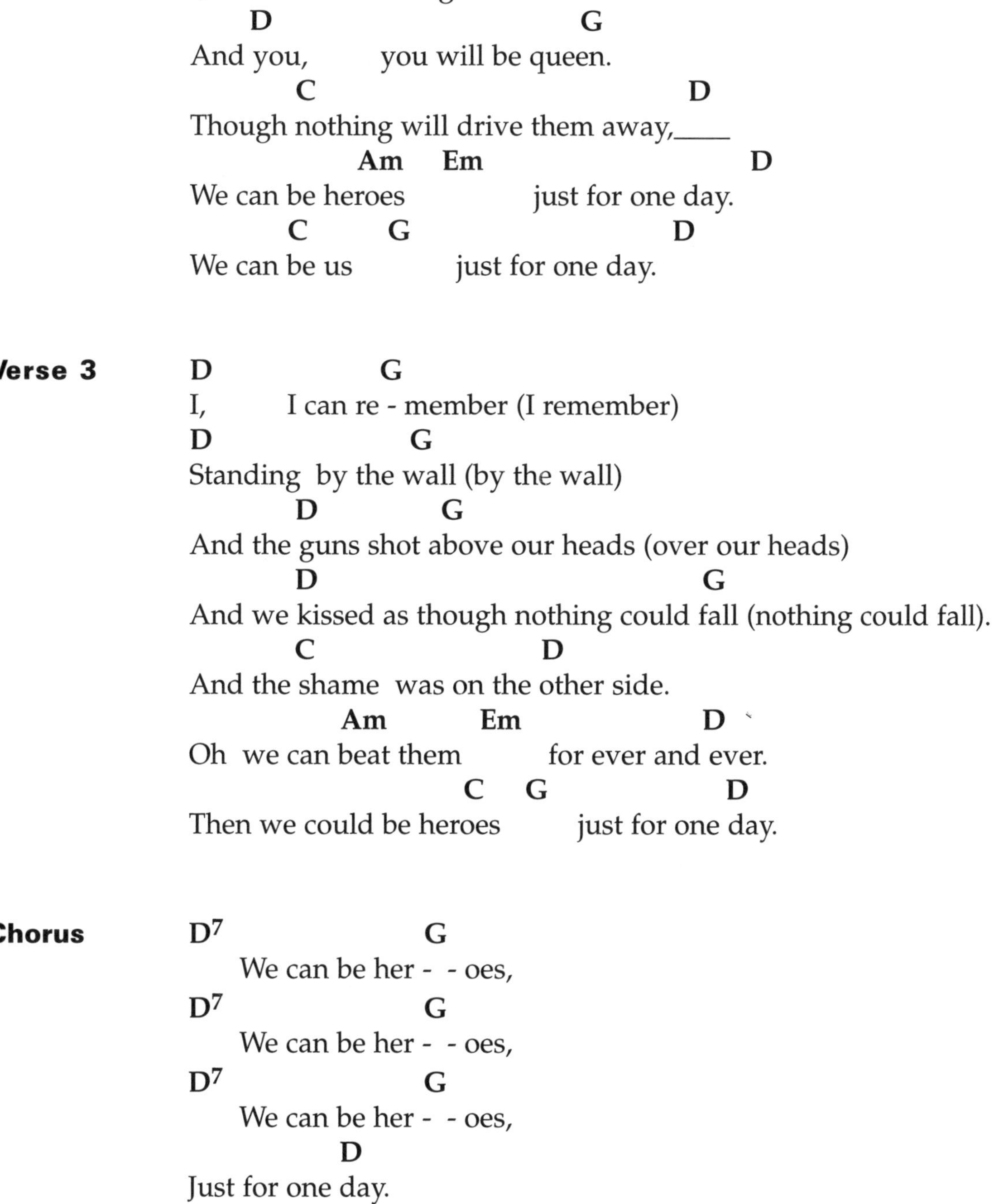

```
Verse 2   D                         G
          I,         I will be king
                 D                            G
          And you,        you will be queen.
                    C                                 D
          Though nothing will drive them away,____
                          Am     Em                      D
          We can be heroes              just for one day.
                   C         G                       D
          We can be us            just for one day.


Verse 3   D                 G
          I,         I can re - member (I remember)
          D                 G
          Standing  by the wall (by the wall)
                    D          G
          And the guns shot above our heads (over our heads)
                    D                                    G
          And we kissed as though nothing could fall (nothing could fall).
                    C                      D
          And the shame  was on the other side.
                        Am          Em                 D
          Oh  we can beat them          for ever and ever.
                                     C     G             D
          Then we could be heroes          just for one day.


Chorus    D7                G
               We can be her -  - oes,
          D7                G
               We can be her -  - oes,
          D7                G
               We can be her -  - oes,
                    D
          Just for one day.
```

Hey Joe

Words and Music by
WILLIAM ROBERTS

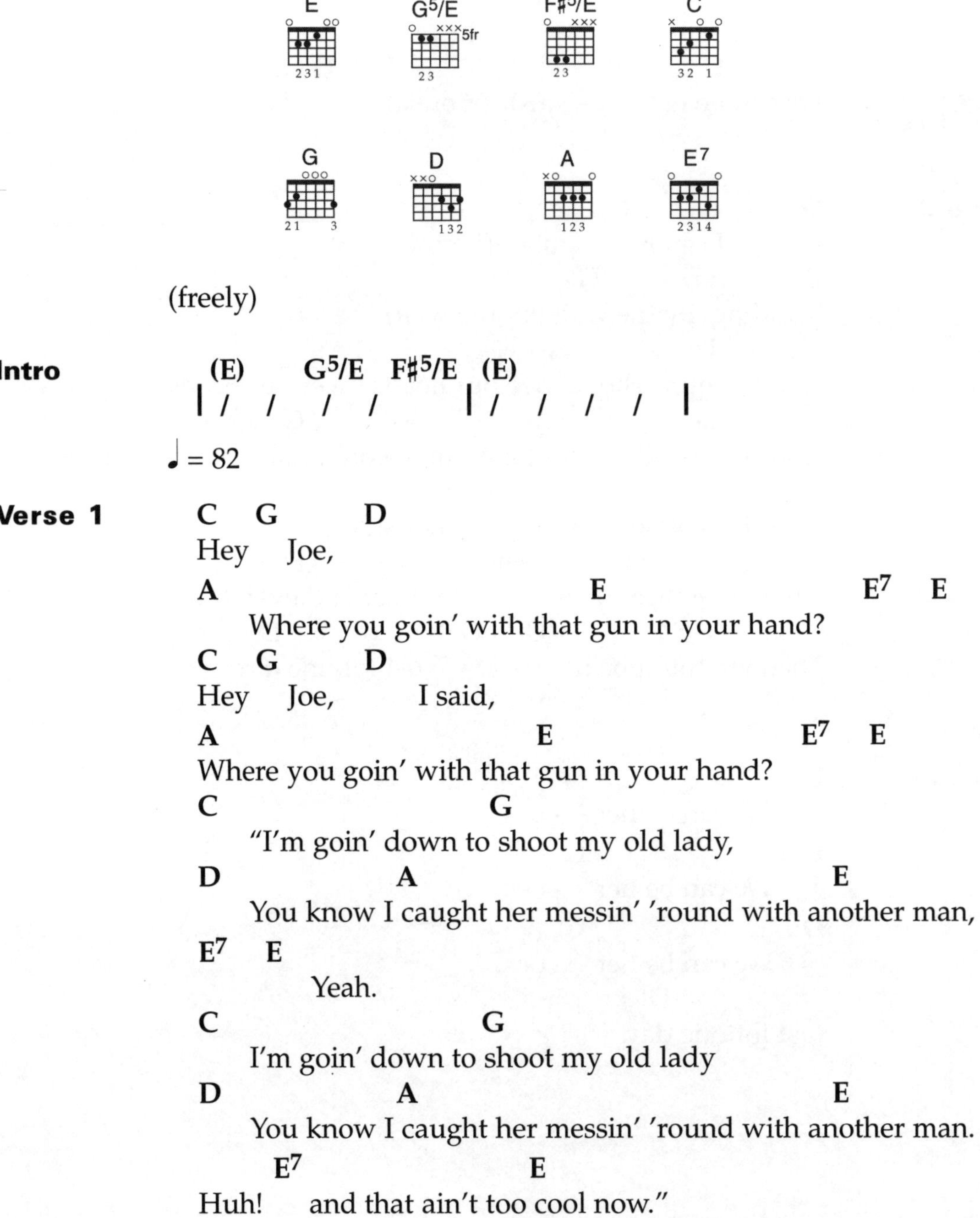

(freely)

Intro
(E) G5/E F♯5/E (E)
| / / / / | / / / / |

♩ = 82

Verse 1
C G D
Hey Joe,
A E E7 E
Where you goin' with that gun in your hand?
C G D
Hey Joe, I said,
A E E7 E
Where you goin' with that gun in your hand?
C G
"I'm goin' down to shoot my old lady,
D A E
You know I caught her messin' 'round with another man,
E7 E
Yeah.
C G
I'm goin' down to shoot my old lady
D A E
You know I caught her messin' 'round with another man.
E7 E
Huh! and that ain't too cool now."

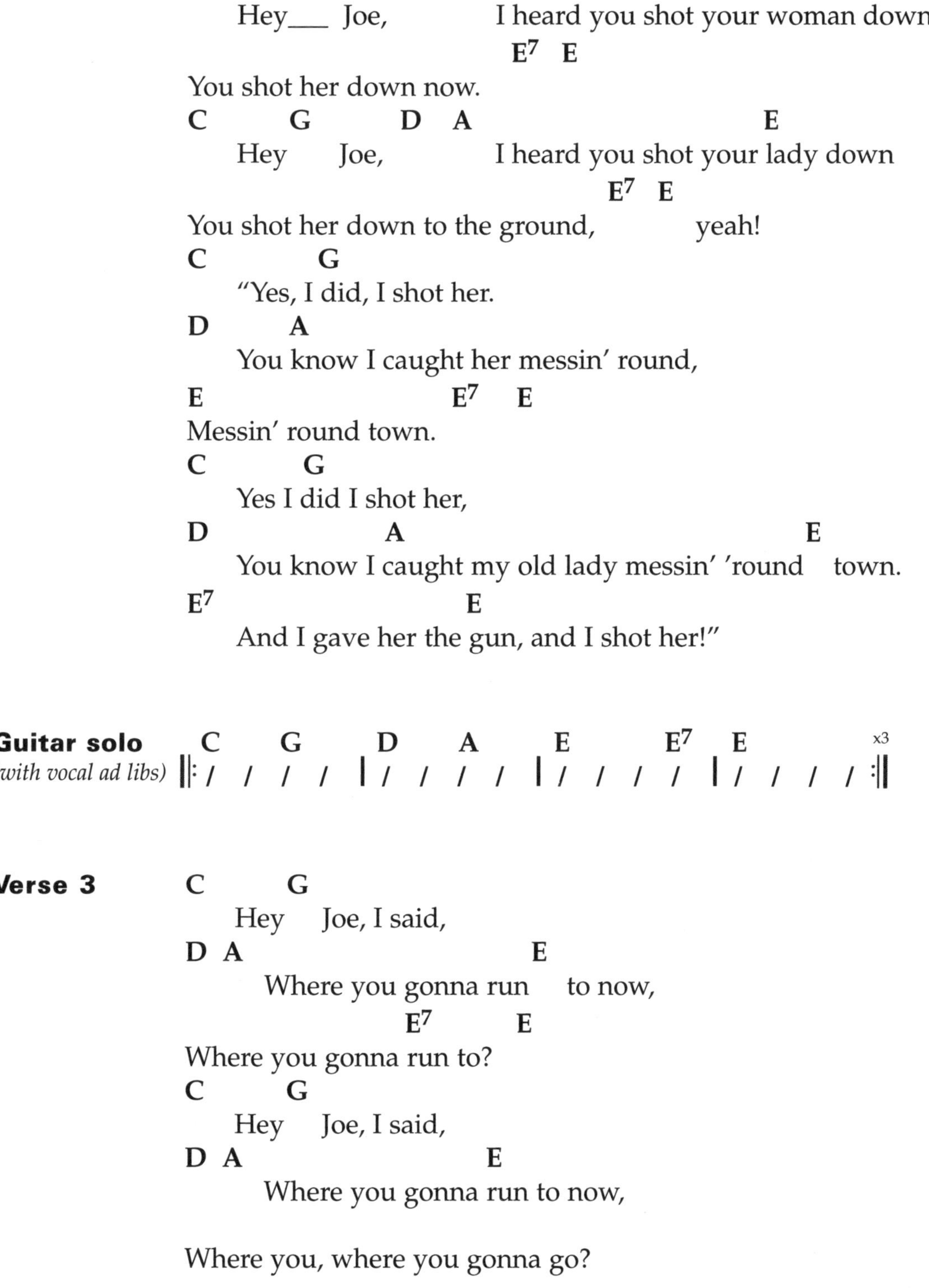

Verse 2

C G D A E
Hey___ Joe, I heard you shot your woman down,
E^7 E
You shot her down now.
C G D A E
Hey Joe, I heard you shot your lady down
E^7 E
You shot her down to the ground, yeah!
C G
"Yes, I did, I shot her.
D A
You know I caught her messin' round,
E E^7 E
Messin' round town.
C G
Yes I did I shot her,
D A E
You know I caught my old lady messin' 'round town.
E^7 E
And I gave her the gun, and I shot her!"

Guitar solo
(with vocal ad libs)

C G D A E E^7 E x3
𝄆 / / / / | / / / / | / / / / | / / / / 𝄇

Verse 3

C G
Hey Joe, I said,
D A E
Where you gonna run to now,
E^7 E
Where you gonna run to?
C G
Hey Joe, I said,
D A E
Where you gonna run to now,

Where you, where you gonna go?

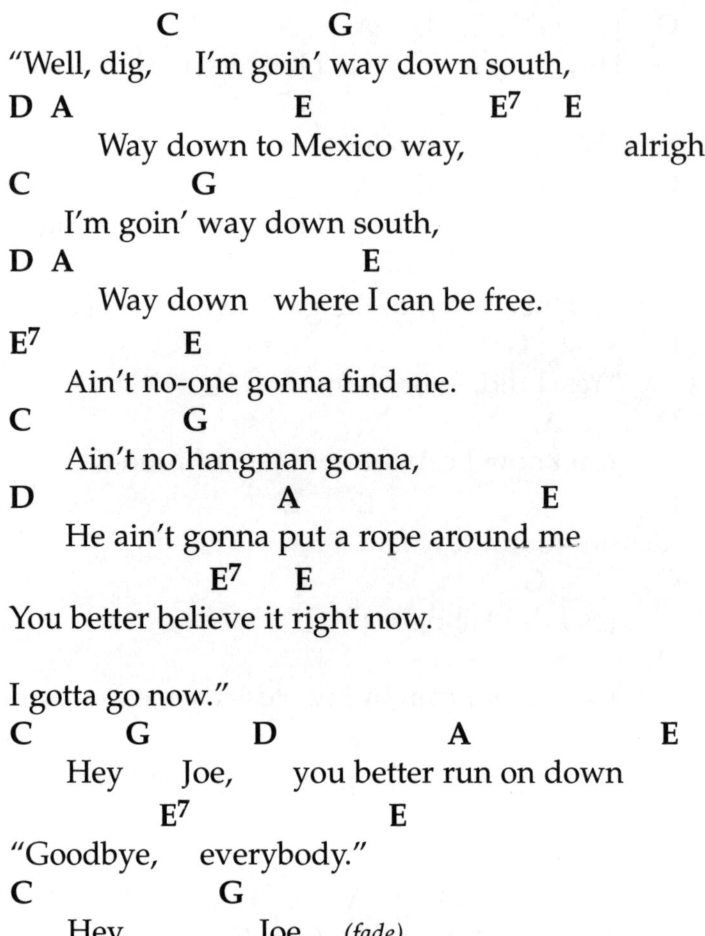

C **G**
"Well, dig, I'm goin' way down south,
D **A** **E** **E^7** **E**
Way down to Mexico way, alright.
C **G**
I'm goin' way down south,
D **A** **E**
Way down where I can be free.
E^7 **E**
Ain't no-one gonna find me.
C **G**
Ain't no hangman gonna,
D **A** **E**
He ain't gonna put a rope around me
E^7 **E**
You better believe it right now.

I gotta go now."
C **G** **D** **A** **E**
Hey Joe, you better run on down
E^7 **E**
"Goodbye, everybody."
C **G**
Hey______ Joe. *(fade)*

Hey You

Words and Music by
GEORGE ROGER WATERS

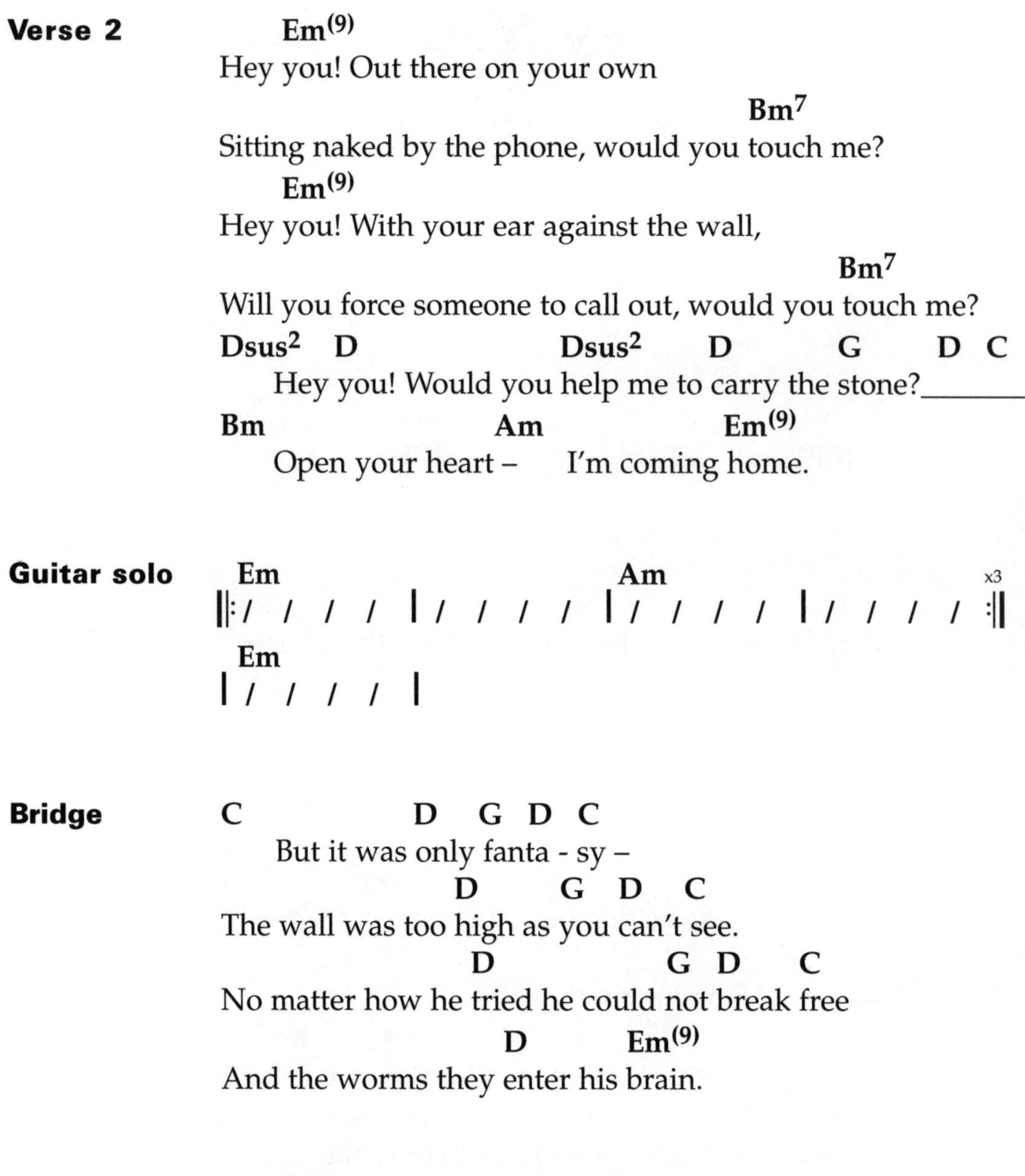

Verse 2

Em$^{(9)}$
Hey you! Out there on your own
Bm^7
Sitting naked by the phone, would you touch me?
Em$^{(9)}$
Hey you! With your ear against the wall,
Bm^7
Will you force someone to call out, would you touch me?
Dsus^2 D Dsus^2 D G D C
Hey you! Would you help me to carry the stone?________
Bm Am Em$^{(9)}$
Open your heart – I'm coming home.

Guitar solo

Em Am x3
‖: / / / / | / / / / | / / / / | / / / / :‖
Em
| / / / / |

Bridge

C D G D C
But it was only fanta - sy –
D G D C
The wall was too high as you can't see.
D G D C
No matter how he tried he could not break free
D Em$^{(9)}$
And the worms they enter his brain.

Link 2

Em$^{(9)}$ Em Em$^{(9)}$ Em Dsus^2 Dm Dsus^2 Dm x4
‖: (brain) / / / | / / / / :‖

Verse 3

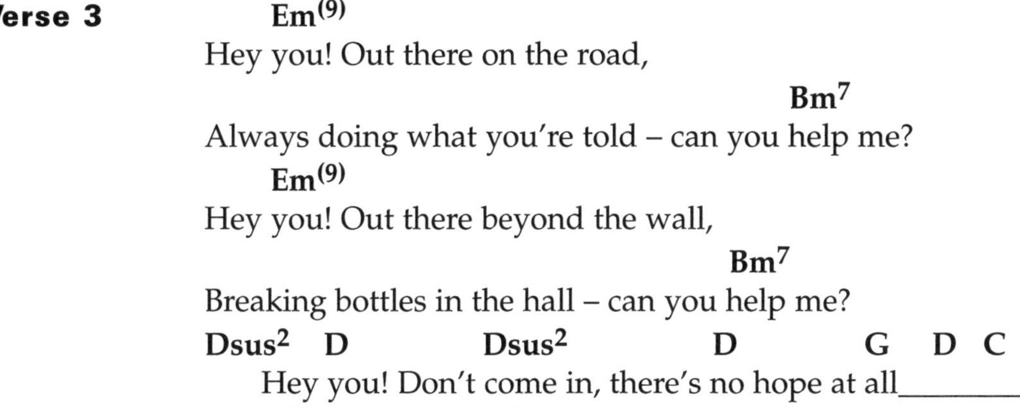

Em$^{(9)}$
Hey you! Out there on the road,
Bm^{7}
Always doing what you're told – can you help me?
Em$^{(9)}$
Hey you! Out there beyond the wall,
Bm^{7}
Breaking bottles in the hall – can you help me?
Dsus^{2} D Dsus^{2} D G D C
Hey you! Don't come in, there's no hope at all_______
Bm^{7} Am^{7} Em
Together we stand, divided we fall. ‖

Hickory Wind

Words and Music by
GRAM PARSONS AND BOB BUCHANAN

D7 C G D
213 | 32 1 | 21 3 | 132

♩ = 100

Intro

D7 C
3/4 | / / / | / / / | / / / | / / / |

G
| / / / | / / / | / / / |

Verse 1

G D D7 C G
In South Carolina there are many tall pines.
D D7 C D7
I remember the oak tree that we used to climb.
C D7 G
But now when I'm lonesome, I always pretend
C D G C G
That I'm getting the feel of hickory wind.

Verse 2

D D7 C G
I started out younger at most everything.
D D7 C D7
All the riches and pleasures, what else can life bring?
C D7 G
But it makes me feel better each time it be - gins
C D G C G
Calling me home, hickory wind.

Solo

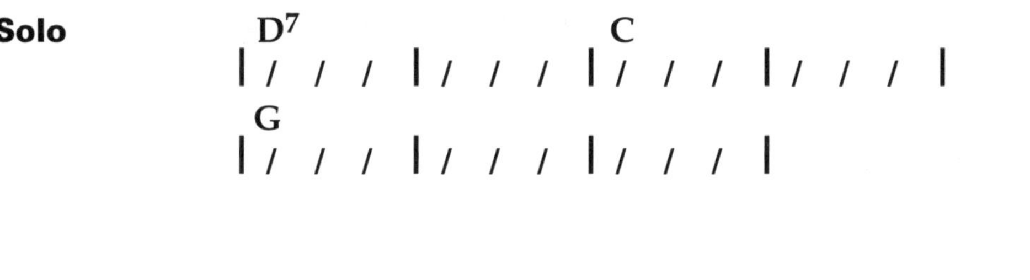
D7 C
G

Verse 3

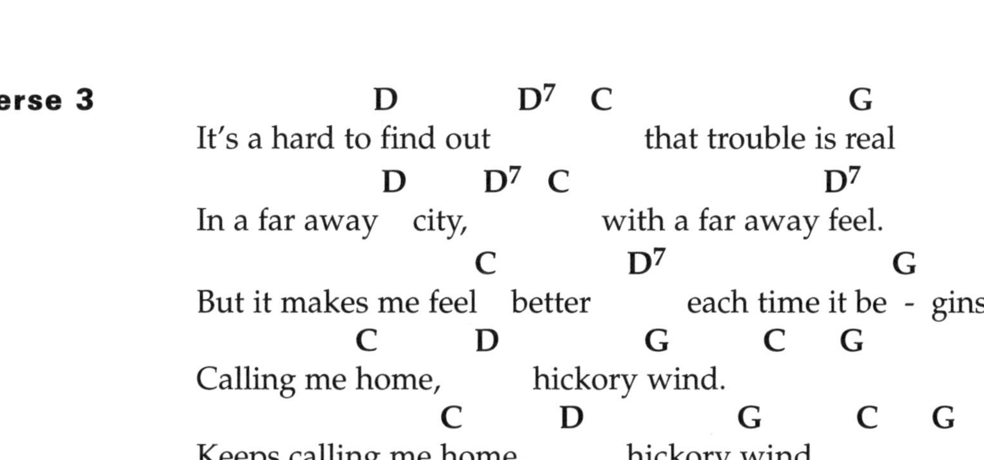
D D7 C G
It's a hard to find out that trouble is real
D D7 C D7
In a far away city, with a far away feel.
C D7 G
But it makes me feel better each time it be - gins
C D G C G
Calling me home, hickory wind.
C D G C G
Keeps calling me home, hickory wind.

A House Is Not A Motel

Words and Music by
ARTHUR LEE

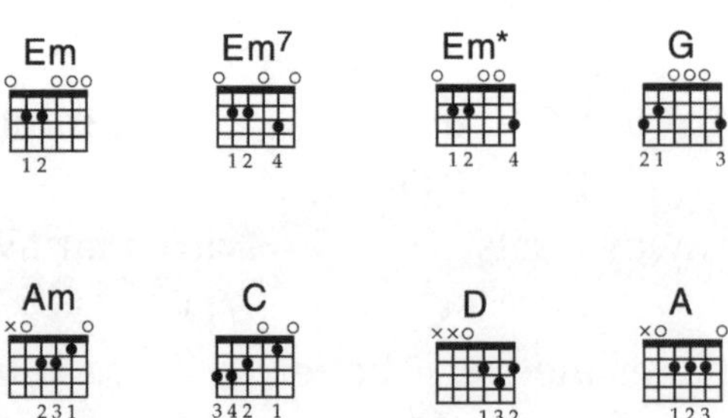

♩ = 155

Intro

```
     Em       Em7  Em        Em*  Em        Em7  Em        Em*
4/4 ||: / / / / | / / / / | / / / / | / / / / :||
```

Verse 1

```
Em                    G
     At my house I've got no shackles,
Am                  C
You can come and look if you want to:
Em                    G
     Through the halls you'll see the mantles
Am                     C
Where the light shines dim all around you.
Am                     D
     And the streets are paved with gold,
       Am                   D                  (Em)
And if someone asks you,    you can call my name.
```

Link

```
 Em        Em7  Em        Em*  Em        Em7  Em        Em*
| (name.) | / / / / | / / / / | / / / / |
```

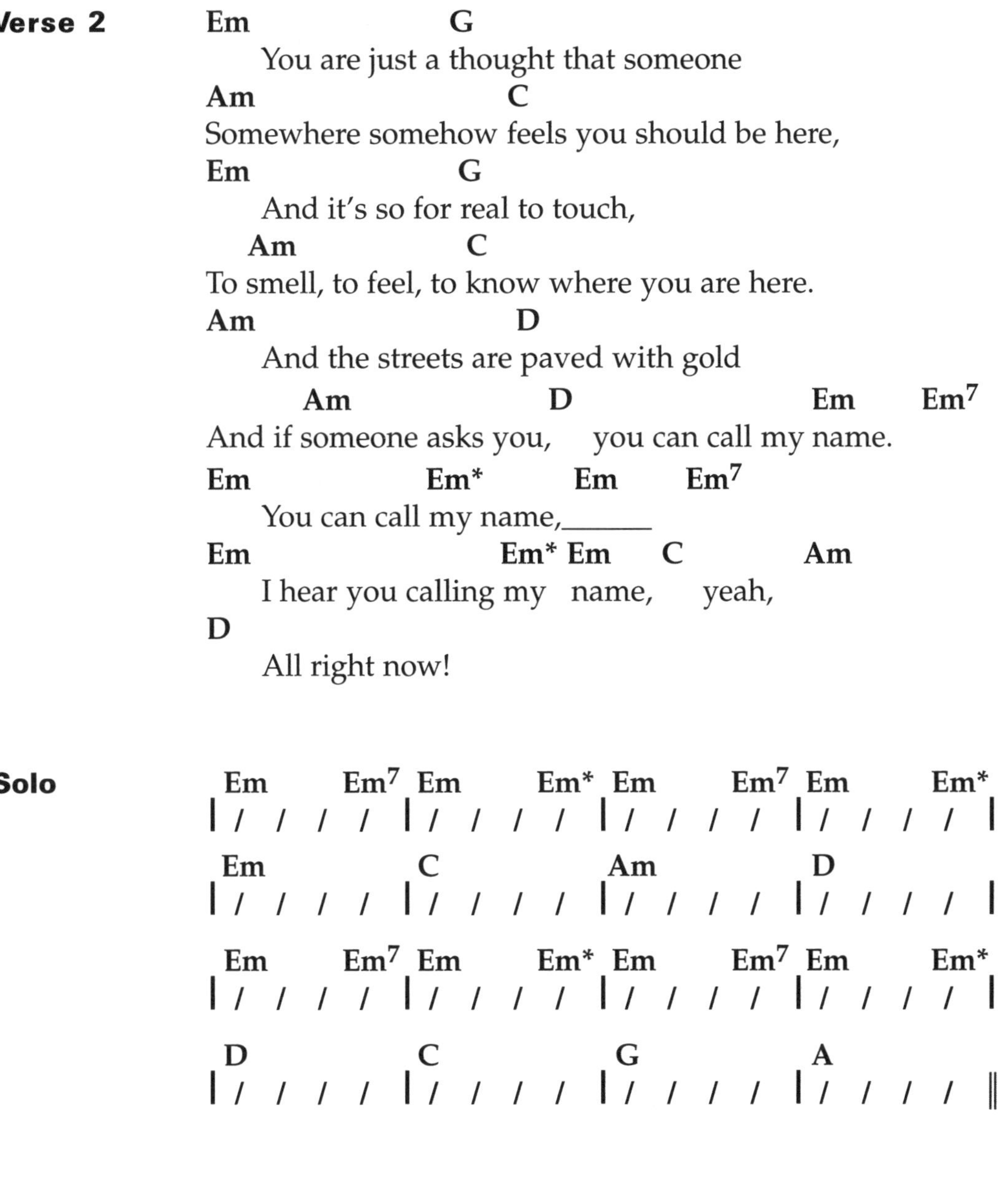

Verse 2

Em G
You are just a thought that someone
Am C
Somewhere somehow feels you should be here,
Em G
And it's so for real to touch,
Am C
To smell, to feel, to know where you are here.
Am D
And the streets are paved with gold
Am D Em Em^7
And if someone asks you, you can call my name.
Em Em* Em Em^7
You can call my name,______
Em Em* Em C Am
I hear you calling my name, yeah,
D
All right now!

Solo

| Em Em^7 | Em Em* | Em Em^7 | Em Em* |
| / / / / | / / / / | / / / / | / / / / |

| Em | C | Am | D |
| / / / / | / / / / | / / / / | / / / / |

| Em Em^7 | Em Em* | Em Em^7 | Em Em* |
| / / / / | / / / / | / / / / | / / / / |

| D | C | G | A |
| / / / / | / / / / | / / / / | / / / / ||

Link 2

||: Em Em^7 | Em Em* | Em Em^7 | Em Em* :||
||: / / / / | / / / / | / / / / | / / / / :||

Verse 3

```
Em                    G
     By the time that I'm through singing
     Am                  C
The bells from the schools of wars will be ringing:
Em                     G
     More confusions, blood transfusions,
      Am                   C
The news today will be the movies for tomorrow.
Am                   D
     And the water's turned to blood,
       Am                D                  Em      Em7
And if you don't think so   go turn on your tub
Em                   Em*      Em     Em7
     And if it's mixed      with mud
    Em          Em*  Em     Em7
You'll see it turn     to gray.
Em                   Em* Em     Em7
     And you can call my   name,
Em                    Em* Em
     I hear you calling my   name.
```

N.C.

| *4 bars drums only* | *4 bars lead guitar only* |

Coda/ Guitar solo

```
   Em      Em7 Em      Em*
||: / / / / | / / / /  :|| repeat to fade
```

House Of The Rising Sun

Traditional
Arranged by ALAN PRICE

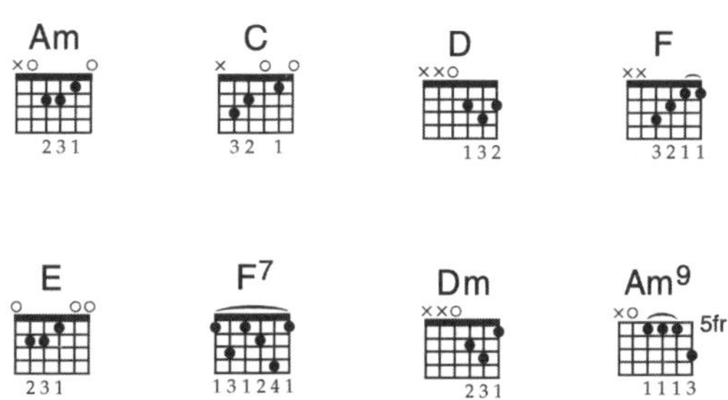

♩. = 78

Intro

```
        Am      C       D       F       Am      E       Am      E
6/8  |  /  /  | /  /  | /  /  | /  /  | /  /  | /  /  | /  /  | /  /  ||
```

Verse 1

```
           Am  C        D            F
There is a  house in New Orleans
           Am      C      E
They call the Rising Sun,
              Am      C      D                      F
And it's been the ruin of many a poor boy,
         Am    E
And God, I know I'm one.
```

Link

```
  Am        C       D       F       Am      E       Am      E
| (one.)  | /  /  | /  /  | /  /  | /  /  | /  /  | /  /  | /  /  ||
```

Verse 2

```
        Am    C     D       F7
My mother was a tailor.
        Am        C       E
She sewed my new blue jeans.
        Am   C    D       F
My father was a gambling man
Am      E
Down in New Orleans.
```

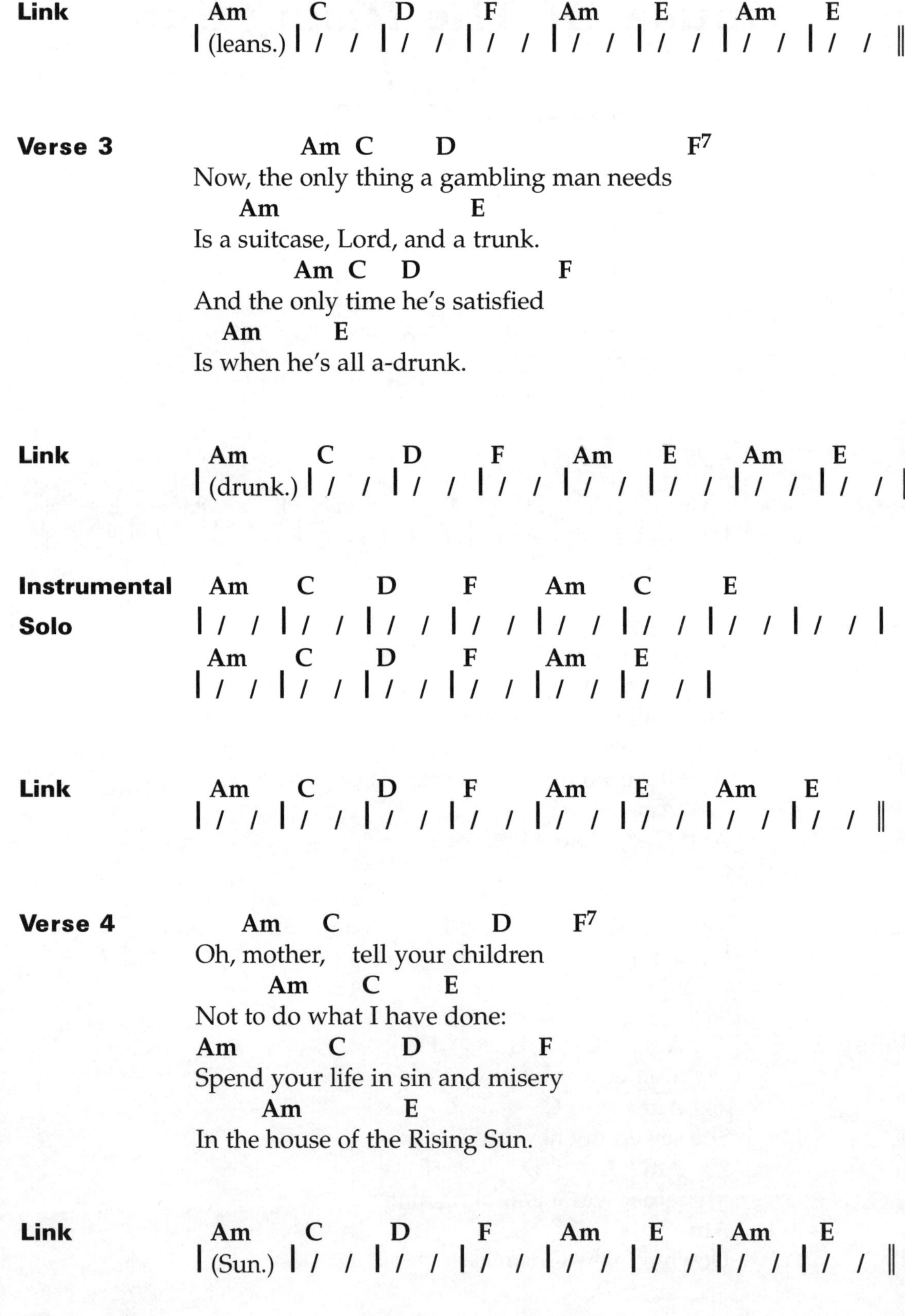

Link

Am C D F Am E Am E
| (leans.) | / / | / / | / / | / / | / / | / / | / / ||

Verse 3

            Am C   D   F7
Now, the only thing a gambling man needs
   Am   E
Is a suitcase, Lord, and a trunk.
        Am C   D   F
And the only time he's satisfied
  Am   E
Is when he's all a-drunk.

Link

Am C D F Am E Am E
| (drunk.) | / / | / / | / / | / / | / / | / / | / / ||

Instrumental Solo

Am C D F Am C E
| / / | / / | / / | / / | / / | / / | / / | / / |
Am C D F Am E
| / / | / / | / / | / / | / / | / / |

Link

Am C D F Am E Am E
| / / | / / | / / | / / | / / | / / | / / | / / ||

Verse 4

   Am   C   D   F7
Oh, mother,   tell your children
      Am   C   E
Not to do what I have done:
Am   C   D   F
Spend your life in sin and misery
     Am   E
In the house of the Rising Sun.

Link

Am C D F Am E Am E
| (Sun.) | / / | / / | / / | / / | / / | / / | / / ||

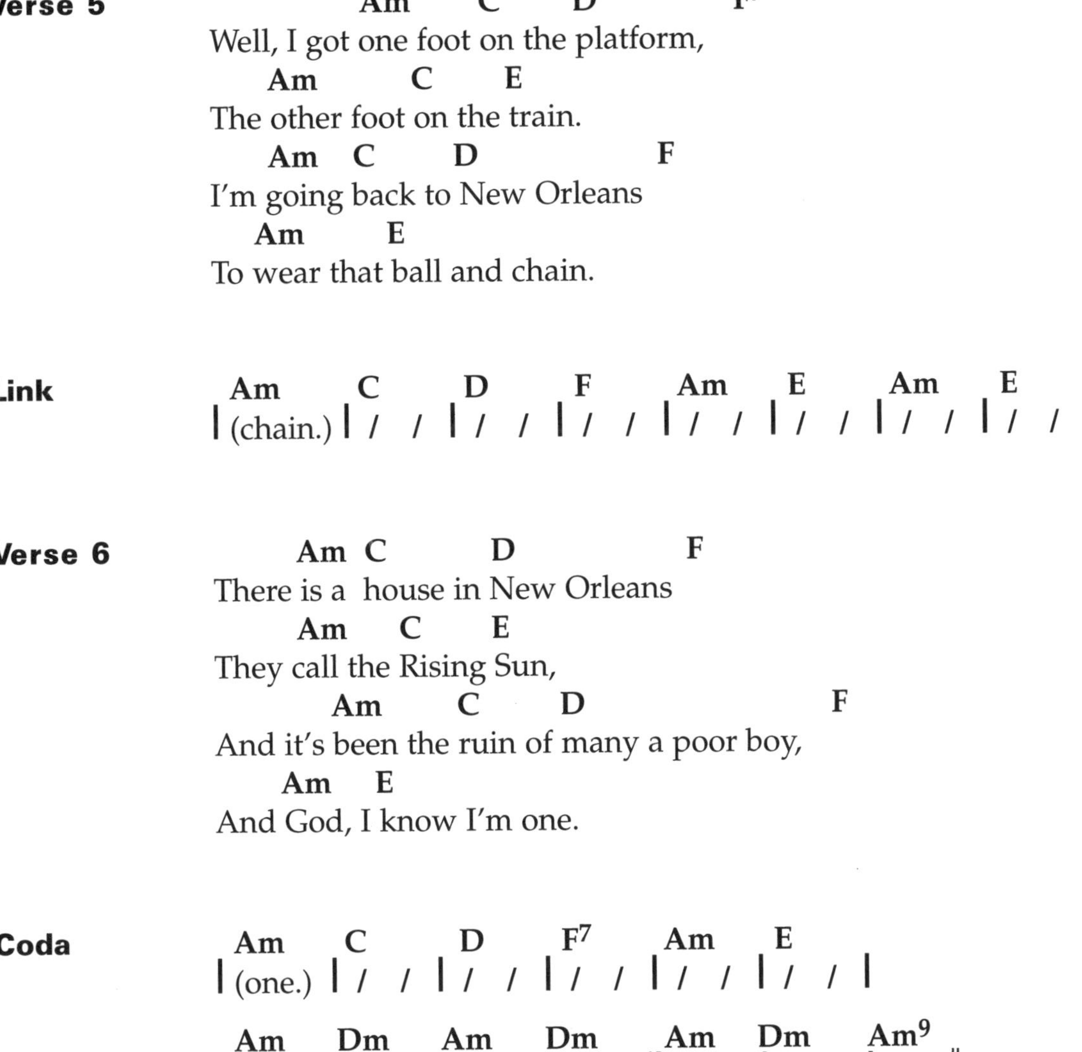

Verse 5

Am C D F^7
Well, I got one foot on the platform,
Am C E
The other foot on the train.
Am C D F
I'm going back to New Orleans
Am E
To wear that ball and chain.

Link

Am C D F Am E Am E
| (chain.) | / / | / / | / / | / / | / / | / / | / / ||

Verse 6

Am C D F
There is a house in New Orleans
Am C E
They call the Rising Sun,
Am C D F
And it's been the ruin of many a poor boy,
Am E
And God, I know I'm one.

Coda

Am C D F^7 Am E
| (one.) | / / | / / | / / | / / | / / |

Am Dm Am Dm Am Dm Am^9
||: / / | / / | / / | / / :|| / / | / / | / ||

Hungry Like The Wolf

Words and Music by
SIMON LE BON, ANDY TAYLOR, ROGER TAYLOR,
JOHN TAYLOR AND NICK RHODES

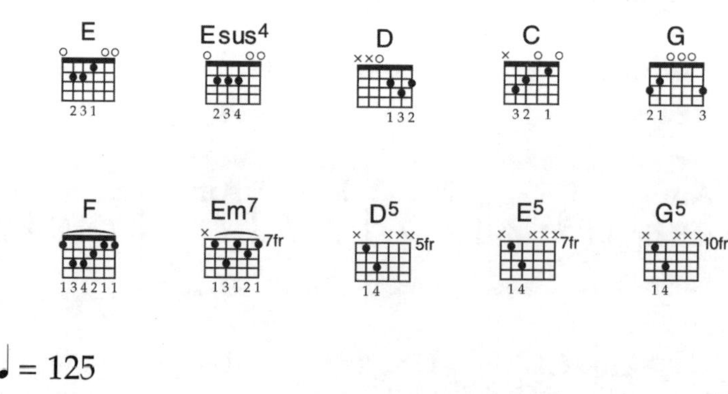

♩ = 125

Intro

E Esus4 E Esus4
‖: / / / / | / / / / :‖

Verse 1

E Esus4 E Esus4 E
Darken the city, night is a wire;
Esus4 E Esus4 E
Steam in the subway, earth is afire.
D
Do do do, do do do, do do do, do do do,
E Esus4 E Esus4 E
Do do do.
Esus4 E Esus4 E
Woman, you want me, give me a sign
Esus4 E Esus4 E
And catch my breathing even clo - ser behind.
D
Do do do, do do do, do do do, do do do,
E Esus4 E Esus4 E
Do do do.

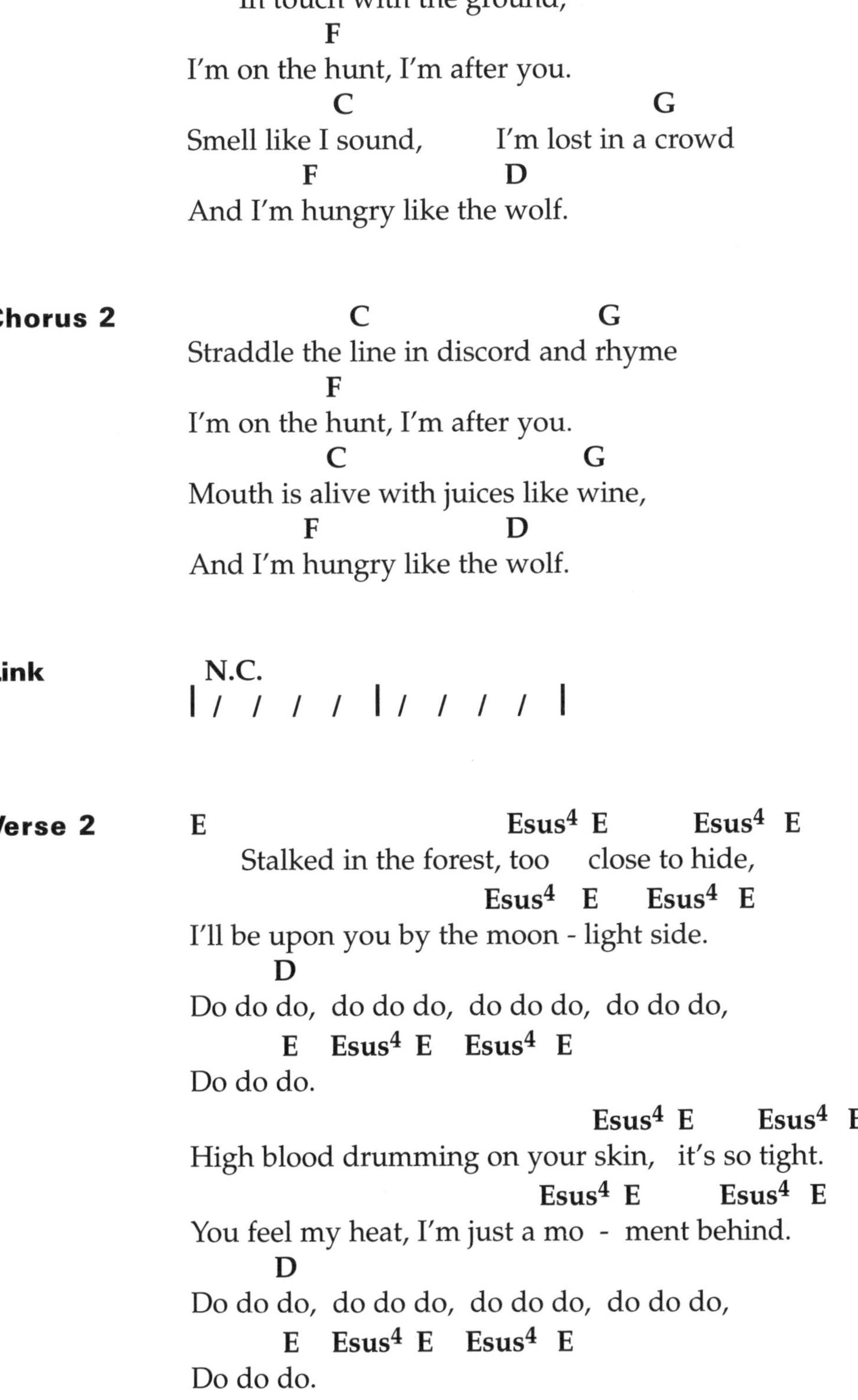

Chorus 1

C G
In touch with the ground,
F
I'm on the hunt, I'm after you.
C G
Smell like I sound, I'm lost in a crowd
F D
And I'm hungry like the wolf.

Chorus 2

C G
Straddle the line in discord and rhyme
F
I'm on the hunt, I'm after you.
C G
Mouth is alive with juices like wine,
F D
And I'm hungry like the wolf.

Link

N.C.
| / / / / | / / / / |

Verse 2

E Esus4 E Esus4 E
Stalked in the forest, too close to hide,
Esus4 E Esus4 E
I'll be upon you by the moon - light side.
D
Do do do, do do do, do do do, do do do,
E Esus4 E Esus4 E
Do do do.
Esus4 E Esus4 E
High blood drumming on your skin, it's so tight.
Esus4 E Esus4 E
You feel my heat, I'm just a mo - ment behind.
D
Do do do, do do do, do do do, do do do,
E Esus4 E Esus4 E
Do do do.

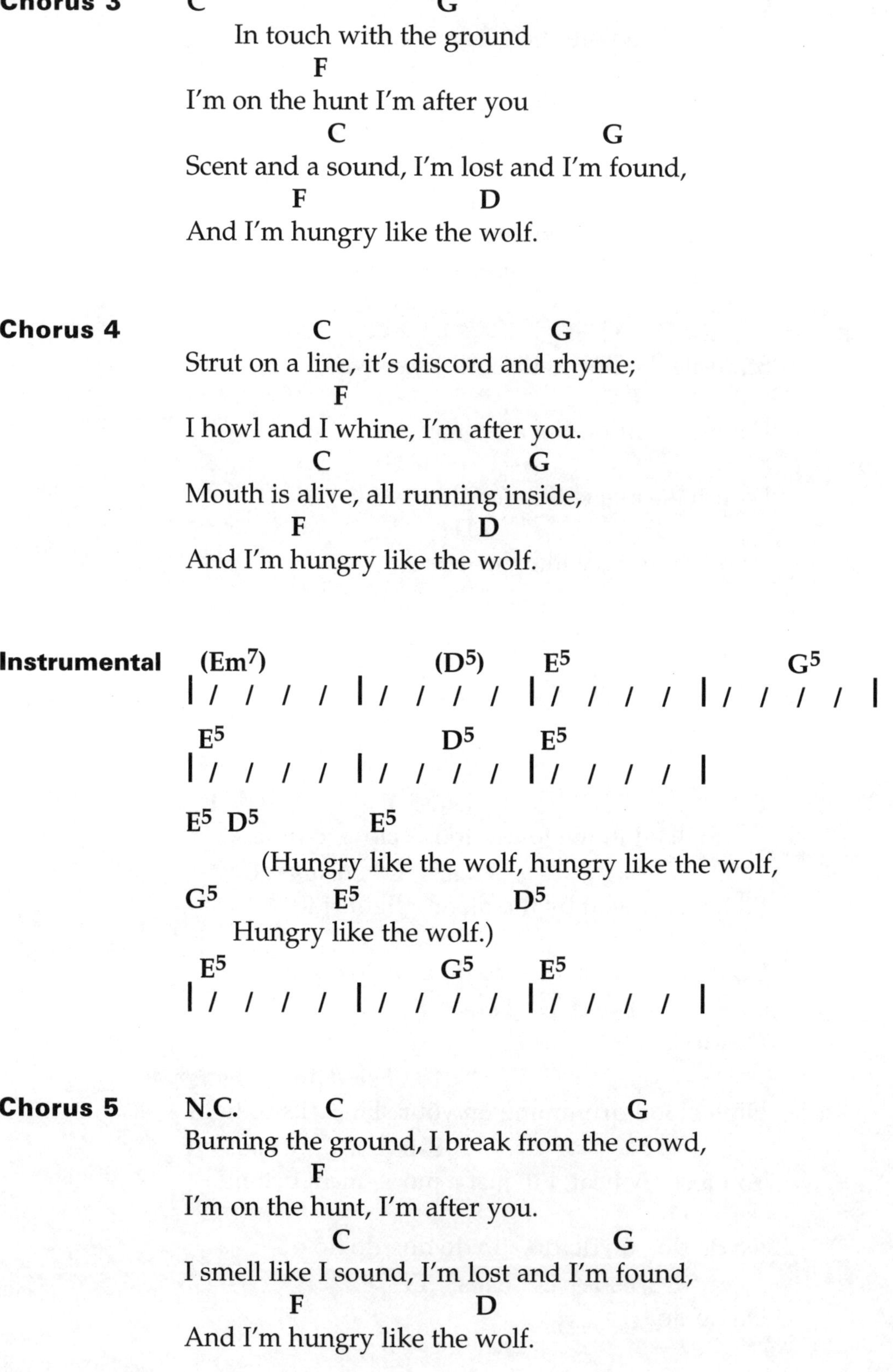
Chorus 3
C G
In touch with the ground
F
I'm on the hunt I'm after you
C G
Scent and a sound, I'm lost and I'm found,
F D
And I'm hungry like the wolf.
Chorus 4
C G
Strut on a line, it's discord and rhyme;
F
I howl and I whine, I'm after you.
C G
Mouth is alive, all running inside,
F D
And I'm hungry like the wolf.
Instrumental
(Em7) (D5) E5 G5
E5 D5 E5
E5 D5 E5
(Hungry like the wolf, hungry like the wolf,
G5 E5 D5
Hungry like the wolf.)
E5 G5 E5
Chorus 5
N.C. C G
Burning the ground, I break from the crowd,
F
I'm on the hunt, I'm after you.
C G
I smell like I sound, I'm lost and I'm found,
F D
And I'm hungry like the wolf.

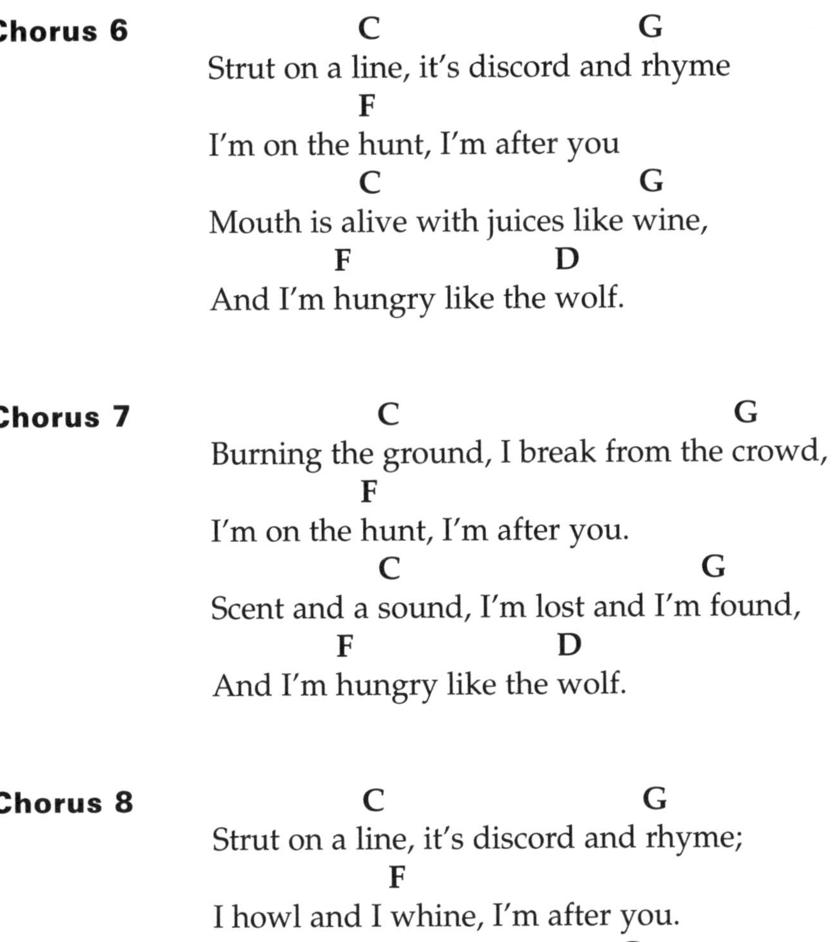

Chorus 6

C G
Strut on a line, it's discord and rhyme
F
I'm on the hunt, I'm after you
C G
Mouth is alive with juices like wine,
F D
And I'm hungry like the wolf.

Chorus 7

C G
Burning the ground, I break from the crowd,
F
I'm on the hunt, I'm after you.
C G
Scent and a sound, I'm lost and I'm found,
F D
And I'm hungry like the wolf.

Chorus 8

C G
Strut on a line, it's discord and rhyme;
F
I howl and I whine, I'm after you.
C G
Mouth is alive, all running inside… *(fade)*

I Got You Babe

Words and Music by
SONNY BONO

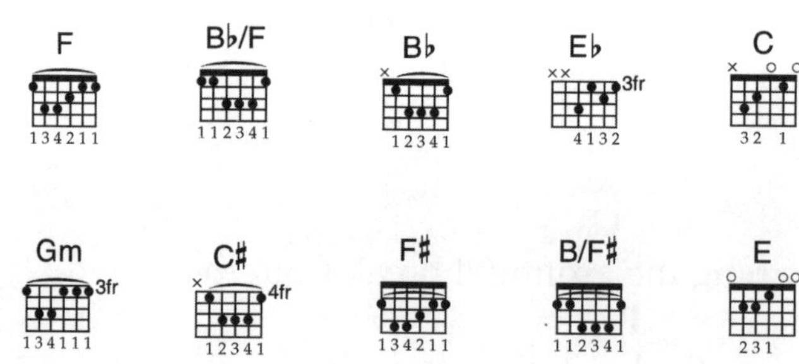

♩. = 72

Intro

12/8 | **F** / / **B♭/F** / / | **F** / / **B♭/F** / / |

Verse 1

```
      F                                  B♭/F
They say we're young and we don't know,
      F                      B♭  E♭       C
We won't find out until____     we grow.
       F              B♭/F
Well I don't know        if all that's true
          F                  B♭    E♭     C
'Cause you got me and baby I got you.
```

Chorus

```
F       B♭/F         F                B♭/F
Babe,          I got you babe,
        F              B♭/F
I got you babe.
```

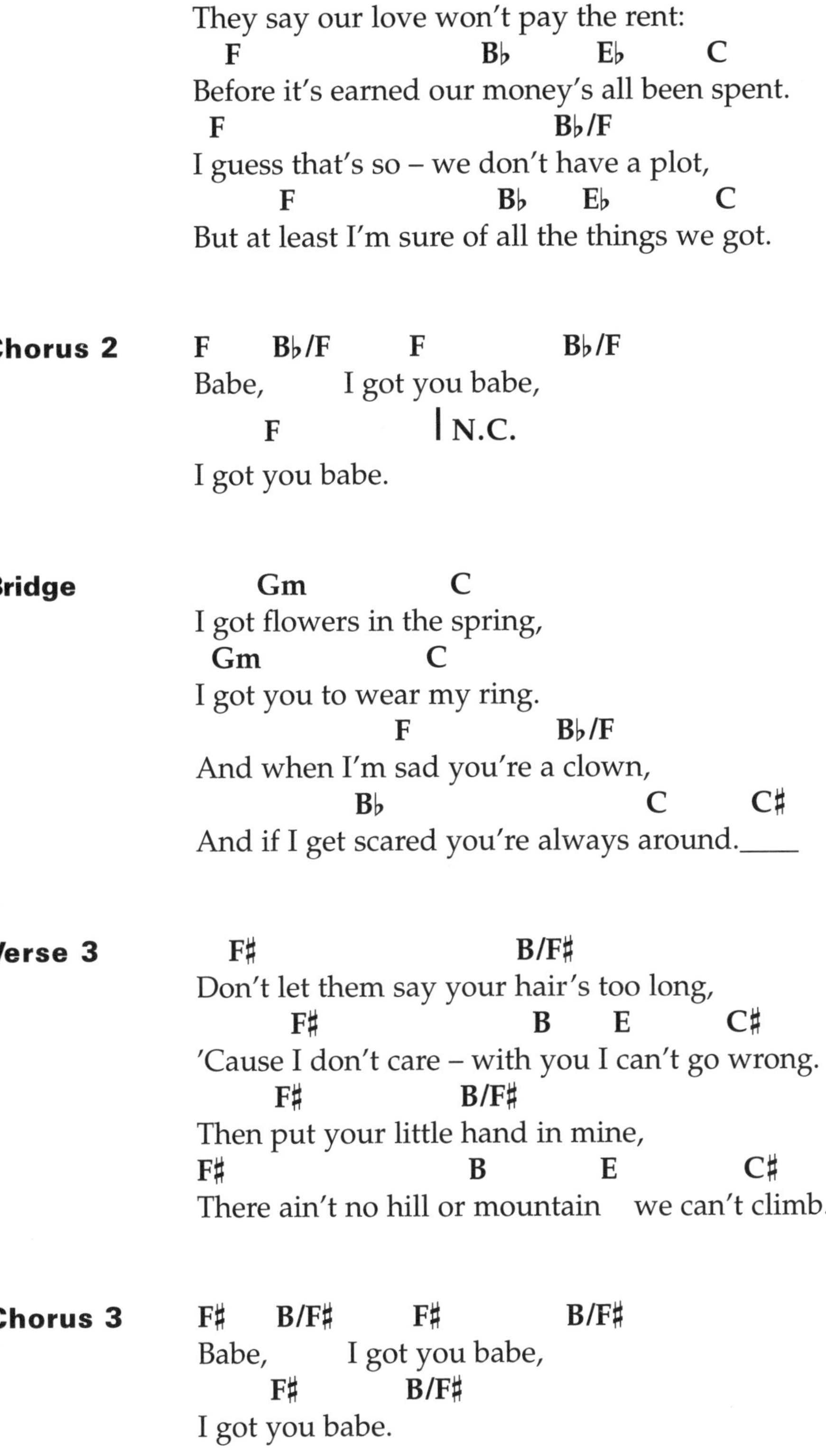

```
Verse 2     F                            B♭/F
            They say our love won't pay the rent:
              F                      B♭      E♭      C
            Before it's earned our money's all been spent.
             F                              B♭/F
            I guess that's so – we don't have a plot,
                   F                   B♭     E♭        C
            But at least I'm sure of all the things we got.


Chorus 2    F     B♭/F       F          B♭/F
            Babe,        I got you babe,
                F              | N.C.
            I got you babe.


Bridge          Gm             C
            I got flowers in the spring,
              Gm             C
            I got you to wear my ring.
                          F           B♭/F
            And when I'm sad you're a clown,
                       B♭                     C       C♯
            And if I get scared you're always around.____


Verse 3       F♯                         B/F♯
            Don't let them say your hair's too long,
                    F♯                   B     E        C♯
            'Cause I don't care – with you I can't go wrong.
                   F♯             B/F♯
            Then put your little hand in mine,
            F♯                      B          E           C♯
            There ain't no hill or mountain    we can't climb.


Chorus 3    F♯    B/F♯       F♯         B/F♯
            Babe,        I got you babe,
                 F♯         B/F♯
            I got you babe.
```

Link

F♯ B/F♯ F♯ C♯
| / / / / | / / / / |

Coda

F♯ B/F♯
I got you to hold my hand,
F♯ C♯
I got you to understand.
F♯ B/F♯
I got you to walk with me,
F♯ C♯
I got you to talk with me.
F♯ B/F♯
I got you to kiss goodnight,
F♯ C♯
I got you to hold me tight.
F♯ B/F♯
I got you, I won't let go;
F♯ C♯
I got you to love me so.

Link

F♯ B/F♯ F♯ C♯
| / / / / | / / / / |

N.C. B F♯
I got you babe,
F♯ B/F♯ F♯ C♯
I got you babe.
F♯ B/F♯
‖: I got you babe,
F♯ C♯
I got you babe. :‖ *repeat to fade*

I Walk The Line

Words and Music by
JOHNNY CASH

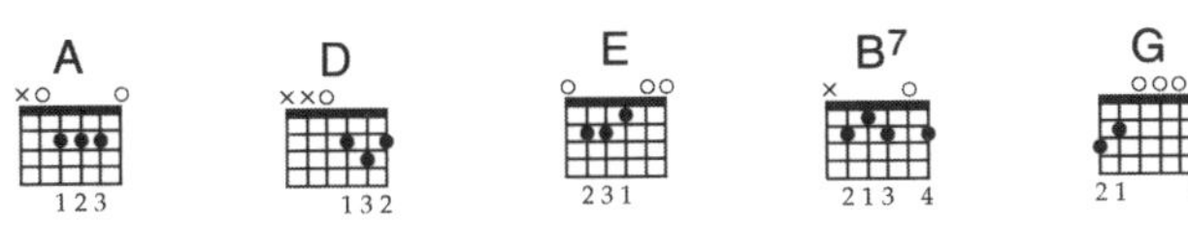

Capo 1st fret

♩ = 112

ntro

```
    A                 D                 A                 E
4/4 | /  /  /  /  | /  /  /  /  | /  /  /  /  | /  /  /  /  |
    B7                E
    | /  /  /  /  | /  /  /  /  | /  /  /  /  | /  /  /  /  ||
```

Verse 1

```
          B7                              E
I keep a close watch on this heart of mine
             B7                       E
I keep my eyes wide open all the time
             A                          E
I keep the ends out for the tie that binds
                 B7              E
Because you're mine, I walk the line.
```

Link

A

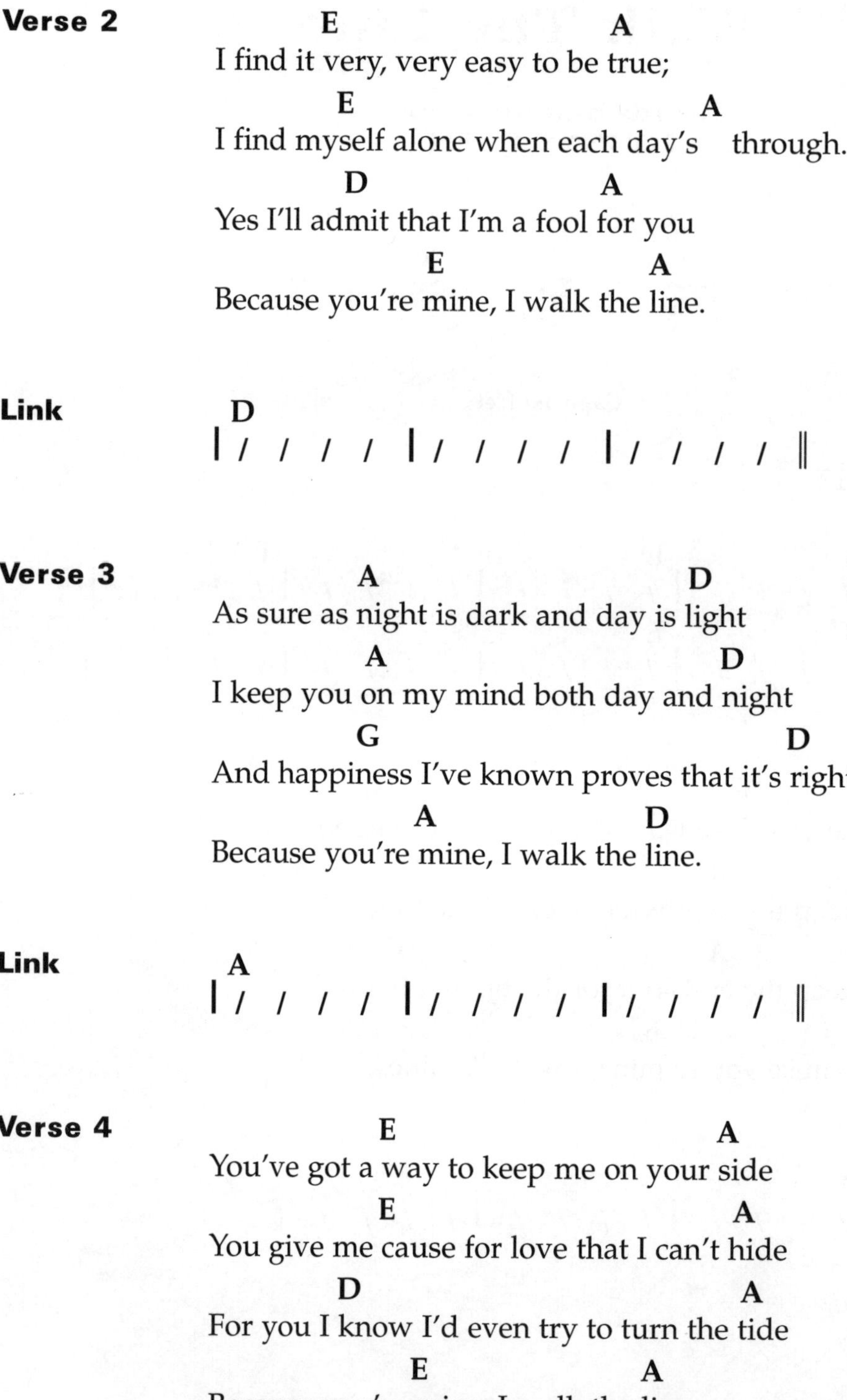

Verse 2

E A
I find it very, very easy to be true;
E A
I find myself alone when each day's through.
D A
Yes I'll admit that I'm a fool for you
E A
Because you're mine, I walk the line.

Link

D
| / / / / | / / / / | / / / / ||

Verse 3

A D
As sure as night is dark and day is light
A D
I keep you on my mind both day and night
G D
And happiness I've known proves that it's right
A D
Because you're mine, I walk the line.

Link

A
| / / / / | / / / / | / / / / ||

Verse 4

E A
You've got a way to keep me on your side
E A
You give me cause for love that I can't hide
D A
For you I know I'd even try to turn the tide
E A
Because you're mine, I walk the line.

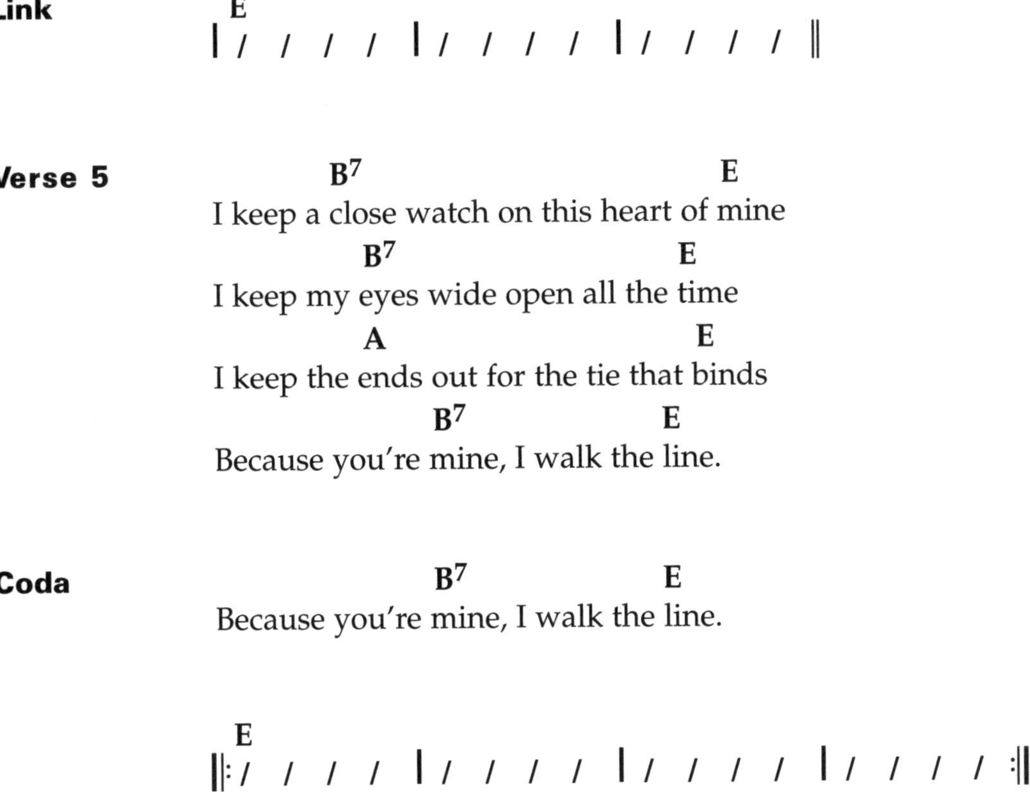

Link

E
| / / / / | / / / / | / / / / ||

Verse 5

B7 E
I keep a close watch on this heart of mine
B7 E
I keep my eyes wide open all the time
A E
I keep the ends out for the tie that binds
B7 E
Because you're mine, I walk the line.

Coda

B7 E
Because you're mine, I walk the line.

E
||: / / / / | / / / / | / / / / | / / / / :||

repeat to fade

I'm Into Something Good

Words and Music by
GERRY GOFFIN AND CAROLE KING

C F C7 G D Dm7 G7

32 1 | 134211 | 3241 | 21 3 | 132 | 312 | 32 1

♩ = 132

Intro

C F C F C F C F
4/4 | / / / / | / / / / | / / / / | / / / / |

Verse 1

C F C F
Woke up this morning feeling fine,
C F C7
There's something special on my mind.
F C
Last night I met a new girl in the neighbourhood, whoa yeah.

Chorus

G F
Something tells me I'm into something
C F C F
Good.
(Something tells me I'm into something

Verse 2

C F C F
She's the kind of girl who's not too shy,
Good.)
C F C7
And I can tell I'm her kind of guy.
F C
She danced close to me like I hoped she would.

(She danced with me like I hoped she would).

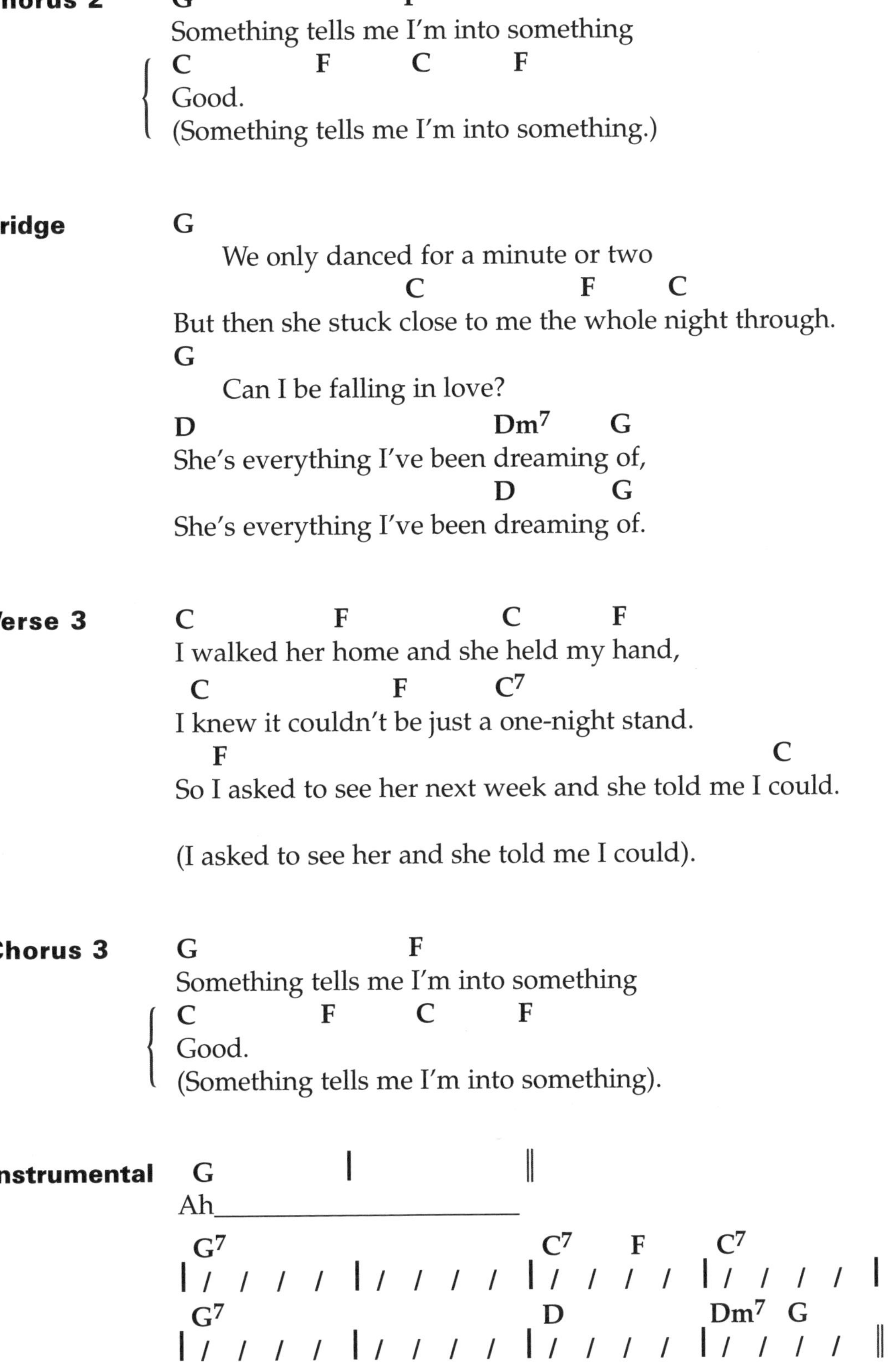

Chorus 2

G F
Something tells me I'm into something
C F C F
Good.
(Something tells me I'm into something.)

Bridge

G
We only danced for a minute or two
C F C
But then she stuck close to me the whole night through.
G
Can I be falling in love?
D Dm^7 G
She's everything I've been dreaming of,
D G
She's everything I've been dreaming of.

Verse 3

C F C F
I walked her home and she held my hand,
C F C^7
I knew it couldn't be just a one-night stand.
F C
So I asked to see her next week and she told me I could.

(I asked to see her and she told me I could).

Chorus 3

G F
Something tells me I'm into something
C F C F
Good.
(Something tells me I'm into something).

Instrumental

G | ||
Ah____________________

G^7 C^7 F C^7
| / / / / | / / / / | / / / / | / / / / |
G^7 D Dm^7 G
| / / / / | / / / / | / / / / | / / / / ||

Verse 4

C F C F
I walked her home and she held my hand,
C F C^7
I knew it couldn't be just a one-night stand.
F C
So I asked to see her next week and she told me I could.

(I asked to see her and she told me I could).

Chorus 4

G F
Something tells me I'm into something
C F C F
Good.
(Something tells me I'm into something).

Chorus 5

G F
Something tells me I'm into something
C F C F
Good.
(Something tells me I'm into something).

Coda

G F
To something good, oh yeah, something
C F C F G
Good. to something good.
(Something tells me I'm into something)
F C
Oh yeah, something good to something
(Something tells me I'm into something)
G F C
Good, something good, something good. *(fade)*

It's A Hard Life

Words and Music by
FREDDIE MERCURY

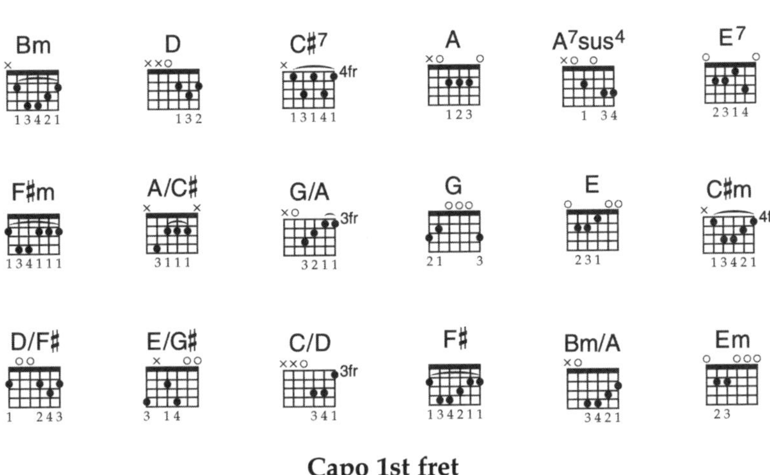

Capo 1st fret

(freely)

Intro

Bm
I don't want my freedom,
D **C♯7** **N.C.**
There's no reason for living with a broken
♩ = 79
A **A7sus4** **A** **A7sus4**
heart.

Verse 1

A **E7** **F♯m** **D** **A/C♯** **Bm**
This is a tricky situation, I've only got myself to blame.
A **G/A**
It's just a simple fact of life, it can happen to any one.
D **A/C♯** **Bm** **F♯m**
You win, you lose, it's a chance you have to take with love.
D **A/C♯**
Oh yeah, I fell in love,
Bm **F♯m** **G**
But now you say it's over and I'm falling apart.
E
Yeah, yeah.

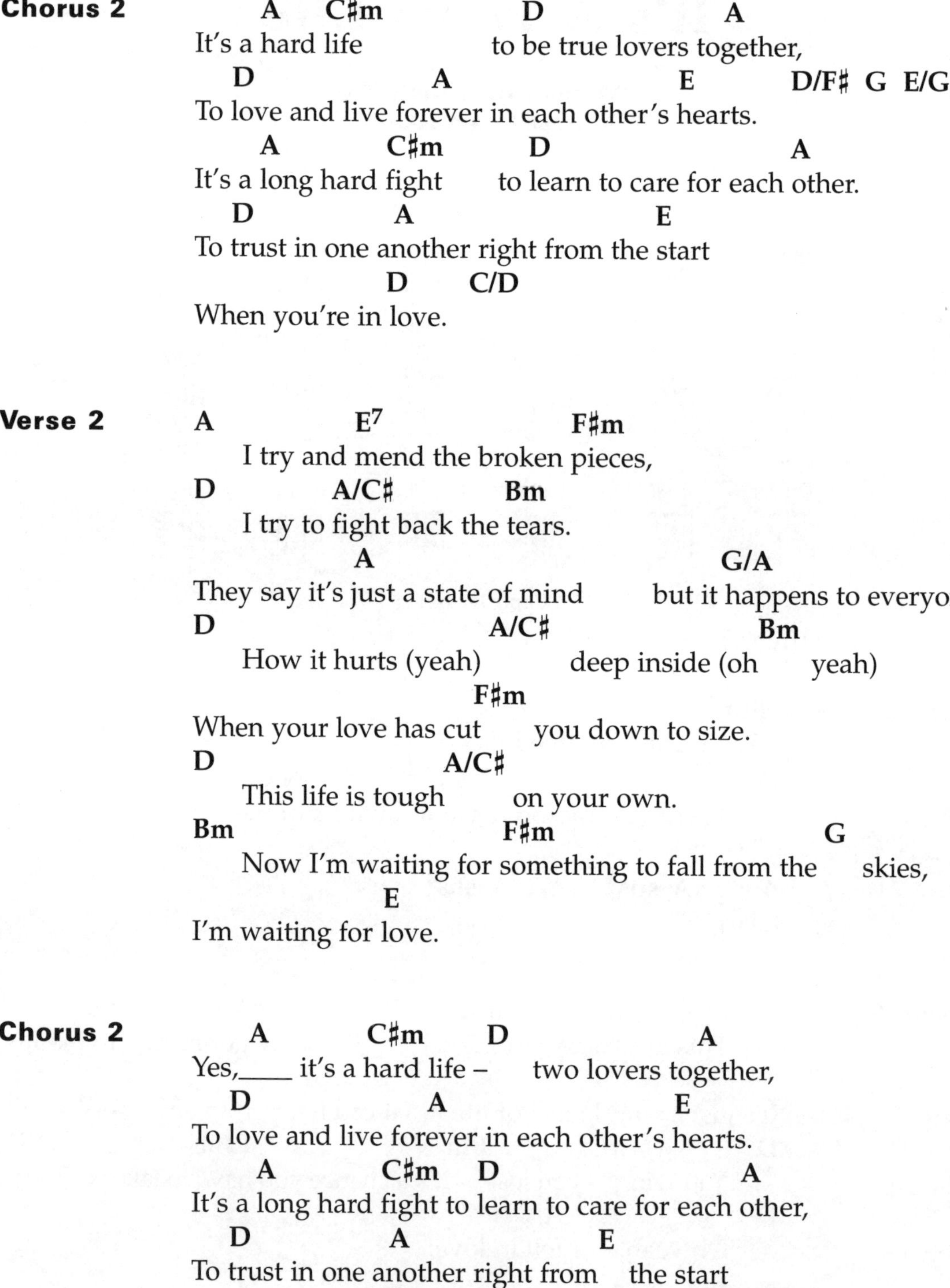

Chorus 2

A C♯m D A
It's a hard life to be true lovers together,
D A E D/F♯ G E/G♯
To love and live forever in each other's hearts.
A C♯m D A
It's a long hard fight to learn to care for each other.
D A E
To trust in one another right from the start
D C/D
When you're in love.

Verse 2

A E^7 F♯m
I try and mend the broken pieces,
D A/C♯ Bm
I try to fight back the tears.
A G/A
They say it's just a state of mind but it happens to everyone
D A/C♯ Bm
How it hurts (yeah) deep inside (oh yeah)
F♯m
When your love has cut you down to size.
D A/C♯
This life is tough on your own.
Bm F♯m G
Now I'm waiting for something to fall from the skies,
E
I'm waiting for love.

Chorus 2

A C♯m D A
Yes,____ it's a hard life – two lovers together,
D A E
To love and live forever in each other's hearts.
A C♯m D A
It's a long hard fight to learn to care for each other,
D A E
To trust in one another right from the start
D C/D
When you're in love.

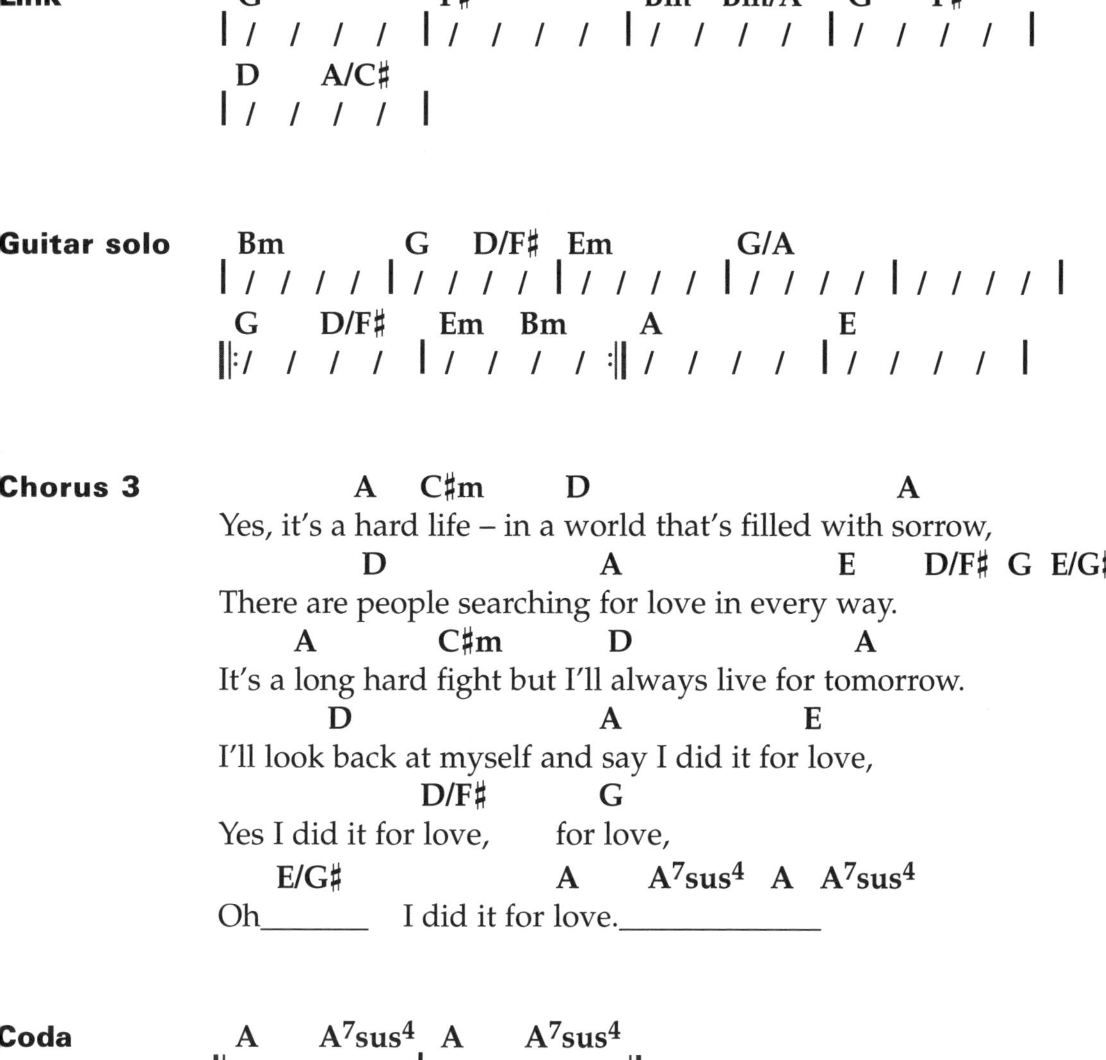
Link
G F♯ Bm Bm/A G F♯
D A/C♯
Guitar solo
Bm G D/F♯ Em G/A
G D/F♯ Em Bm A E
Chorus 3
A C♯m D A
Yes, it's a hard life – in a world that's filled with sorrow,
D A E D/F♯ G E/G♯
There are people searching for love in every way.
A C♯m D A
It's a long hard fight but I'll always live for tomorrow.
D A E
I'll look back at myself and say I did it for love,
D/F♯ G
Yes I did it for love, for love,
E/G♯ A A7sus4 A A7sus4
Oh___ I did it for love.___
Coda
A A7sus4 A A7sus4

The Killing Moon

Words and Music by
IAN McCULLOCH, WILLIAM SARGEANT,
LESLIE PATTINSON AND PETE DE FREITAS

Bm Bm/A G Em C Cm

♩ = 124

Intro

```
    Bm                 Bm/A               G
4/4 ||: / / / / | / / / / | / / / / | / / / / :||
    Em                                    C
    | / / / / | / / / / | / / / / | / / / / ||
```

Verse 1

```
    Em
Under blue moon I saw you,
    C
So soon you'll take me
Em
Up in your arms.

Too late to beg you
    C
Or cancel it though I know it must be
    Em                C
The killing time, unwillingly mine.
```

Chorus 1

```
G     Cm                     G     Cm
Fate       up against your will
                          G     Cm
Through the thick and thin.
                 G     Cm
He will wait until
                      G     Cm
You give yourself to him.______
```

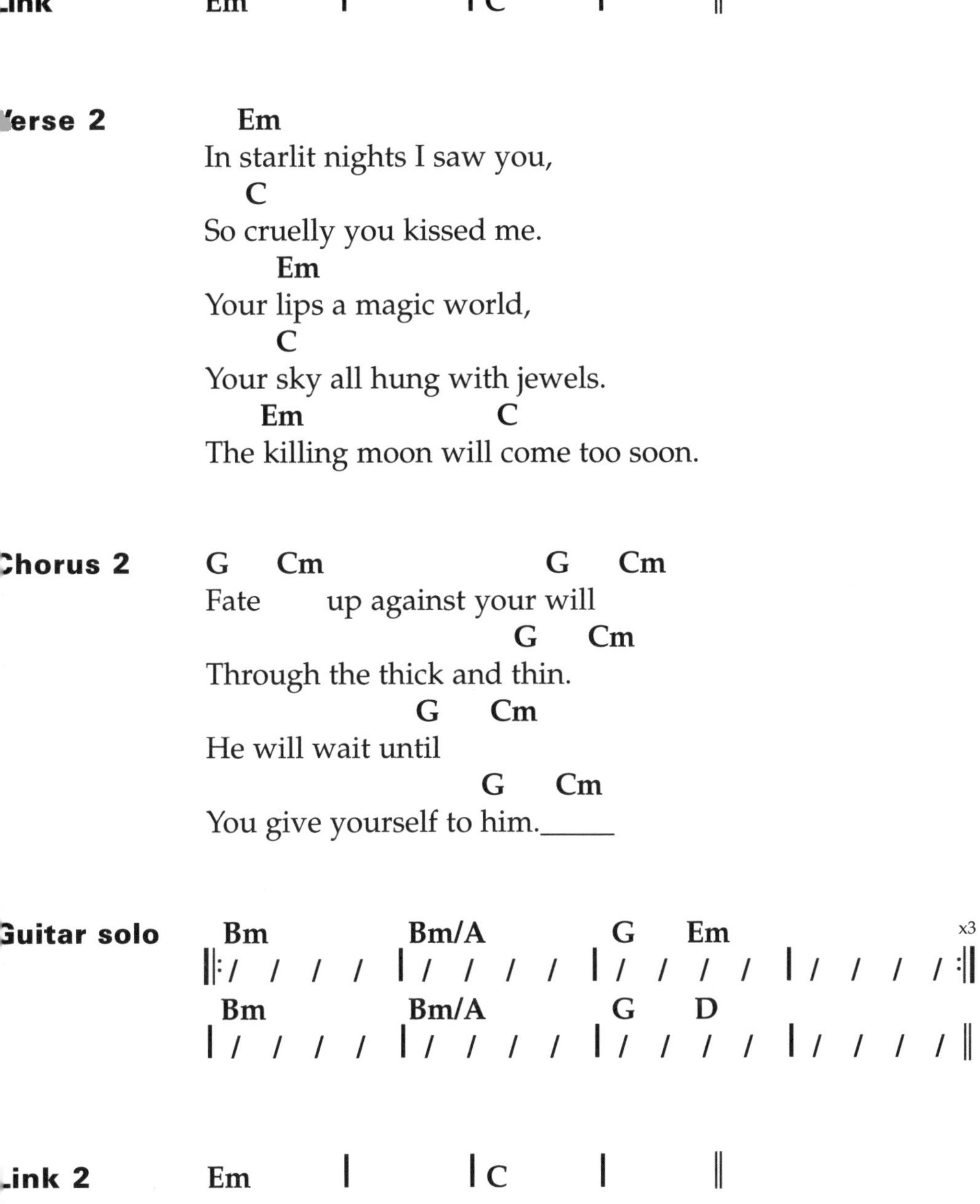

Link Em | | C | ||

Verse 2

Em
In starlit nights I saw you,
C
So cruelly you kissed me.
Em
Your lips a magic world,
C
Your sky all hung with jewels.
Em C
The killing moon will come too soon.

Chorus 2

G Cm G Cm
Fate up against your will
G Cm
Through the thick and thin.
G Cm
He will wait until
G Cm
You give yourself to him.______

Guitar solo

Bm Bm/A G Em x3
||: / / / / | / / / / | / / / / | / / / / :||
Bm Bm/A G D
| / / / / | / / / / | / / / / | / / / / ||

Link 2 Em | | C | ||

Verse 3

```
    Em
Under blue moon I saw you,
    C
So soon you'll take me
Em
Up in your arms.

Too late to beg you
    C
Or cancel it though I know it must be
      Em              C
The killing time, unwillingly mine.
```

Chorus 3

```
G    Cm                   G    Cm
Fate      up against your will
                       G    Cm
Through the thick and thin.
                G    Cm
He will wait until
                    G    Cm
You give yourself to him._____
```

Chorus 4

```
G    Cm                   G       Cm
Fate      up against your   will
                       G    Cm
Through the thick and thin.
                 G     Cm
He will wait un -  - til
                    G      Cm
You give yourself to   him,
                    G    Cm
You give yourself to him._____
```

Link 3
(with vocal ad lib.)

```
   G            Cm           G            Cm        x3
||: /  /  /  /  | /  /  /  /  | /  /  /  /  | /  /  /  / :||
```

Chorus 5

```
G      Cm                          G         Cm
Fate        up against your     will
                              G      Cm
Through the thick and thin.
                       G        Cm
He will wait un -  - til
                           G          Cm
You give yourself to     him,
                           G      Cm
You give yourself to him._____
```

Link 4
(with vocal ad lib.)

```
   G                Cm                G                 Cm
||: /  /  /  /  | /  /  /  /  | /  /  /  /  | /  /  /  / :||
   G                Cm
| /  /  /  /  | /  /  /  / ||
```

Chorus 6

```
    G     Cm                  G             Cm
||: Fate        up against your will
                        G           Cm
   Through the thick and thin.
                   G        Cm
   He will wait until
                     G  Cm    G      Cm
   You give your -  - self to him.          :||  repeat to fade.
```

Let Love Rule

Words and Music by
LENNY KRAVITZ

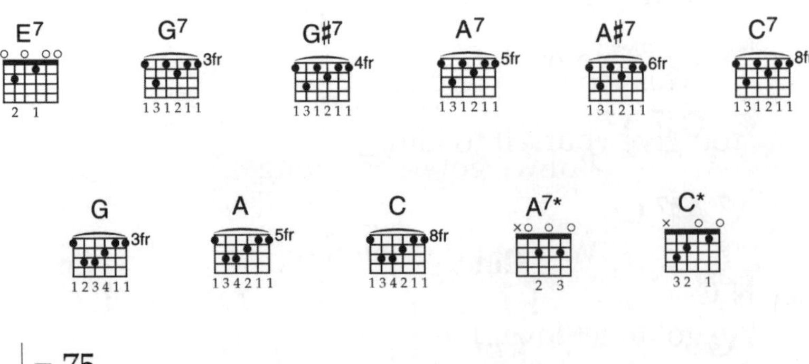

♩ = 75

Intro

$\frac{4}{4}$
E^7 G^7
Love is gentle as a rose,
E^7 G^7
And love can conquer any war.
G^7 $G\sharp^7$ A^7
It's time to take a stand:
A^7 $A\sharp^7$ C^7
Brothers and sisters join hands.
N.C.
We got to let love rule,

Chorus

G A C G^7
Let love rule._____

We got to let love rule,
G A C G^7
Let love rule._____

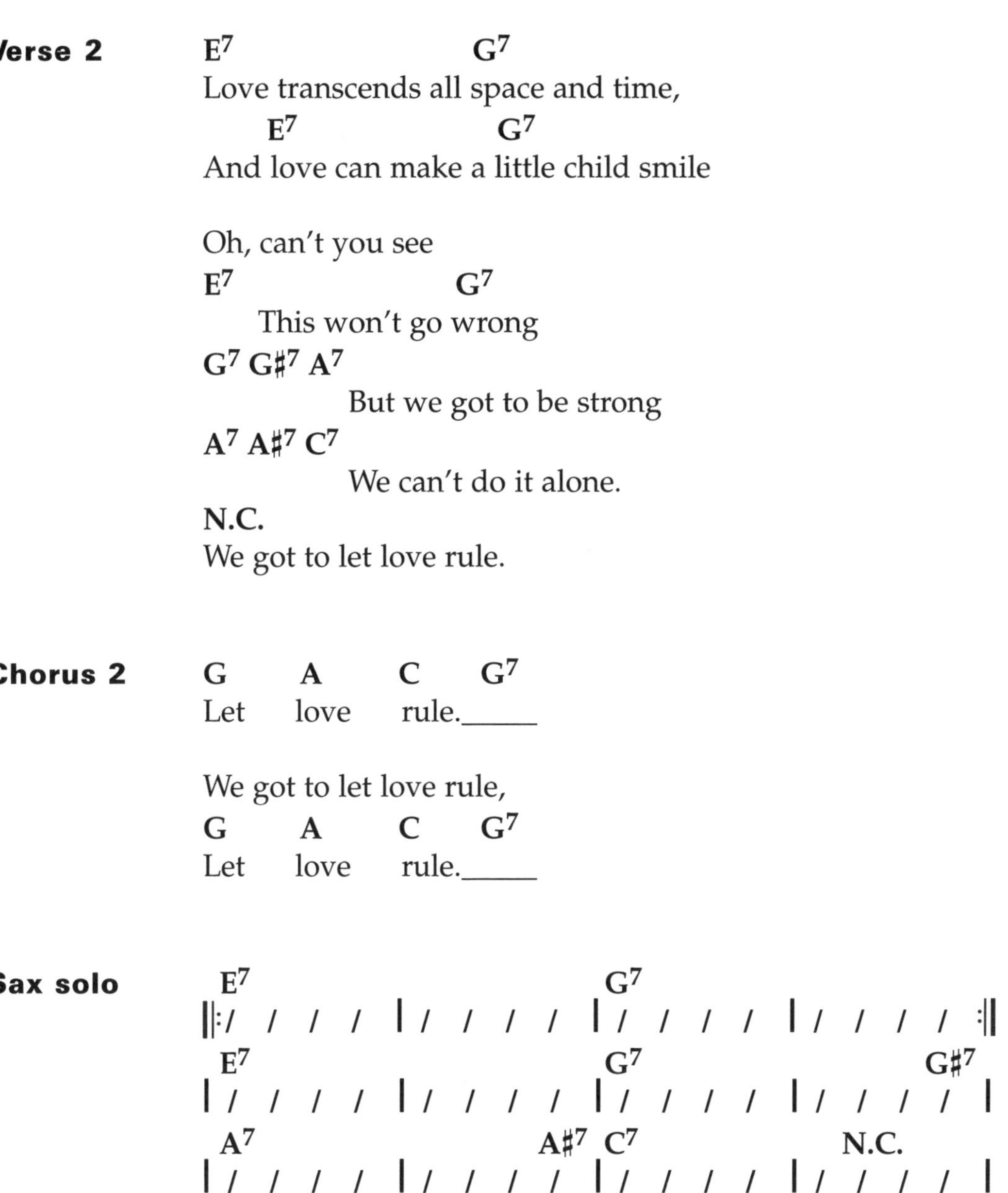

Verse 2

```
E7                      G7
Love transcends all space and time,
     E7                  G7
And love can make a little child smile

Oh, can't you see
E7                     G7
     This won't go wrong
G7 G♯7 A7
          But we got to be strong
A7 A♯7 C7
          We can't do it alone.
N.C.
We got to let love rule.
```

Chorus 2

```
G      A      C      G7
Let    love   rule.______

We got to let love rule,
G      A      C      G7
Let    love   rule.______
```

Sax solo

```
 E7                              G7
‖: / / / / | / / / / | / / / / | / / / / :‖
 E7                              G7                       G♯7
| / / / / | / / / / | / / / / | / / / / |
 A7                      A♯7 C7              N.C.
| / / / / | / / / / | / / / / | / / / / |
 G                A               C               G7
| / / / / | / / / / | / / / / | / / / / ‖
```

Chorus 3

```
G      A      C     G7
Let    love   rule.______

You got to got to got to
G                 A      C     G7
Let  (let love rule)  love   rule.______

You got to, got to, got to, yeah!
G                                      A
Let (let, let, let, let      love    rule) love
                  C     G7
(Let        love)  rule.______
G      A      C     G7
Let    love   rule.______
```

Coda

(with vocal ad lib.)

```
    G             A7*           C*            G7
||: /  /  /  /  | /  /  /  /  | /  /  /  /  | /  /  /  /  :||
```

repeat to fade

Mandolin Wind

Words and Music by
ROD STEWART

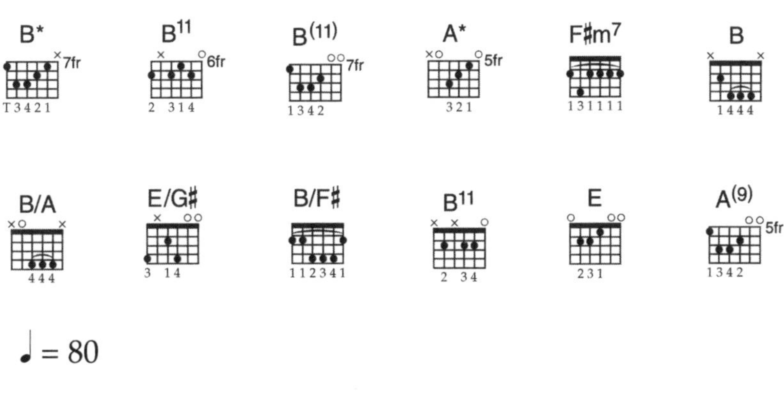

♩ = 80

Intro

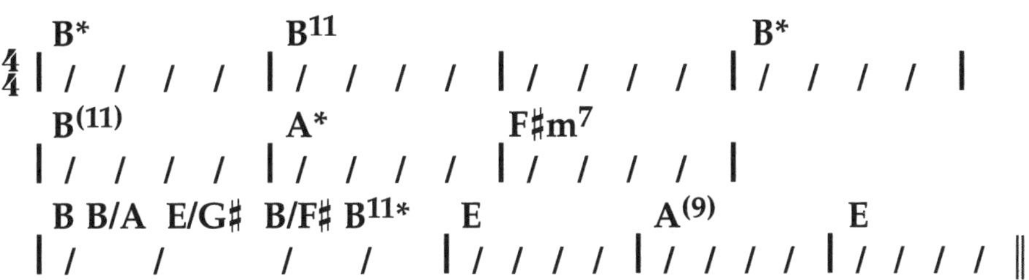

Verse 1

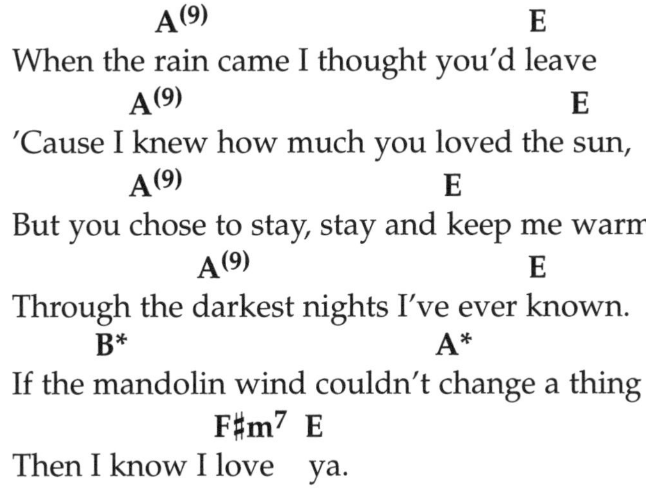
A(9) E
When the rain came I thought you'd leave
A(9) E
'Cause I knew how much you loved the sun,
A(9) E
But you chose to stay, stay and keep me warm
A(9) E
Through the darkest nights I've ever known.
B* A*
If the mandolin wind couldn't change a thing
F♯m7 E
Then I know I love ya.

Link

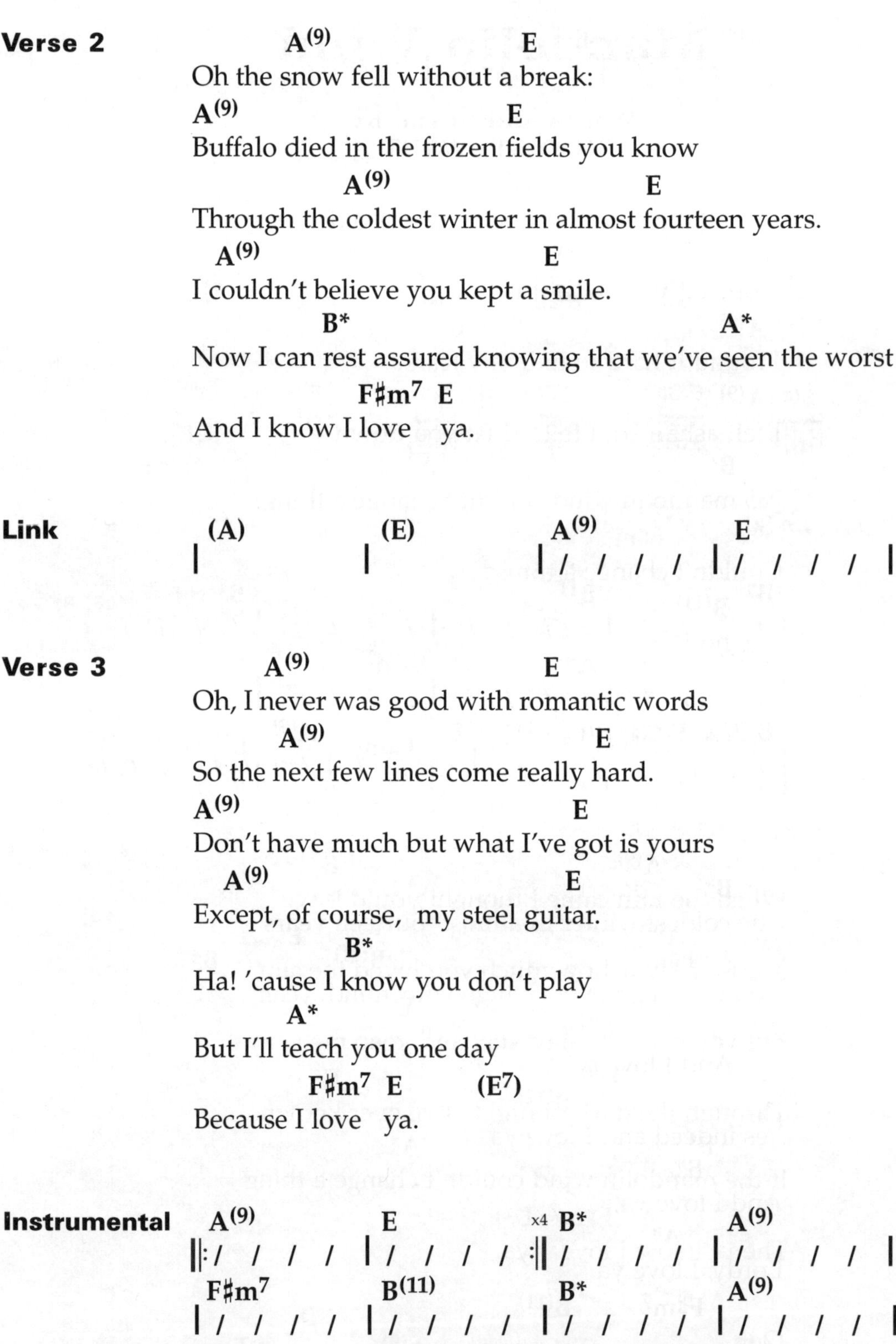

Verse 2

```
            A(9)                   E
Oh the snow fell without a break:
A(9)                          E
Buffalo died in the frozen fields you know
                A(9)                       E
Through the coldest winter in almost fourteen years.
  A(9)                           E
I couldn't believe you kept a smile.
          B*                                          A*
Now I can rest assured knowing that we've seen the worst
              F#m7  E
And I know I love   ya.
```

Link

```
 (A)          (E)          A(9)         E
|            |            |/ / / / /   |/ / / / /   |
```

Verse 3

```
        A(9)                       E
Oh, I never was good with romantic words
         A(9)                         E
So the next few lines come really hard.
A(9)                             E
Don't have much but what I've got is yours
  A(9)                           E
Except, of course,  my steel guitar.
           B*
Ha! 'cause I know you don't play
       A*
But I'll teach you one day
           F#m7  E      (E7)
Because I love   ya.
```

Instrumental

```
  A(9)          E           x4  B*           A(9)
||: / / / /   | / / / /   :|| / / / /     | / / / / /   |
  F#m7          B(11)           B*           A(9)
| / / / / /   | / / / / /    | / / / / /   | / / / / /   |
  F#m7          B  B/A  E/G#  B/F#  B11*   E
| / / / / /   | /     /       /     /    | / / / / /   ||
```

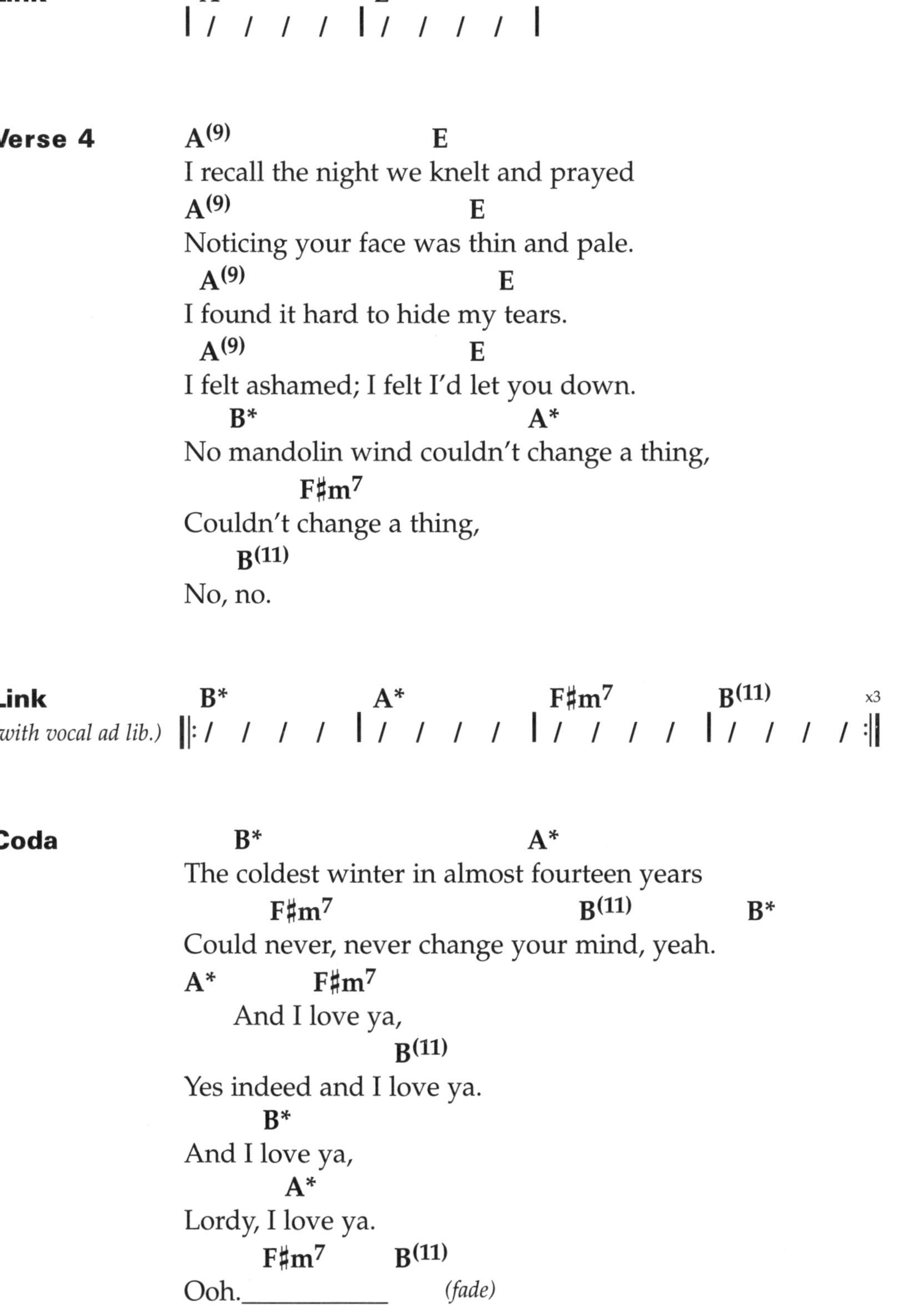
Link
A(9) E
| / / / / | / / / / |
Verse 4
A(9) E
I recall the night we knelt and prayed
A(9) E
Noticing your face was thin and pale.
A(9) E
I found it hard to hide my tears.
A(9) E
I felt ashamed; I felt I'd let you down.
B* A*
No mandolin wind couldn't change a thing,
F♯m7
Couldn't change a thing,
B(11)
No, no.
Link
(with vocal ad lib.)
B* A* F♯m7 B(11) x3
||: / / / / | / / / / | / / / / | / / / / :||
Coda
B* A*
The coldest winter in almost fourteen years
F♯m7 B(11) B*
Could never, never change your mind, yeah.
A* F♯m7
And I love ya,
B(11)
Yes indeed and I love ya.
B*
And I love ya,
A*
Lordy, I love ya.
F♯m7 B(11)
Ooh.__________ (fade)

Lola

Words and Music by
RAYMOND DAVIES

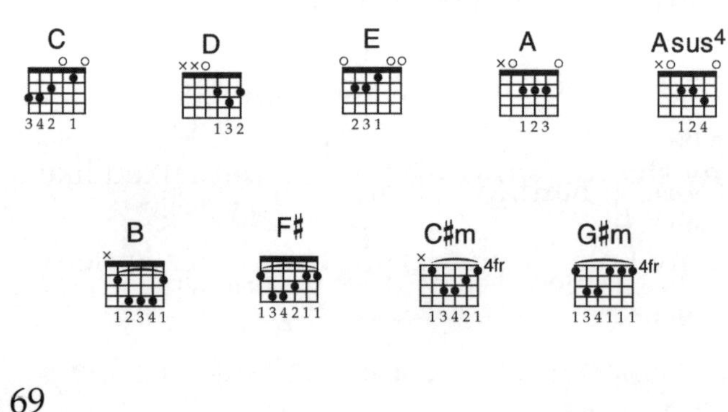

♩ = 69

Intro

```
C              D   E
| /  /  /  /   | /  /  /  /  ||
```

Verse 1

```
E
I met her in a club down in old Soho
              A                               D                    E
Where you drink champagne and it tastes just like cherry-cola.
             A         Asus4    A
C.O.L.A.,  cola.
    E
She walked up to me and she asked me to dance
 A                                      D                          E
I asked her her name and in a dark brown voice she said, "Lola."
            A         D                  C        D
L.O.L.A., Lola,         ler-ler-ler-ler-Lola.
```

Link 1

```
E
| /  /  /  /  | /  /  /  /  ||
```

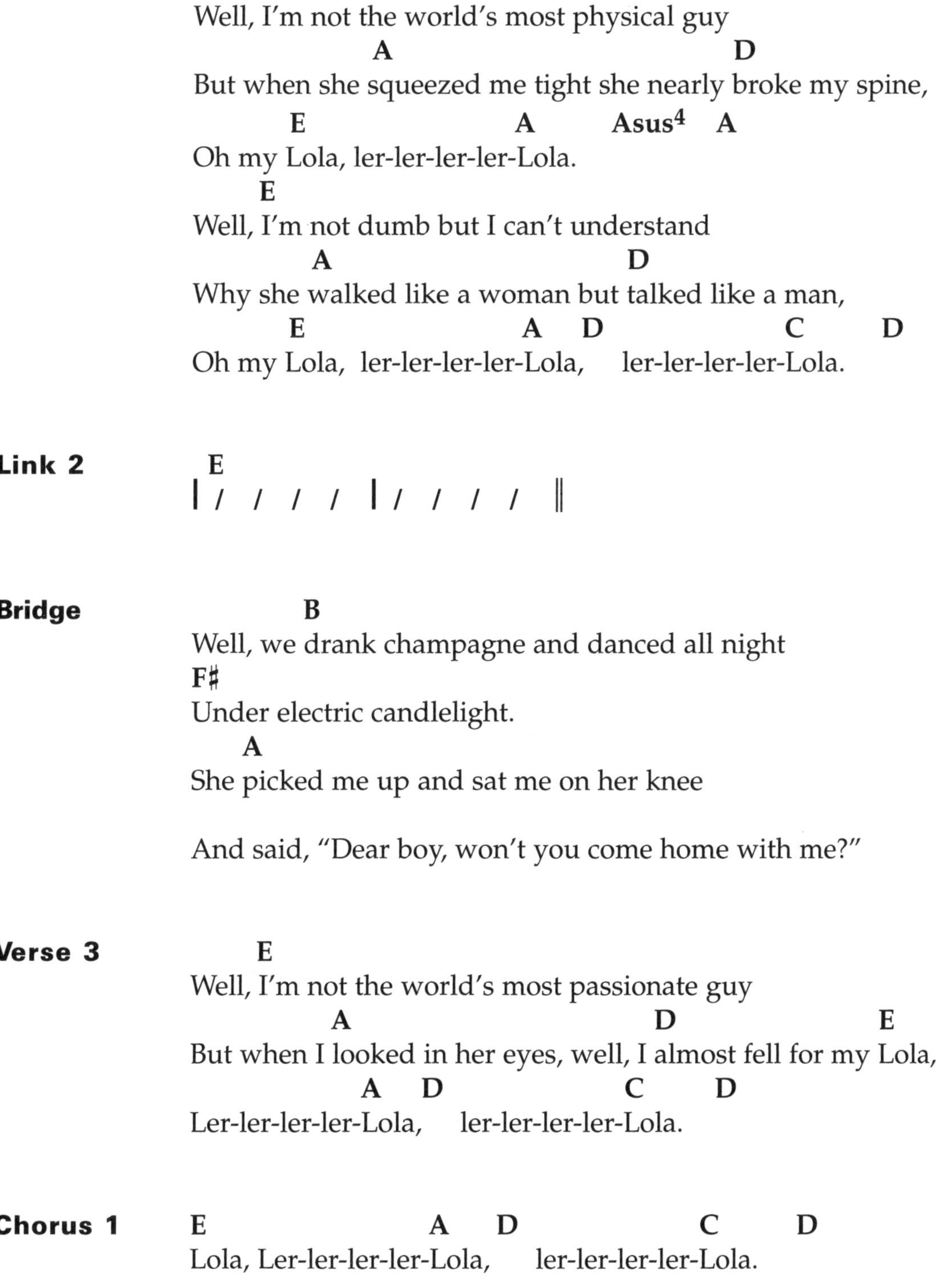

Verse 2

E
Well, I'm not the world's most physical guy
A D
But when she squeezed me tight she nearly broke my spine,
E A Asus4 A
Oh my Lola, ler-ler-ler-ler-Lola.
E
Well, I'm not dumb but I can't understand
A D
Why she walked like a woman but talked like a man,
E A D C D
Oh my Lola, ler-ler-ler-ler-Lola, ler-ler-ler-ler-Lola.

Link 2

E
| / / / / | / / / / ||

Bridge

B
Well, we drank champagne and danced all night
F♯
Under electric candlelight.
A
She picked me up and sat me on her knee

And said, "Dear boy, won't you come home with me?"

Verse 3

E
Well, I'm not the world's most passionate guy
A D E
But when I looked in her eyes, well, I almost fell for my Lola,
A D C D
Ler-ler-ler-ler-Lola, ler-ler-ler-ler-Lola.

Chorus 1

E A D C D
Lola, Ler-ler-ler-ler-Lola, ler-ler-ler-ler-Lola.

Link 3 E
| / / / / | / / / / ‖

Bridge 2
```
 A       C♯m  B    A       C♯m  B
I pushed her away, I walked to the door,
 A  C♯m  B          E     G♯m   C♯m
I fell to the floor, I got down on my knees,
    B
Then I looked at her and she at me.
```

Verse 4
```
     E
Well, that's the way that I want it to stay,
    A                    D                  E
And I always want it to be that way for my Lola,
              A      Asus4  A
Ler-ler-ler-ler-Lola.
E
Girls will be boys and boys will be girls,
    A                         D                           E
It's a mixed-up, muddled-up, shook-up world except for Lola,
              A
Ler-ler-ler-ler-Lola.
```

Bridge 3
```
     B
Well, I left home just a week before
    F♯
And I'd never ever kissed a woman before,
   A
But Lola smiled and took me by the hand

And said, "Little boy, I'm gonna make you a man."
```

Verse 5

```
         E
Well, I'm not the world's most masculine man
         A                                      D
But I know what I am and I'm glad I'm a man,
                E                             A       D                         C          D
And so is Lola,  ler-ler-ler-ler-Lola,     ler-ler-ler-ler-Lola.
```

Chorus 2

```
   E                             A       D                       C          D
||: Lola, ler-ler-ler-ler-Lola,    ler-ler-ler-ler-Lola.          :||
```
repeat to fade

Love Shack

Words and Music by
CATHERINE PIERSON, FREDERICK SCHNEIDER,
KEITH STRICKLAND AND CYNTHIA WILSON

E♭ (3fr, 4132) C* (8fr, 3211) C6 (8fr, 3241) B♭* (6fr, 3211) B♭6/9 (7fr, 2134)

C (32 1) Gm7 (3fr, 131111) B♭ (12341) F (134211) A♭ (4fr, 134211)

♩ = 130

Intro

N.C.
4/4 | *[4 bars drums]* |

N.C.
If you see a faded sign at the side of the road that says:
E♭ C* C6
Fifteen miles to the Love_____ Shack.
B♭* B♭6/9 C* C6 B♭* B♭6/9
Love Shack, yeah,____ yeah.

Verse 1

C Gm7 B♭ C
I'm heading down the Atlanta highway,_____
Gm7 B♭ C Gm7
Looking for the love get-away,
B♭ C Gm7 B♭
Heading for the love get-away.
C Gm7 B♭
I got me a car, it's as big as a whale
C Gm7 B♭
And we´re heading on down to the Love Shack.
C Gm7 B♭
I got me a Chrysler, it seats about twenty,
C Gm7 B♭
So hurry up and bring your jukebox money.

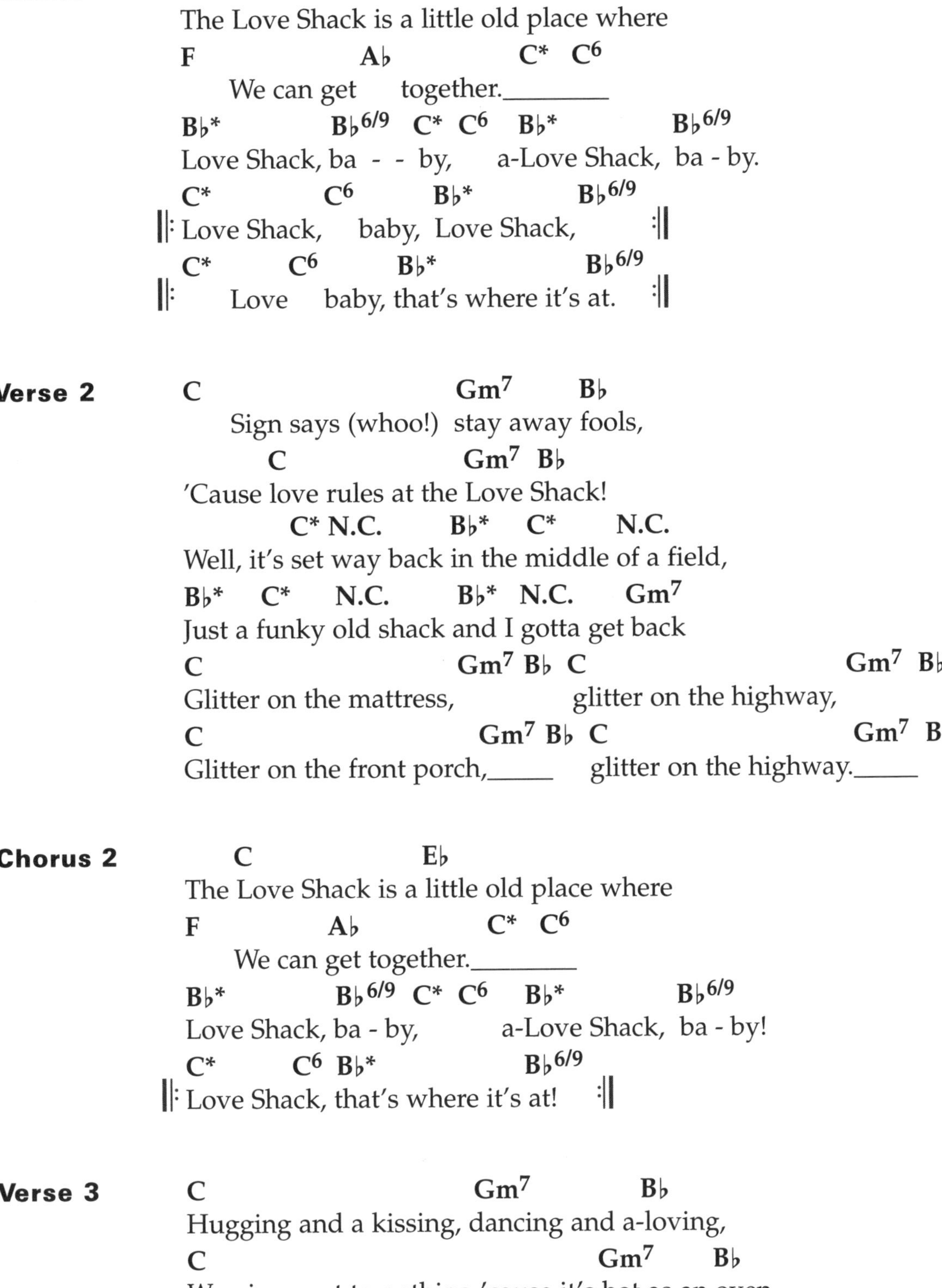

Chorus

C Eb
The Love Shack is a little old place where
F Ab C* C6
We can get together.
Bb* Bb6/9 C* C6 Bb* Bb6/9
Love Shack, ba - - by, a-Love Shack, ba - by.
C* C6 Bb* Bb6/9
||: Love Shack, baby, Love Shack, :||
C* C6 Bb* Bb6/9
||: Love baby, that's where it's at. :||

Verse 2

C Gm7 Bb
Sign says (whoo!) stay away fools,
C Gm7 Bb
'Cause love rules at the Love Shack!
C* N.C. Bb* C* N.C.
Well, it's set way back in the middle of a field,
Bb* C* N.C. Bb* N.C. Gm7
Just a funky old shack and I gotta get back
C Gm7 Bb C Gm7 Bb
Glitter on the mattress, glitter on the highway,
C Gm7 Bb C Gm7 Bb
Glitter on the front porch, glitter on the highway.

Chorus 2

C Eb
The Love Shack is a little old place where
F Ab C* C6
We can get together.
Bb* Bb6/9 C* C6 Bb* Bb6/9
Love Shack, ba - by, a-Love Shack, ba - by!
C* C6 Bb* Bb6/9
||: Love Shack, that's where it's at! :||

Verse 3

C Gm7 Bb
Hugging and a kissing, dancing and a-loving,
C Gm7 Bb
Wearing next to nothing 'cause it's hot as an oven.

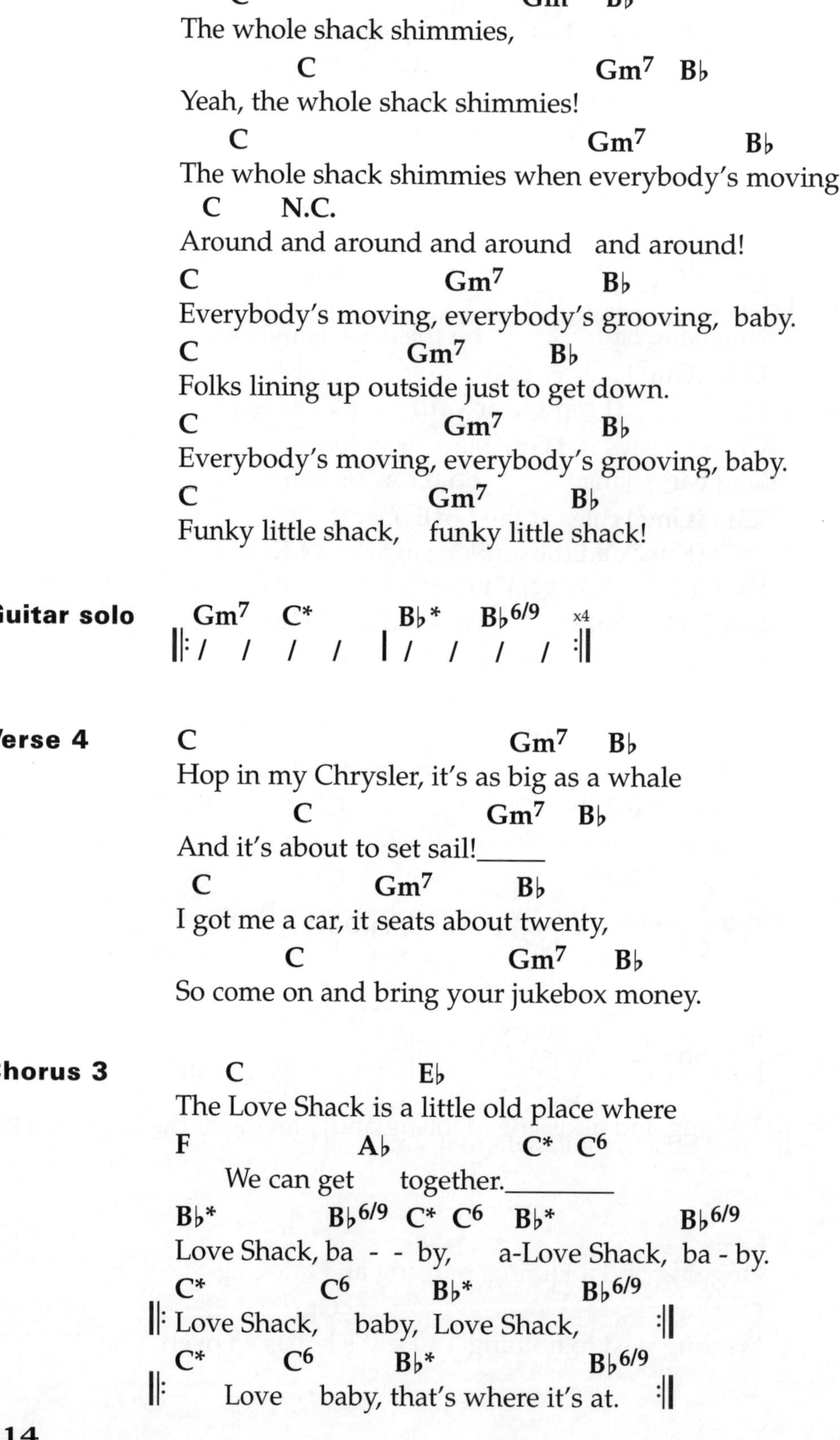

C Gm7 B♭
The whole shack shimmies,
C Gm7 B♭
Yeah, the whole shack shimmies!
C Gm7 B♭
The whole shack shimmies when everybody's moving
C N.C.
Around and around and around and around!
C Gm7 B♭
Everybody's moving, everybody's grooving, baby.
C Gm7 B♭
Folks lining up outside just to get down.
C Gm7 B♭
Everybody's moving, everybody's grooving, baby.
C Gm7 B♭
Funky little shack, funky little shack!

Guitar solo
Gm7 C* B♭* B♭6/9 x4
||: / / / / | / / / / :||

Verse 4
C Gm7 B♭
Hop in my Chrysler, it's as big as a whale
C Gm7 B♭
And it's about to set sail!_____
C Gm7 B♭
I got me a car, it seats about twenty,
C Gm7 B♭
So come on and bring your jukebox money.

Chorus 3
C E♭
The Love Shack is a little old place where
F A♭ C* C6
We can get together.________
B♭* B♭6/9 C* C6 B♭* B♭6/9
Love Shack, ba - - by, a-Love Shack, ba - by.
C* C6 B♭* B♭6/9
||: Love Shack, baby, Love Shack, :||
C* C6 B♭* B♭6/9
||: Love baby, that's where it's at. :||

Link (C) Gm7 B♭ x4

‖: / / / / | / / / / :‖

Coda
(C) (Gm7)
Bang bang bang on the door, baby!
(C*) (Gm7) (B♭)
(Knock a little louder, baby)
(C) (Gm7)
Bang bang bang on the door, baby!
(C*) (Gm7) (B♭)
(I can´t hear you)
(C) (Gm7)
Bang bang bang on the door, baby!
(C*) (Gm7) (B♭)
(Knock a little louder, sugar)
(C) (Gm7)
Bang bang bang on the door, baby!
(C*) (Gm7) (B♭)
(I can't hear you)
C* B♭6/9
‖: Bang bang bang on the door, baby! :‖
C* B♭6/9 C* B♭6/9
Bang bang, (on the door, baby), bang bang, (on the door)
C* B♭6/9 C* B♭6/9
Bang bang, (on the door, baby), bang bang,
C* N.C.
Your what? Tin roof, rusted!
C* C6 B♭* B♭6/9 x3
‖: Love Shack, baby, Love Shack! :‖
C* C6 B♭ B♭6/9 C
Hugging and a-kissing, dancing and a-loving at the Love Shack. ‖

Lyin' Eyes

Words and Music by
DON HENLEY AND GLENN FREY

G Gmaj7 C Am7 D7 C/G

D/F♯ Em7 Bm7 G9 A Am

♩ = 130

Intro

G	Gmaj7	C	
/ / / /	/ / / /	/ / / /	/ / / /
Am7	**D7**	**G**	
/ / / /	/ / / /	/ / / /	/ / / /

Verse 1

G Gmaj7 C
City girls just seem to find out early
Am7 D7
How to open doors with just a smile.____
G Gmaj7 C
A rich old man and she won't have to wor - ry:
Am7 C G
She'll dress up all in lace and go in style.___

Verse 2

G Gmaj7 C
Late at night a big old house gets lonely –
Am7 D7
I guess every form of refuge has its price.
G Gmaj7 C
And it breaks her heart to think her love is only
Am7 C G C D7
Given to a man with hands as cold as ice.

Verse 3

G Gmaj7 C
So she tells him she must go out for the evening
Am7 D7
To comfort an old friend who's feeling down.
G Gmaj7 C
But he knows where she's going as she's leaving:
Am7 C G D7 G
She is headed for the cheating side of town.

Chorus

N.C. G C/G G C G
You can't hide______ your lyin' eyes,
D/F♯ Em7 Bm7 Am7 D7
And your smile______ is a thin disguise.
G G9 C A
I thought by now______ you'd realize_____
Am D7 G
There ain't no way to hide your lyin' eyes.

Link

G Gmaj7 C
| (eyes.) | / / / / | / / / / | / / / / |
Am7 D7 G
| / / / / | / / / / | / / / / | / / / / ||

Verse 4

G Gmaj7 C
On the other side of town a boy is wait - ing
Am7 D7
With fiery eyes and dreams no-one could steal.
G Gmaj7 C
She drives on through the night anticipating
Am7 C G C D7
'Cause he makes her feel the way she used to feel.

Verse 5

G Gmaj^7 C
She rushes to his arms, they fall together;
Am^7 D^7
She whispers that it's only for awhile.
G Gmaj^7 C
She swears that soon she'll be coming back forever.
Am^7 C G D^7 G
She pulls away and leaves him with a smile.____

Chorus 2

N.C. G C/G G C G
You can't hide______ your lyin' eyes,
D/F♯ Em^7 Bm^7 Am^7 D^7
And your smile______ is a thin disguise.
G G^9 C A
I thought by now______ you'd realize______
Am D^7 G
There ain't no way to hide your lyin' eyes.

Link

G Gmaj^7 C
| (eyes.) | / / / / | / / / / | / / / / |
Am^7 D^7 G
| / / / / | / / / / | / / / / | / / / / ||

Verse 6

G Gmaj^7 C
She gets up and pours herself a strong one
Am^7 D^7
And stares out at the stars up in the sky.
G Gmaj^7 C
Another night, it's gonna be a long one.
Am^7 C G C D^7
She draws the shade and hangs her head to cry.

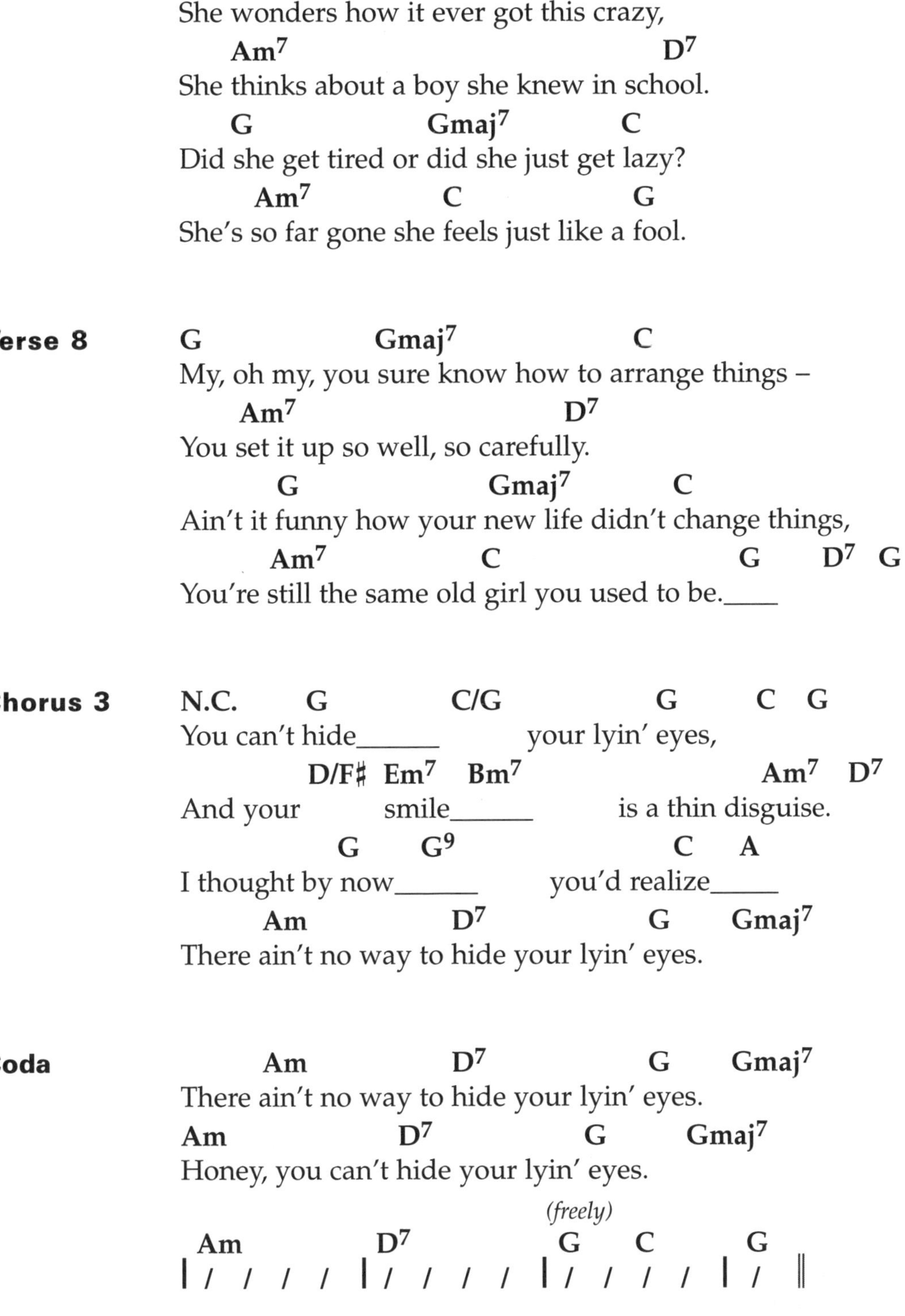

Verse 7

G Gmaj^7 C
She wonders how it ever got this crazy,
Am^7 D^7
She thinks about a boy she knew in school.
G Gmaj^7 C
Did she get tired or did she just get lazy?
Am^7 C G
She's so far gone she feels just like a fool.

Verse 8

G Gmaj^7 C
My, oh my, you sure know how to arrange things –
Am^7 D^7
You set it up so well, so carefully.
G Gmaj^7 C
Ain't it funny how your new life didn't change things,
Am^7 C G D^7 G
You're still the same old girl you used to be.____

Chorus 3

N.C. G C/G G C G
You can't hide______ your lyin' eyes,
D/F♯ Em^7 Bm^7 Am^7 D^7
And your smile______ is a thin disguise.
G G^9 C A
I thought by now______ you'd realize_____
Am D^7 G Gmaj^7
There ain't no way to hide your lyin' eyes.

Coda

Am D^7 G Gmaj^7
There ain't no way to hide your lyin' eyes.
Am D^7 G Gmaj^7
Honey, you can't hide your lyin' eyes.

(freely)
Am D^7 G C G
| / / / / | / / / / | / / / / | / ‖

Man Of The World

Words and Music by
PETER GREEN

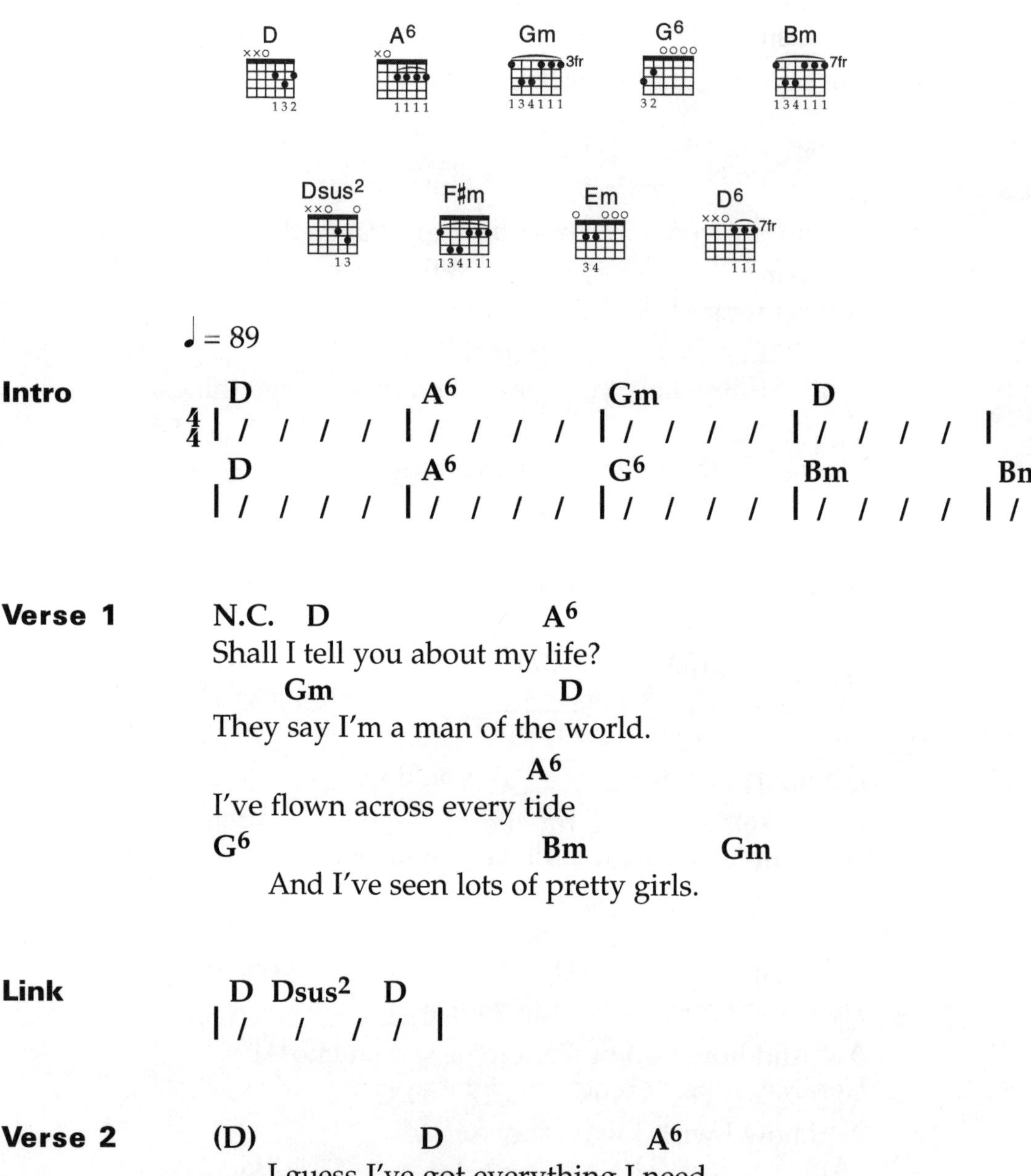

♩ = 89

Intro

4/4 | D / / / / | A6 / / / / | Gm / / / / | D / / / / |
| D / / / / | A6 / / / / | G6 / / / / | Bm / / / / | Bm / |

Verse 1

```
N.C.    D                    A6
Shall I tell you about my life?
      Gm                    D
They say I'm a man of the world.
                           A6
I've flown across every tide
G6                         Bm           Gm
     And I've seen lots of pretty girls.
```

Link

```
 D  Dsus2   D
| /    /   /  / |
```

Verse 2

```
(D)               D                A6
     I guess I've got everything I need,
Gm                        D
     I wouldn't ask for more.
```

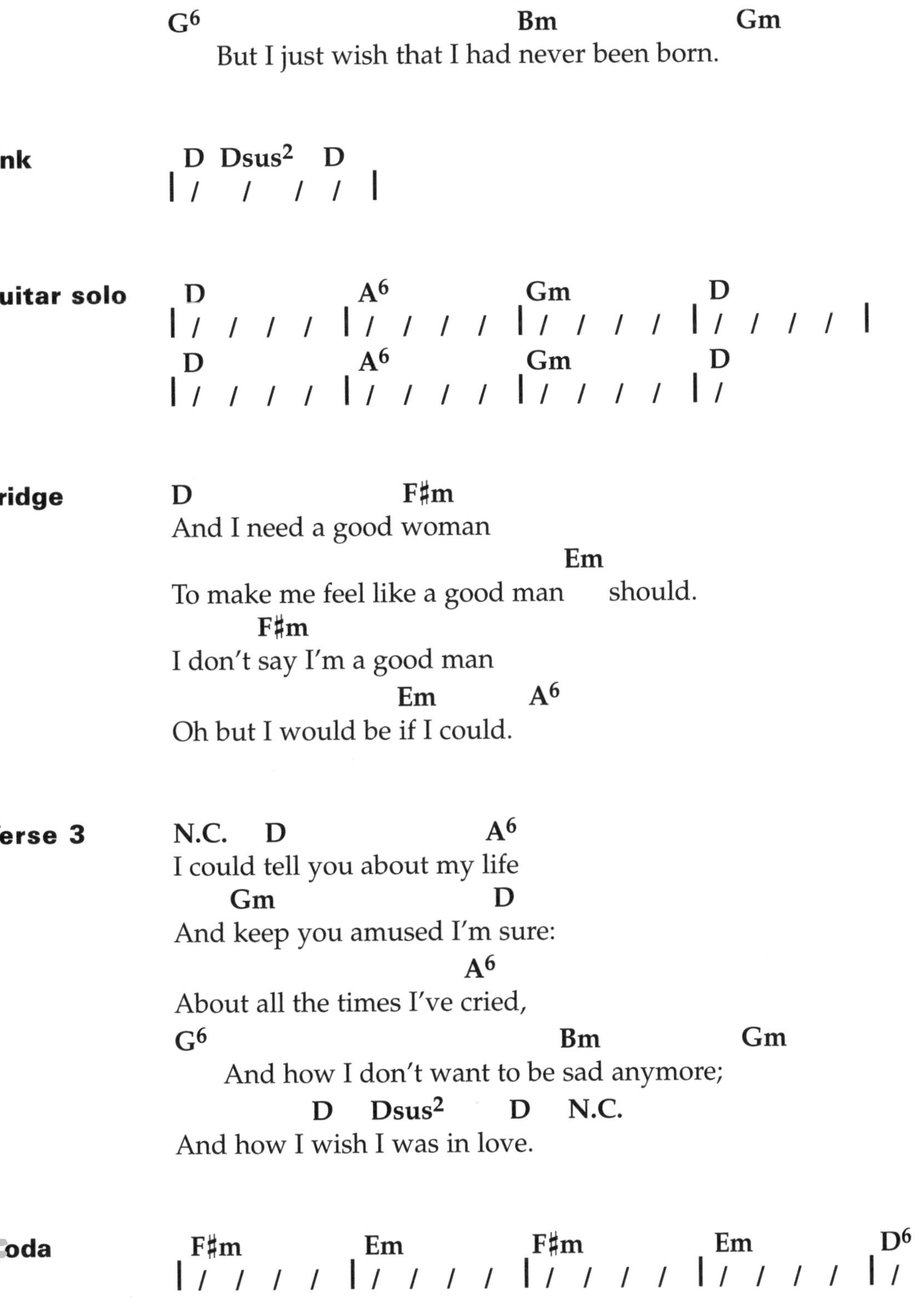

```
                              A6
And there's no one I'd rather be,
G6                            Bm              Gm
      But I just wish that I had never been born.
```

Link

```
  D  Dsus2   D
| /   /   /  /  |
```

Guitar solo

```
  D               A6              Gm              D
| /  /  /  /    | /  /  /  /    | /  /  /  /    | /  /  /  /  |
  D               A6              Gm              D
| /  /  /  /    | /  /  /  /    | /  /  /  /    | /
```

Bridge

```
D                      F#m
And I need a good woman
                                      Em
To make me feel like a good man      should.
          F#m
I don't say I'm a good man
                        Em          A6
Oh but I would be if I could.
```

Verse 3

```
N.C.   D                 A6
I could tell you about my life
      Gm                 D
And keep you amused I'm sure:
                            A6
About all the times I've cried,
G6                              Bm              Gm
      And how I don't want to be sad anymore;
               D    Dsus2      D    N.C.
And how I wish I was in love.
```

Coda

```
  F#m             Em              F#m             Em              D6
| /  /  /  /    | /  /  /  /    | /  /  /  /    | /  /  /  /    | /  ||
```

The Man With The Child In His Eyes

Words and Music by
KATE BUSH

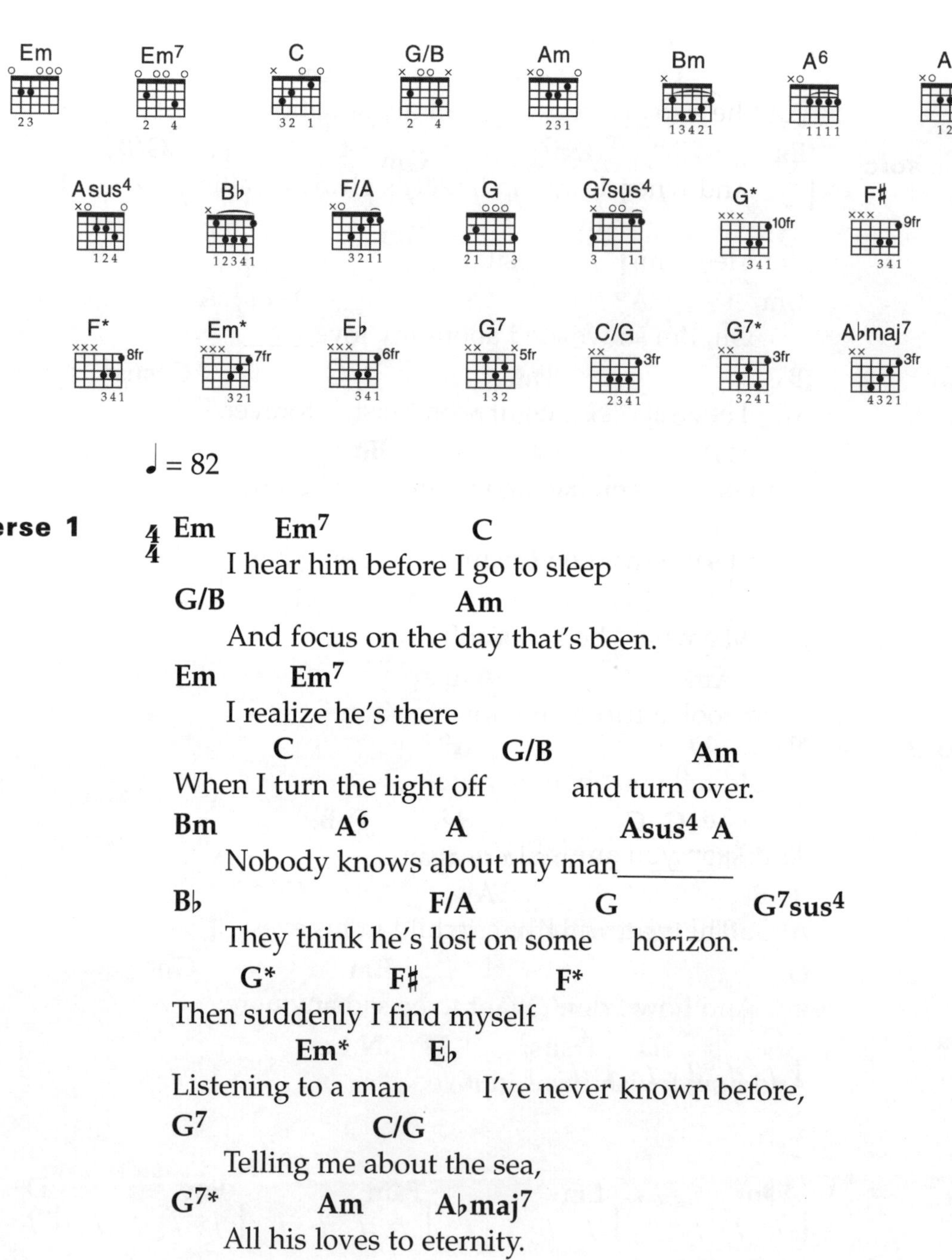

♩ = 82

Verse 1

4/4

Em Em7 C
I hear him before I go to sleep
G/B Am
And focus on the day that's been.
Em Em7
I realize he's there
C G/B Am
When I turn the light off and turn over.
Bm A6 A Asus4 A
Nobody knows about my man______
B♭ F/A G G7sus4
They think he's lost on some horizon.
G* F♯ F*
Then suddenly I find myself
Em* E♭
Listening to a man I've never known before,
G7 C/G
Telling me about the sea,
G7* Am A♭maj7
All his loves to eternity.

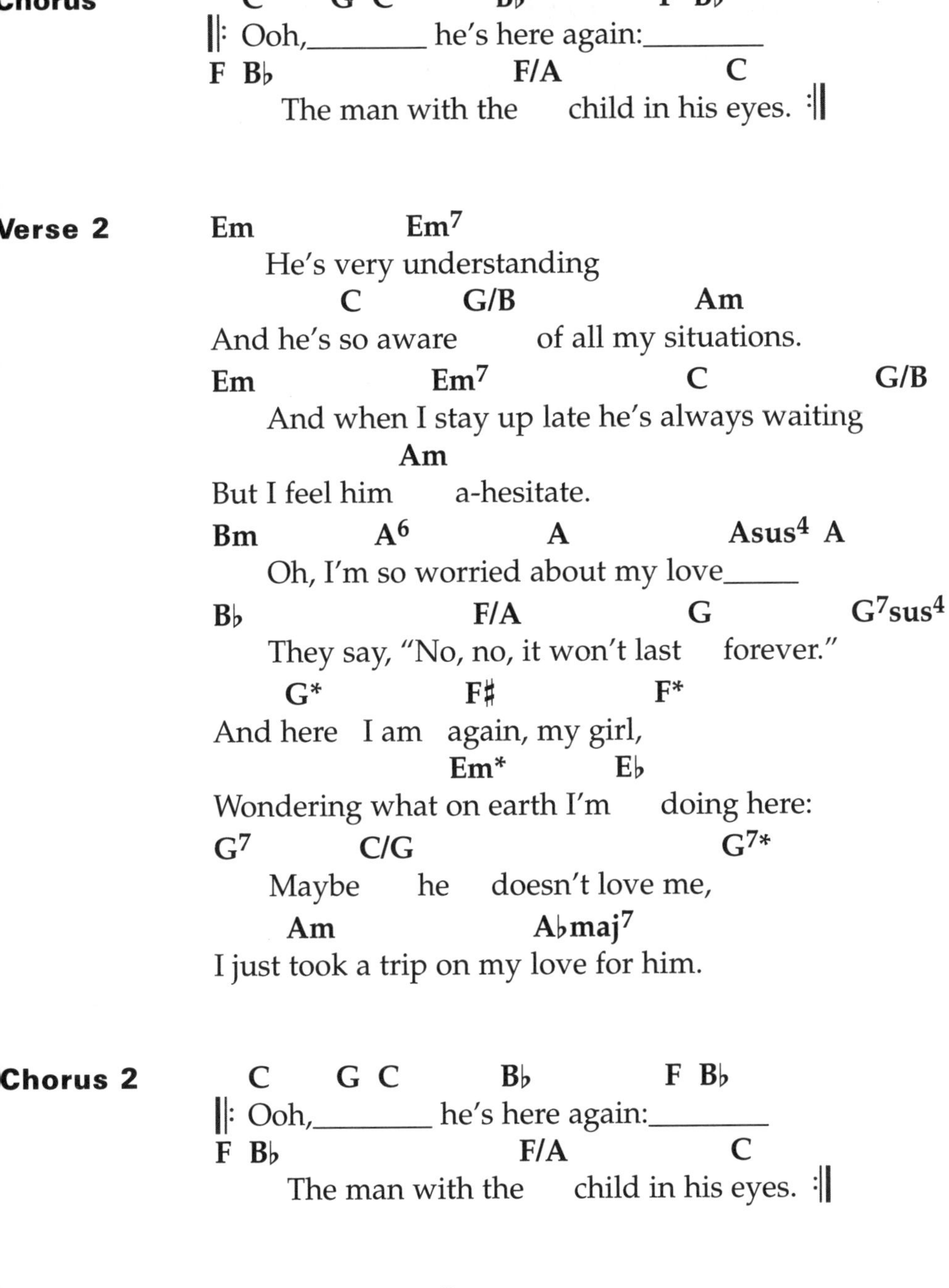

Chorus

C G C B♭ F B♭
‖: Ooh,________ he's here again:________
F B♭ F/A C
The man with the child in his eyes. :‖

Verse 2

Em Em^7
He's very understanding
C G/B Am
And he's so aware of all my situations.
Em Em^7 C G/B
And when I stay up late he's always waiting
Am
But I feel him a-hesitate.
Bm A^6 A Asus^4 A
Oh, I'm so worried about my love_____
B♭ F/A G G^{7}sus^4
They say, "No, no, it won't last forever."
G* F♯ F*
And here I am again, my girl,
Em* E♭
Wondering what on earth I'm doing here:
G^7 C/G G^{7*}
Maybe he doesn't love me,
Am A♭maj^7
I just took a trip on my love for him.

Chorus 2

C G C B♭ F B♭
‖: Ooh,________ he's here again:________
F B♭ F/A C
The man with the child in his eyes. :‖

Coda

C C
| / / / / | / ‖

Mexico

Words and Music by
JAMES TAYLOR

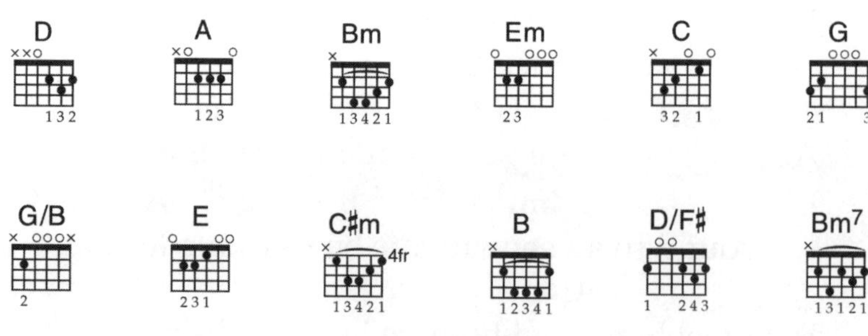

Capo 2nd fret

♩ = 112

Intro

```
      D      A D    Bm    A          Bm    Em   Bm
4/4 ||: /  /  /  / 6/4| /  /  /  /  /  / 4/4| /  /  /  /  |

   [1.                              [2.
      C    G    G/B C                 C    G
6/4 | /  /  /  /  /  /  :|| 6/4 /  /  /  /  /  /  ||
```

Verse 1

```
4/4             G   D                    A      G
     Way down here       you need a rea - son to move,
                D                 A        G
     Feel a fool     running your Stateside games.
                     D              A       G
     Lose your load,      leave your mind behind, baby Jane.
```

Chorus

```
     E    C♯m        B    A
     Oh__________   Mexico,
         E           C♯m   B          A
     You sound so simple I just got to go.
         E         C♯m    B          A
     The sun's so hot  I forgot to go home;
     G          D/F♯        E
     Guess I'll have to go now.
```

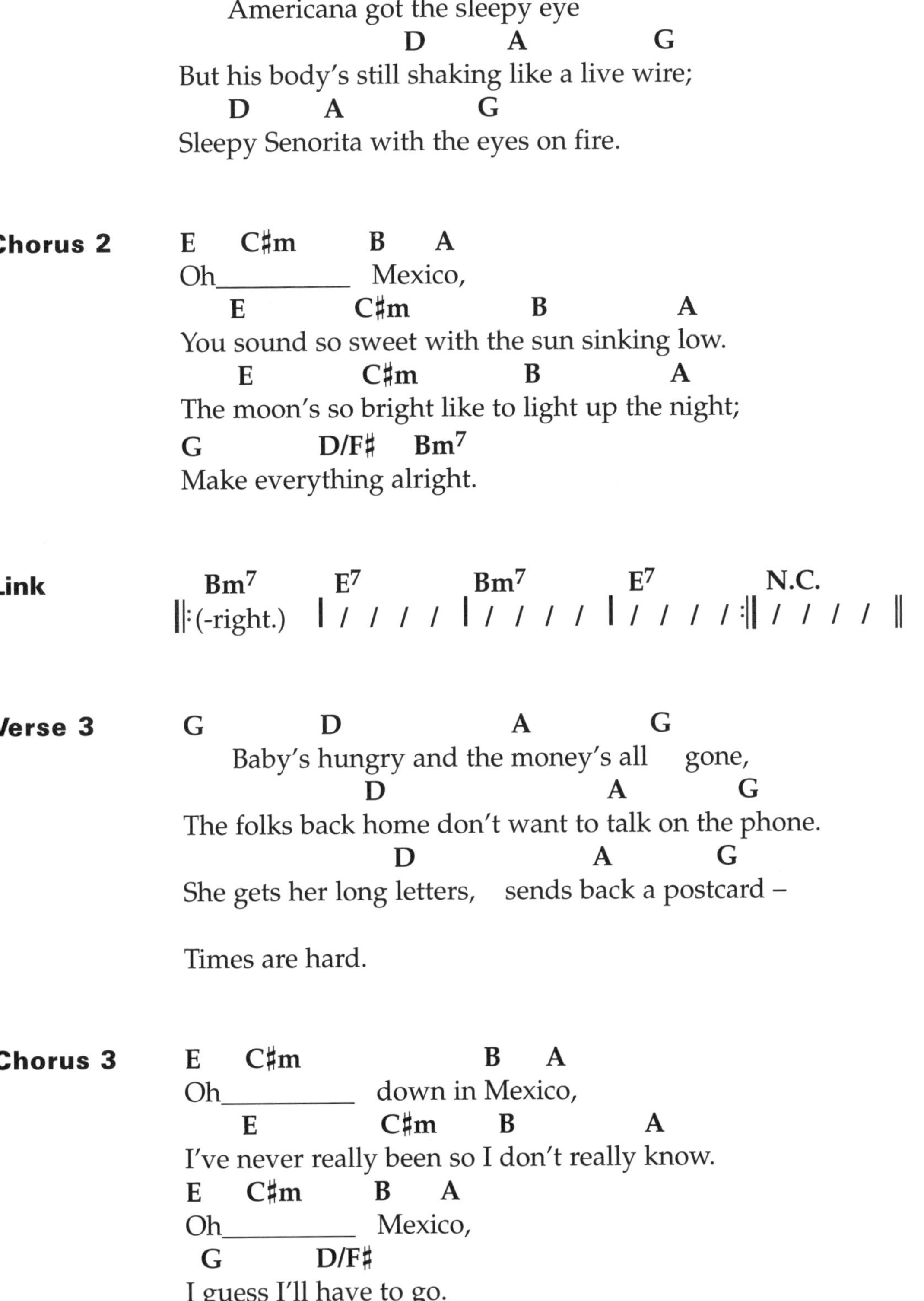

Verse 2

G D A G
Americana got the sleepy eye
D A G
But his body's still shaking like a live wire;
D A G
Sleepy Senorita with the eyes on fire.

Chorus 2

E C♯m B A
Oh__________ Mexico,
E C♯m B A
You sound so sweet with the sun sinking low.
E C♯m B A
The moon's so bright like to light up the night;
G D/F♯ Bm^7
Make everything alright.

Link

Bm^7 E^7 Bm^7 E^7 N.C.
𝄆 (-right.) | / / / / | / / / / | / / / / 𝄇 / / / / ‖

Verse 3

G D A G
Baby's hungry and the money's all gone,
D A G
The folks back home don't want to talk on the phone.
D A G
She gets her long letters, sends back a postcard –

Times are hard.

Chorus 3

E C♯m B A
Oh__________ down in Mexico,
E C♯m B A
I've never really been so I don't really know.
E C♯m B A
Oh__________ Mexico,
G D/F♯
I guess I'll have to go.

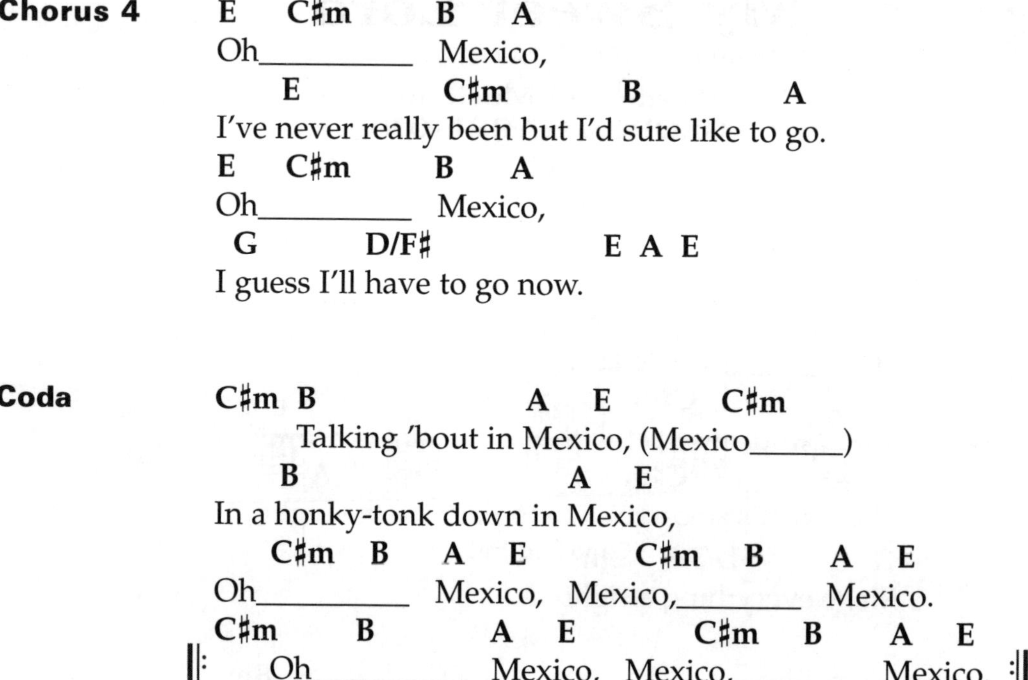

```
Chorus 4   E    C#m        B   A
           Oh_________  Mexico,
              E          C#m        B         A
           I've never really been but I'd sure like to go.
           E    C#m        B   A
           Oh_________  Mexico,
             G         D/F#               E A E
           I guess I'll have to go now.

Coda       C#m B                 A    E        C#m
                Talking 'bout in Mexico, (Mexico______)
               B                   A   E
           In a honky-tonk down in Mexico,
              C#m   B     A   E     C#m  B      A   E
           Oh_________  Mexico,  Mexico,________  Mexico.
           C#m      B        A   E      C#m   B    A   E
        ||:  Oh_________  Mexico,  Mexico,________  Mexico. :||
                                                  repeat to fade
```

My Sweet Lord

Words and Music by
GEORGE HARRISON

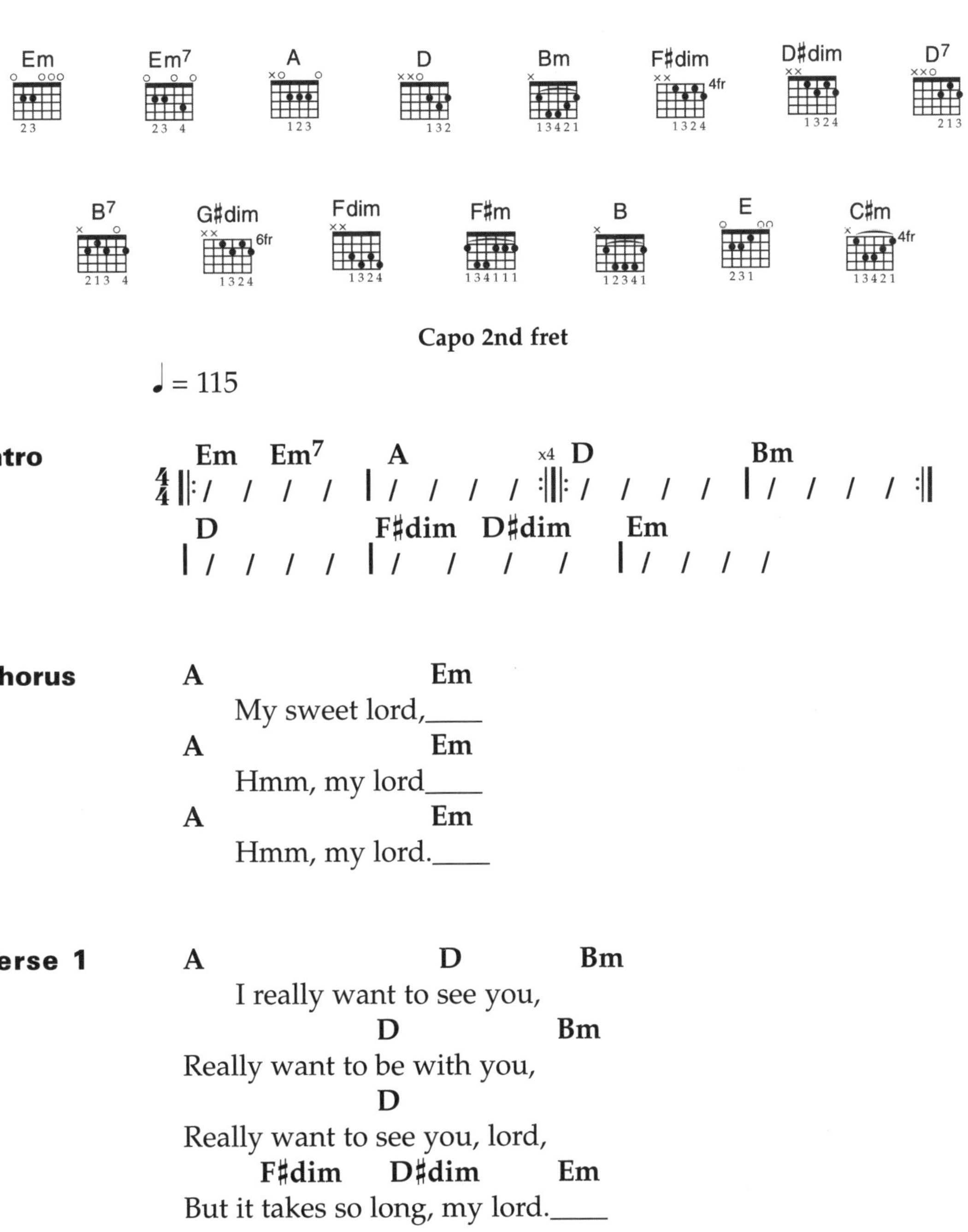

Chorus 2

```
A                  Em
    My sweet lord,____
A                  Em
    Hmm, my lord____
A                  Em
    Hmm, my lord.____
```

Verse 2

```
A                   D          Bm
    I really want to know you,
               D             Bm
Really want to go with you,
               D
Really want to show you, lord,
      F♯dim     D♯dim          Em
But it won't take long, my lord.____
```

Chorus 3

```
      A                          Em
(Hallelujah)     My sweet lord,____
      A                          Em
(Hallelujah)     Hmm my lord,____
      A                          Em
(Hallelujah)     My sweet lord.____
      A
(Hallelujah).
```

Bridge

```
               D
Really want to see you,
               D7
Really want to see you,
               B7
Really want to see you, lord;
               E
Really want to see you, lord,
      G♯dim      Fdim  F♯m
But it takes so long, my    lord.
```

Chorus 4

```
             B                          F♯m
(Hallelujah)       My sweet lord,____
             B                          F♯m
(Hallelujah)       Hmm my lord,____
             B                            F♯m
(Hallelujah)       My my my lord.____
             B
(Hallelujah).
```

Verse 3

```
                    E                   C♯m
I really want to know you (hallelujah),
                   E                      C♯m
Really want to go with you (hallelujah),
                   E
Really want to show you, lord,
       G♯dim         Fdim  F♯m
But it won't take long, my     lord.
```

Chorus 5

```
             B                   F♯m
(Hallelujah)       Hmm-hm-hm,
             B                   F♯m
(Hallelujah)       My sweet lord,
             B                F♯m
(Hallelujah)       My, my   lord.____
             B
(Hallelujah).
```

Guitar solo

```
 E           C♯m          E            C♯m
| / / / / | / / / / | / / / / | / / / / |
 E           G♯dim   Fdim
| / / / / | /   /   /   /   |
```

Chorus 4

F♯m B F♯m B
Hmm, my lord (hare Krishna)
F♯m B
My, my, my lord (hare Krishna)
F♯m B
Oh, my sweet lord (Krishna Krishna)
F♯m B
Ooh________ (hare hare).

Verse 5

E C♯m
Now I really want to see you (hare rama)
E C♯m
Really want to be with you (hare rama)
E
Really want to see you, lord,
G♯dim Fdim F♯m
But it takes so long, my lord.
B F♯m B
(Hallelujah) my lord._____ (Hallelujah)
F♯m B
My, my, my lord (hare Krishna),
F♯m B
My sweet lord (hare Krishna),
F♯m B
My sweet lord (Krishna Krishna),
F♯m B
My lord (hare hare),
F♯m B
Hmm____ (Gurur Brahma),
F♯m B
Hmm____ (Gurur Vishnu),
F♯m B
Hmm____ (Gurur Devo),
F♯m B
Hmm____ (Maheshwara),

```
            F♯m         B
My sweet lord (Gurur Sakshaat),
            F♯m      B
My sweet lord (Parabrahma),
                F♯m        B
My, my, my lord (Tasmai Shree),
                   F♯m          B
My, my, my, my lord (Guruve Namah),
            F♯m      B
My sweet lord (hare rama),
F♯m          B
     (hare Krishna),
              F♯m        B
My sweet lord (hare Krishna),
                 F♯m             B
My sweet lord       (Krishna Krishna)
         F♯m
My lord      (hare hare).   (fade)
```

My Mind's Eye

Words and Music by
STEVE MARRIOTT AND RONNIE LANE

A* Asus4 A7 E A F♯m D

♩ = 114

Intro

A* Asus4 A* A7 A* (E)
4/4 ‖: / / / / | / / / / :‖

Verse 1

A E F♯m
I sit here everyday looking at the sky,
E D
Ever wondering why I dream my dreams away,
E A*
And I'm living for today in my mind's eye.

Link

A* Asus4 A* Asus4 E
| (eye.) | / / / / |

Verse 2

A E F♯m
Things are clearer than before showing me the way
E D
Asking me to stay; I'll never close the door
E A
To all these things and more in my mind's eye.

Link

A* Asus4 A* Asus4 A* A* Asus4 A* Asus4 A*
| (eye.) / / / | / / / / |

Bridge

```
F♯m                           A
Everybody I know says I've changed, yeah.
F♯m                                          D   E   F♯m  E
Laughing behind their hands – I think they're strange.______
```

Verse 3

```
A                    E                     F♯m
People running everywhere, running through my life –
                E                      D
I couldn't give a care because they'll never see
             E7              A*
All that I can see with my mind's eye.
```

Link

```
  A*   Asus4 A* Asus4   E
| (eye.)              | / / / / |
```

Verse 4

```
   A              E
‖: Ah, ah ah ah ah ah,
             F♯m
Ah ah ah ah ah,
             E
Ah ah ah ah ah,
             D
Ah ah ah ah ah,
             E                   A* Asus4 A* Asus4 A*
Ah ah ah ah ah,  ah ah ah ah,
E
   In my mind's eye. :‖ repeat twice to fade
```

(You Make Me Feel Like) A Natural Woman

Words and Music by
GERRY GOFFIN, CAROLE KING AND JERRY WEXLER

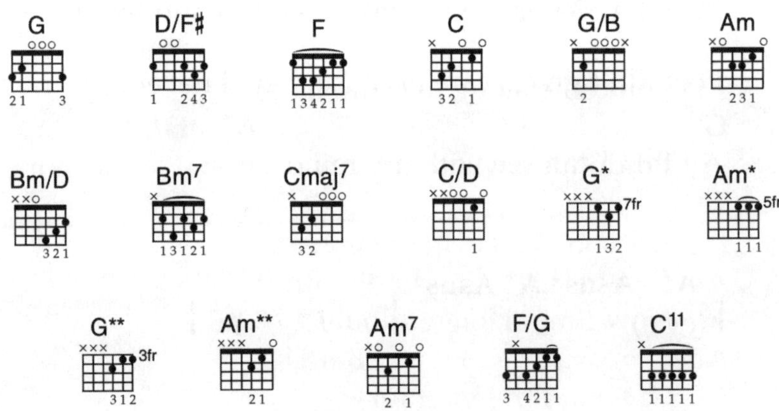

Capo 2nd fret

♩ = 84

Verse 1 3/4

```
G                          D/F♯
     Looking out on          the morning rain,
F                        C           G/B    Am
     I used to feel uninspired
G                                              D/F♯
     And when I know I'd have to face          another day
F                               C        G/B
     Lord, it made me feel so tired.
Am                      Bm/D    Am                    Bm/D
     Before the day I met you          life was so unkind
Am                           Bm7                   Cmaj7   C/D
     Your love was the key to my peace of mind.
```

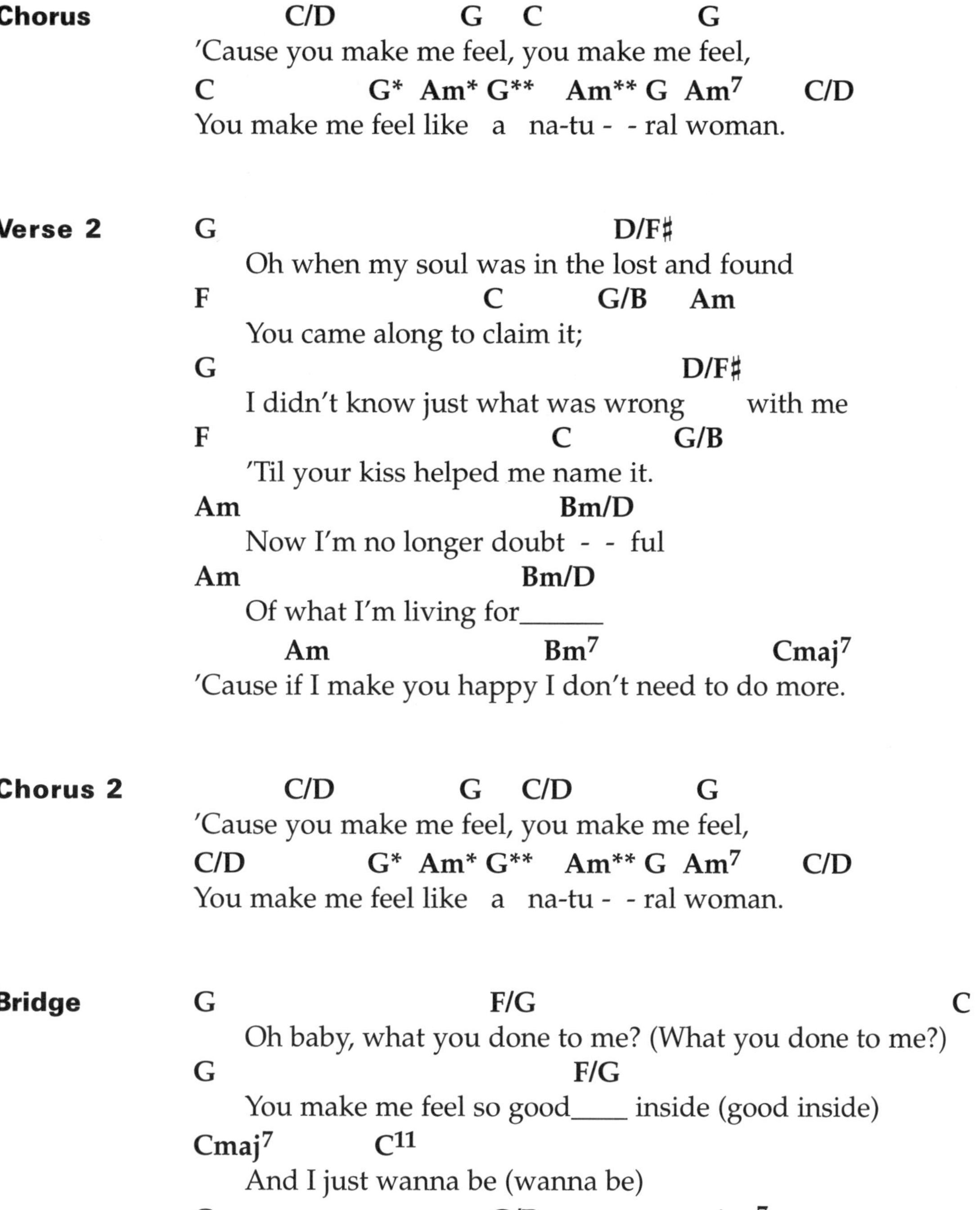

Chorus

C/D G C G
'Cause you make me feel, you make me feel,
C G* Am* G** Am** G Am^7 C/D
You make me feel like a na-tu - - ral woman.

Verse 2

G D/F♯
Oh when my soul was in the lost and found
F C G/B Am
You came along to claim it;
G D/F♯
I didn't know just what was wrong with me
F C G/B
'Til your kiss helped me name it.
Am Bm/D
Now I'm no longer doubt - - ful
Am Bm/D
Of what I'm living for______
Am Bm^7 Cmaj^7
'Cause if I make you happy I don't need to do more.

Chorus 2

C/D G C/D G
'Cause you make me feel, you make me feel,
C/D G* Am* G** Am** G Am^7 C/D
You make me feel like a na-tu - - ral woman.

Bridge

G F/G C
Oh baby, what you done to me? (What you done to me?)
G F/G
You make me feel so good____ inside (good inside)
Cmaj^7 C^{11}
And I just wanna be (wanna be)
C G/B Am^7
Close to you – you make me feel so alive.

Chorus 3

        C/D   G   C   G
You____ make me feel, you make me feel,
C/D   G* Am* G**   Am** G Am^7 C/D
You make me feel like   a   na-tu - - ral,   natural woman.
                 G   C   G
You make me feel,   you know you make me   feel,
C   G* Am* G**   Am** G Am^7
You make me feel like   a   na-tu - - ral woman.
      C/D   G   C   G
You know you make me feel, you make me feel,
C   G* Am* G**   Am** G Am^7 C/D   G
You make me feel like   a   na-tu - - ral woman, natural woman.

Nights In White Satin

Words and Music by
JUSTIN HAYWARD

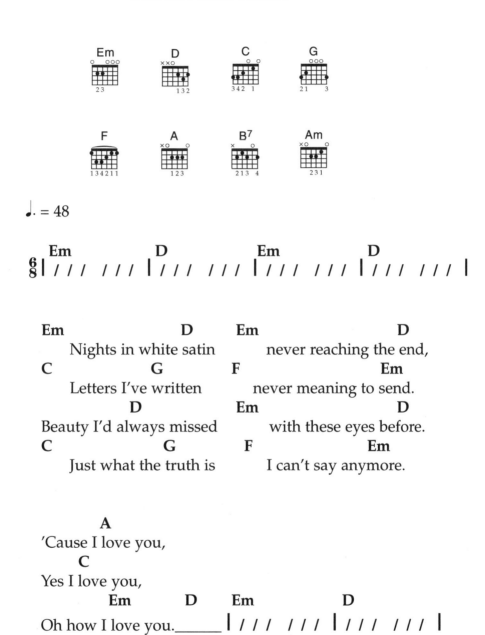

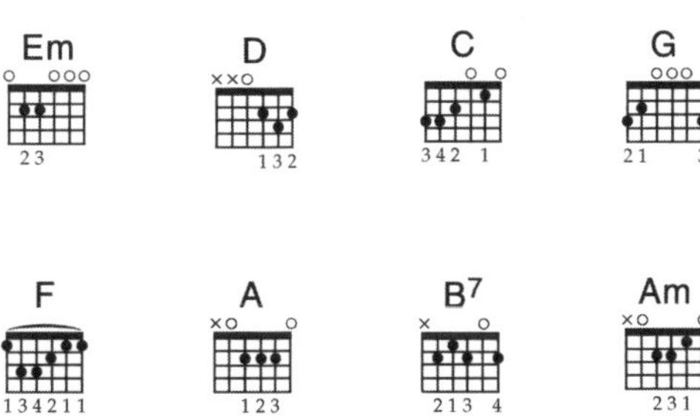

♩. = 48

Intro

Verse 1

Em D Em D
Nights in white satin never reaching the end,
C G F Em
Letters I've written never meaning to send.
D Em D
Beauty I'd always missed with these eyes before.
C G F Em
Just what the truth is I can't say anymore.

Chorus

A
'Cause I love you,
C
Yes I love you,
Em D Em D
Oh how I love you.______ | / / / / / / | / / / / / / |

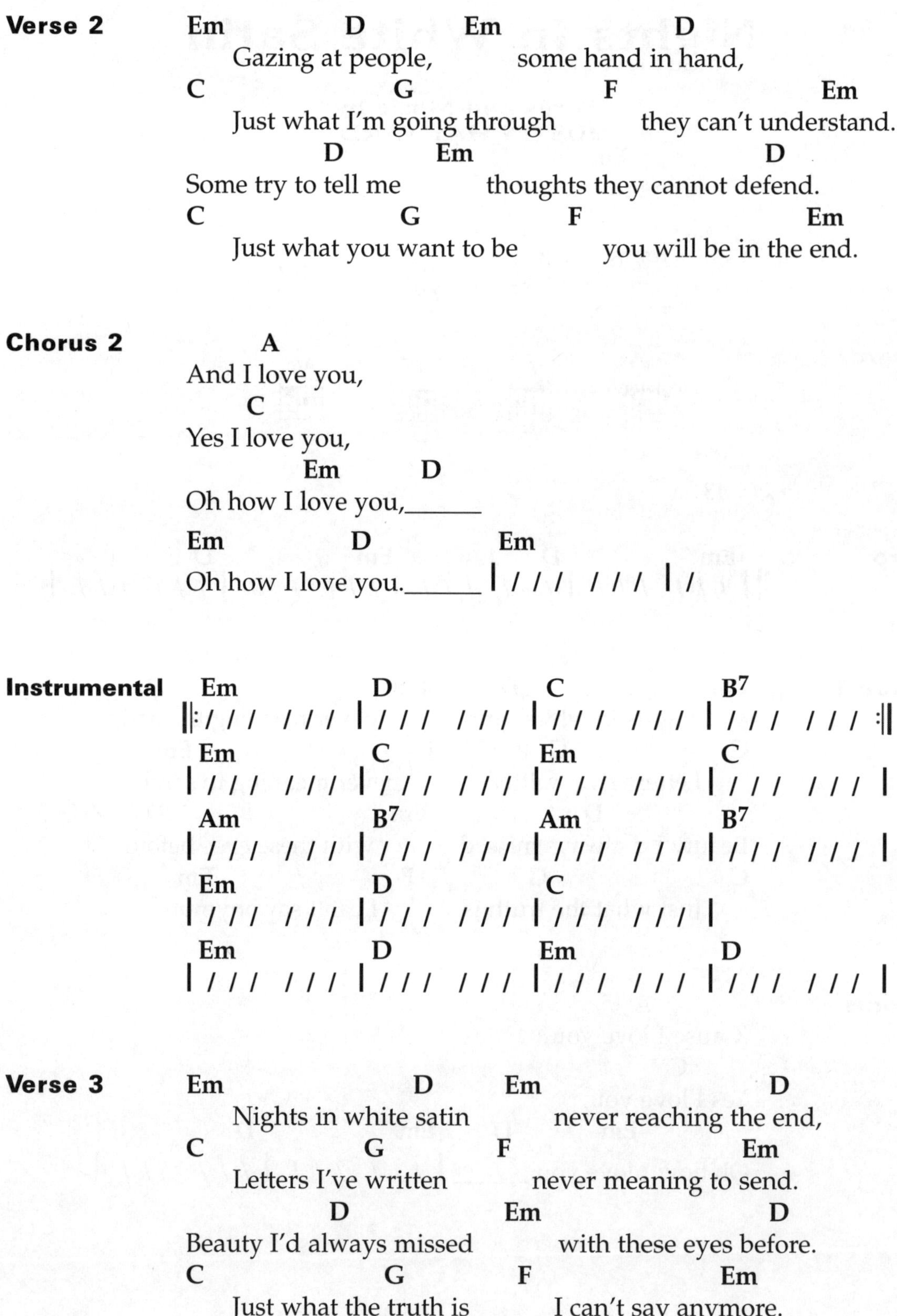
Verse 2
Em D Em D
Gazing at people, some hand in hand,
C G F Em
Just what I'm going through they can't understand.
D Em D
Some try to tell me thoughts they cannot defend.
C G F Em
Just what you want to be you will be in the end.
Chorus 2
A
And I love you,
C
Yes I love you,
Em D
Oh how I love you,
Em D Em
Oh how I love you.
Instrumental
Em D C B7
Em C Em C
Am B7 Am B7
Em D C
Em D Em D
Verse 3
Em D Em D
Nights in white satin never reaching the end,
C G F Em
Letters I've written never meaning to send.
D Em D
Beauty I'd always missed with these eyes before.
C G F Em
Just what the truth is I can't say anymore.

Chorus 3

```
              A
'Cause I love you,
       C
Yes I love you,
              Em          D
Oh how I love you,______
Em                 D        Em
Oh how I love you.
```

Chorus 4

```
              A
'Cause I love you,
       C
Yes I love you,
              Em          D
Oh how I love you,______
Em                 D        Em     ||
Oh how I love you.
```

The One I Love

Words and Music by
MICHAEL MILLS, WILLIAM BERRY,
PETER BUCK AND MICHAEL STIPE

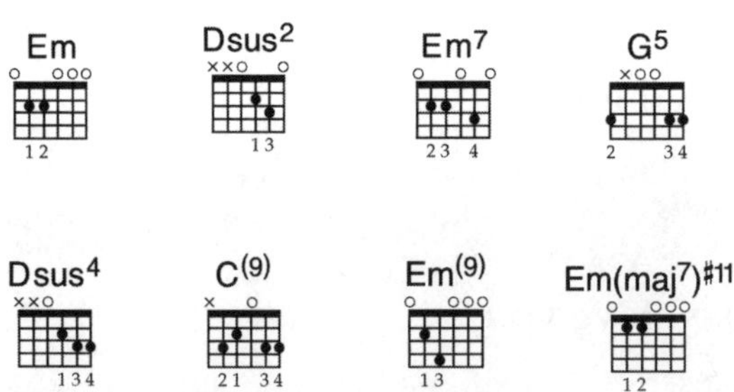

♩ = 125

Intro

```
 Em               Dsus2            Em7              Em
‖: /  /  /  /  |  /  /  /  /  |  /  /  /  /  |  /  /  /  /  :‖
```

Verse 1

```
Em                   Dsus2        Em7      Em
This one goes out to the one I love,
                     Dsus2           Em7          Em
This one goes out to the one I've left behind:
G5               Dsus4   C(9)
     A simple prop to occupy my time.
Em                   Dsus2        Em7      Em
This one goes out to the one I love.
```

Chorus

```
  Em    Dsus2    Em7    Em
Fire.________________________
  Em    Dsus2    Em7    Em
Fire.________________________
```

Verse 2

```
Em                   Dsus2        Em7      Em
This one goes out to the one I love,
                     Dsus2           Em7          Em
This one goes out to the one I've left behind:
```

G^{5} Dsus^{4} C$^{(9)}$
A simple prop to occupy my time.
Em Dsus^{2} Em^{7} Em
This one goes out to the one I love.

Chorus 2

Em Dsus^{2} Em^{7} Em
Fire.________________
Em Dsus^{2} Em^{7} Em
Fire.________________

Guitar solo

G^{5} Dsus^{4} C$^{(9)}$
| / / / / | / / / / | / / / / | / / / / |
Em Dsus^{2} Em$^{(9)}$ Em
| / / / / | / / / / | / / / / | / / / / ||

Verse 3

Em Dsus^{2} Em^{7} Em
This one goes out to the one I love,
Dsus^{2} Em^{7} Em
This one goes out to the one I've left behind.
G^{5} Dsus^{4} C$^{(9)}$
Another prop has occupied my time.
Em Dsus^{2} Em^{7} Em
This one goes out to the one I love.

Chorus 3

Em Dsus^{2} Em^{7} Em
||: Fire.________________
Em Dsus^{2} Em^{7} Em
Fire.________________ :||

(freely)

Coda

Em Dsus^{2} Em(maj^{7})$^{\sharp 11}$ Em
| / / / / | / / / / | / ||

The Passenger

Words and Music by
JAMES OSTERBERG AND RICKY GARDINER

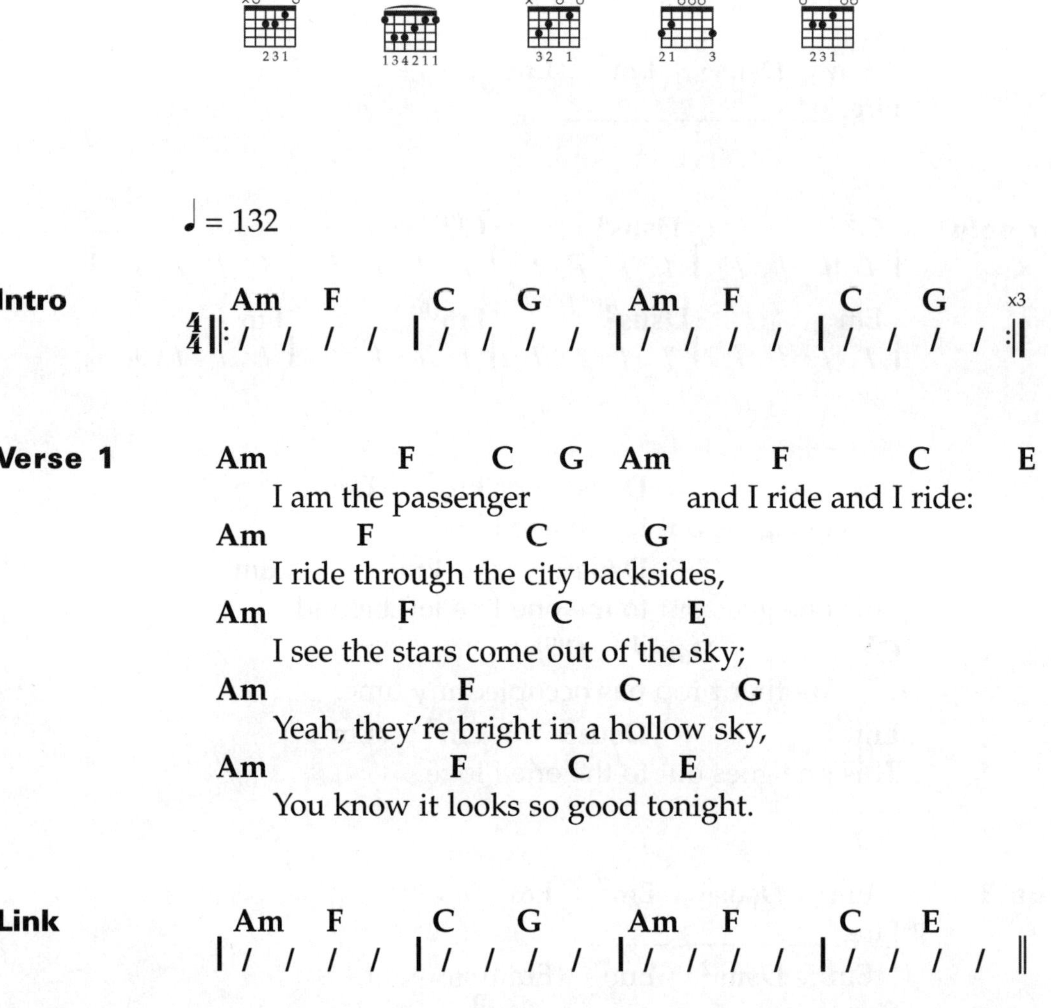

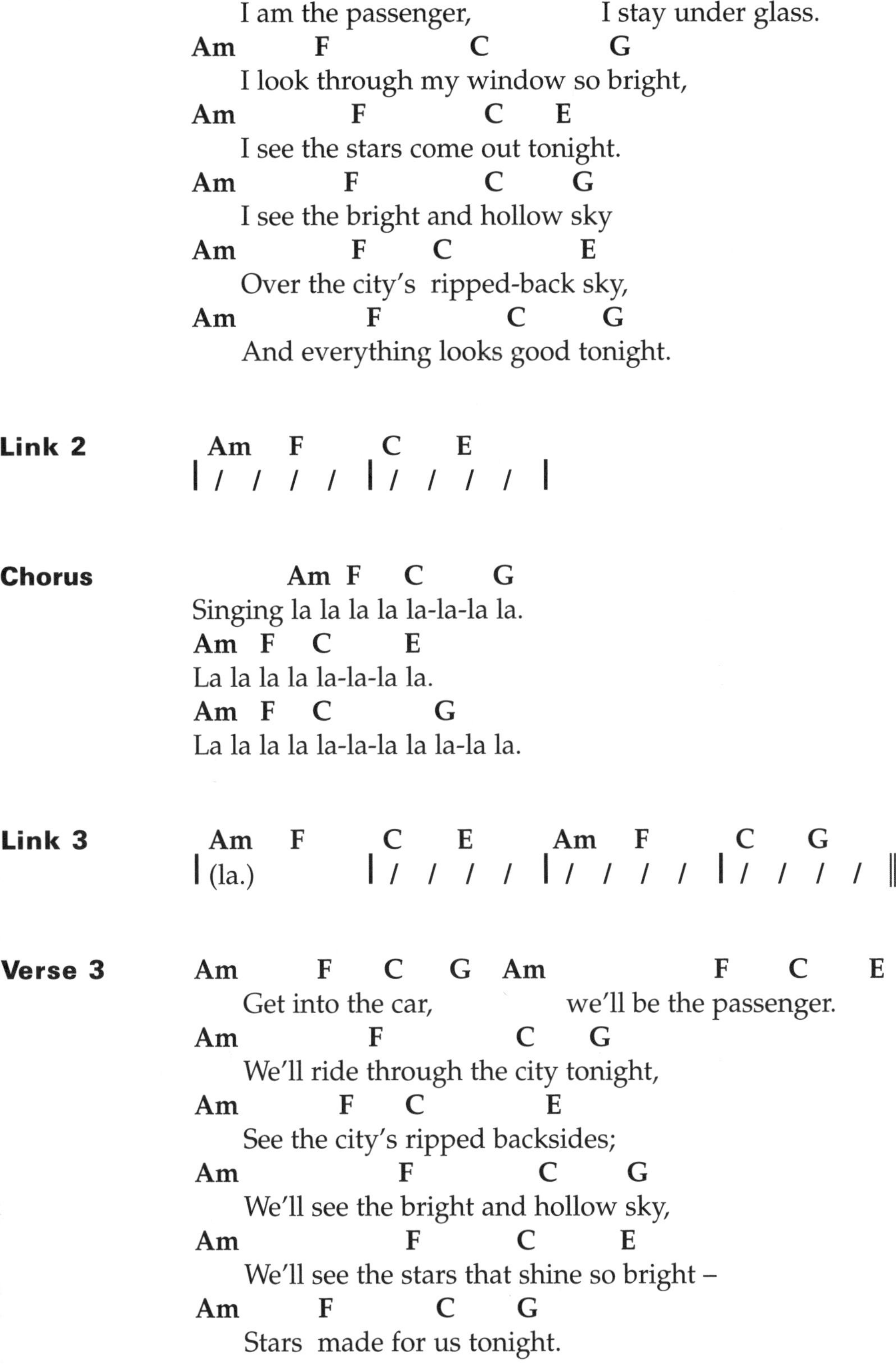

Verse 2

Am F C G Am F C E
I am the passenger, I stay under glass.
Am F C G
I look through my window so bright,
Am F C E
I see the stars come out tonight.
Am F C G
I see the bright and hollow sky
Am F C E
Over the city's ripped-back sky,
Am F C G
And everything looks good tonight.

Link 2

Am F C E
| / / / / | / / / / |

Chorus

Am F C G
Singing la la la la la-la-la la.
Am F C E
La la la la la-la-la la.
Am F C G
La la la la la-la-la la la-la la.

Link 3

Am F C E Am F C G
| (la.) | / / / / | / / / / | / / / / ||

Verse 3

Am F C G Am F C E
Get into the car, we'll be the passenger.
Am F C G
We'll ride through the city tonight,
Am F C E
See the city's ripped backsides;
Am F C G
We'll see the bright and hollow sky,
Am F C E
We'll see the stars that shine so bright –
Am F C G
Stars made for us tonight.

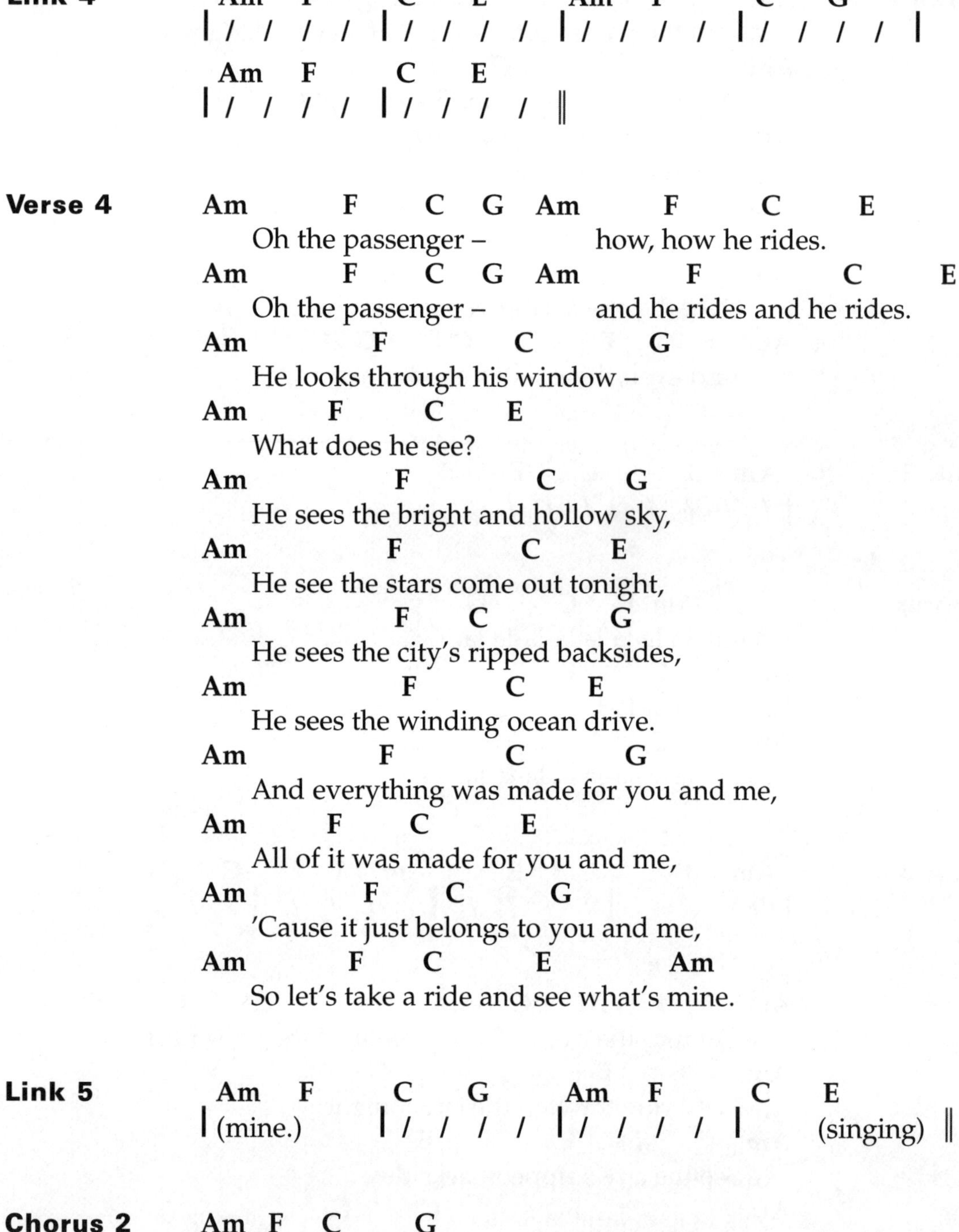

Link 4

| Am F / / / / | C E / / / / | Am F / / / / | C G / / / / |
| Am F / / / / | C E / / / / ||

Verse 4

Am F C G Am F C E
Oh the passenger – how, how he rides.
Am F C G Am F C E
Oh the passenger – and he rides and he rides.
Am F C G
He looks through his window –
Am F C E
What does he see?
Am F C G
He sees the bright and hollow sky,
Am F C E
He see the stars come out tonight,
Am F C G
He sees the city's ripped backsides,
Am F C E
He sees the winding ocean drive.
Am F C G
And everything was made for you and me,
Am F C E
All of it was made for you and me,
Am F C G
'Cause it just belongs to you and me,
Am F C E Am
So let's take a ride and see what's mine.

Link 5

| Am F (mine.) | C G / / / / | Am F / / / / | C E (singing) ||

Chorus 2

Am F C G
La la la la la-la-la la.
Am F C E
La la la la la-la-la la.
Am F C G
La la la la la-la-la la la-la la.

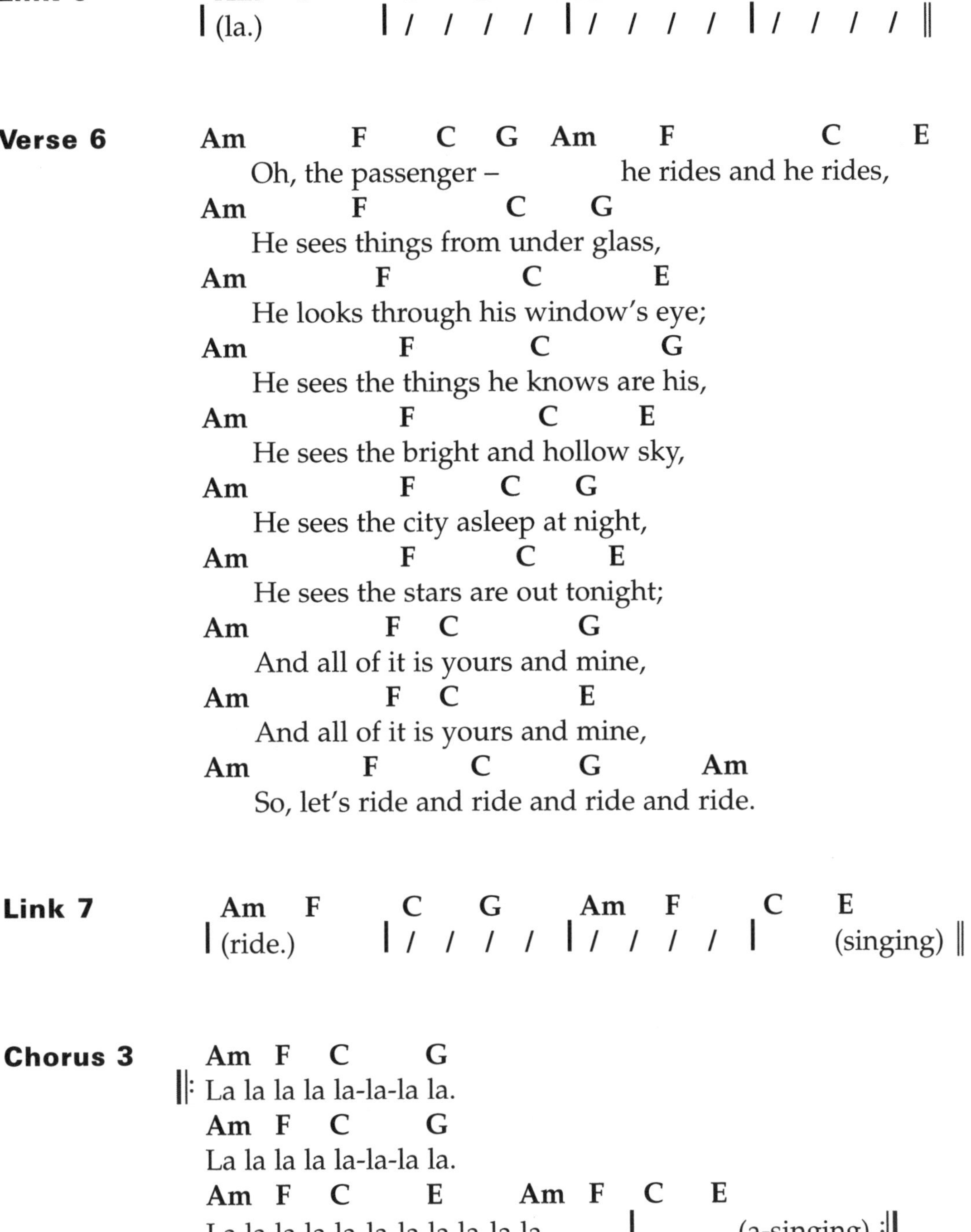

Link 6
Am F C E Am F C G
| (la.) | / / / / | / / / / | / / / / ||

Verse 6
Am F C G Am F C E
Oh, the passenger – he rides and he rides,
Am F C G
He sees things from under glass,
Am F C E
He looks through his window's eye;
Am F C G
He sees the things he knows are his,
Am F C E
He sees the bright and hollow sky,
Am F C G
He sees the city asleep at night,
Am F C E
He sees the stars are out tonight;
Am F C G
And all of it is yours and mine,
Am F C E
And all of it is yours and mine,
Am F C G Am
So, let's ride and ride and ride and ride.

Link 7
Am F C G Am F C E
| (ride.) | / / / / | / / / / | (singing) ||

Chorus 3
Am F C G
||: La la la la la-la-la la.
Am F C G
La la la la la-la-la la.
Am F C E Am F C E
La la la la la-la-la la la-la la. | (a-singing) :||

repeat to fade

Piece Of My Heart

Words by BERT BERNS
Music by JERRY RAGOVOY

F♯m A B C♯m D E G♯m

♩ = 78

Intro

```
    F♯m             A     B      C♯m             B
4/4 | /  /  /  /  | /  /  /  /  | /  /  /  /  | /  /  /  /  |
    D               B
    | /  /  /  /  | /  /  /  /  |

        B
Well, come on, come on, come on, come on.
```

Verse 1

```
E                   A    B     A                E    A    B
Didn't I make you feel     like you were the only man?
A    E                              A
Yeah, didn't I give you nearly everything
                  B
That a woman possibly can?

Honey, you know I did.
C♯m                                 B
But each time I tell myself that I     well, I think I've had enough,
       D                                  B
Oh but I'm gonna show you, baby,   that a woman can be tough:

I want you to come on, come on, come on, come on and
```

Chorus

```
E                A                       B
Take it! Take another little piece of my heart now, baby.
     A   E
(Oh oh, break a!)
         A                      B
Break another little bit of my heart now, darlin', yeah, yeah.
    A   E                 A                       B                 B♭
(Oh oh, have a!) have another little piece of my heart now, baby.
A                                                 G♯m    F♯m   E
    Well you know you've got it   if it makes  you    feel   good.

Oh, yes, indeed.
```

Link

```
 E      A      B      A
| /  /  /  /  | /  /  /  /  |
```

Verse 2

```
        E          A                B
You're out on the streets, looking good,
               A                       E
And baby    deep down in your heart,
                                A      B
I guess you know that it ain't right.     Now-ma, now-ma,

Now-ma, now-ma, now-ma, now-ma,
E                        A     B
    Heel, man, when I cry at night,

Baby and I cry all of the time.
C♯m                                     B
    But each time I tell myself that I – well, I can't stand the pain,
                D                         B
But when you hold me in your arms, I sing it once again:

I said, come on, come on, come on, come on, yeah
```

Chorus 2

```
E                    A                            B
Take it! Take another little piece of my heart now,  baby.
      A   E
(Oh oh, break a!)
           A                           B
Break another little bit of my heart now, darlin', yeah.
     A   E                     A                         B                  B♭
(Oh oh, have a!) have another little piece of my heart now, baby.___
A
     Well, you know you've got it, child,
                G♯m    F♯m    E
If it makes    you     feel   good.
```

Guitar solo

```
 F♯m               A       B          F♯m               A      B
‖: /  /  /  /  | /  /  /  /  | /  /  /  /  | /  /  /  /  :‖
 C♯m               B                  D                  B
|  /  /  /  /  | /  /  /  /  | /  /  /  /  | /  /  /  /  |
                      B
I need you to come on, come on, come on, come on, and
```

Chorus 3

```
E                    A                            B
Take it! Take another little piece of my heart now,  baby.
      A   E                   A                      B
(Oh oh, break a!) break another little bit of my heart
                                 A
Now, darlin', yeah, come on, now.
E                     A                         B                  B♭
(Have a!) have another little piece of my heart now, baby.
A                                  N.C.
     Well, you know you've got it, wah._______
```

```
Chorus 4    E                    A                          B
            Take it! Take another little piece of my heart now,  baby.
                  A   E                    A                          B
            (Oh oh, break a!) break another little bit of my heart
                                           A
            Now, darlin', yeah, yeah, yeah, yeah.
            E                      A                          B                     B♭
            (Have a!) have another little piece of my heart now, baby.____
            A                                                  G♯m   F♯m  E
            You know you've got it, child, if it makes you    feel    good.


Coda          F♯m                 A       B       F♯m
            | /  /  /  /  | /  /  /  /  | /      ||
```

Pinball Wizard

Words and Music by
PETER TOWNSHEND

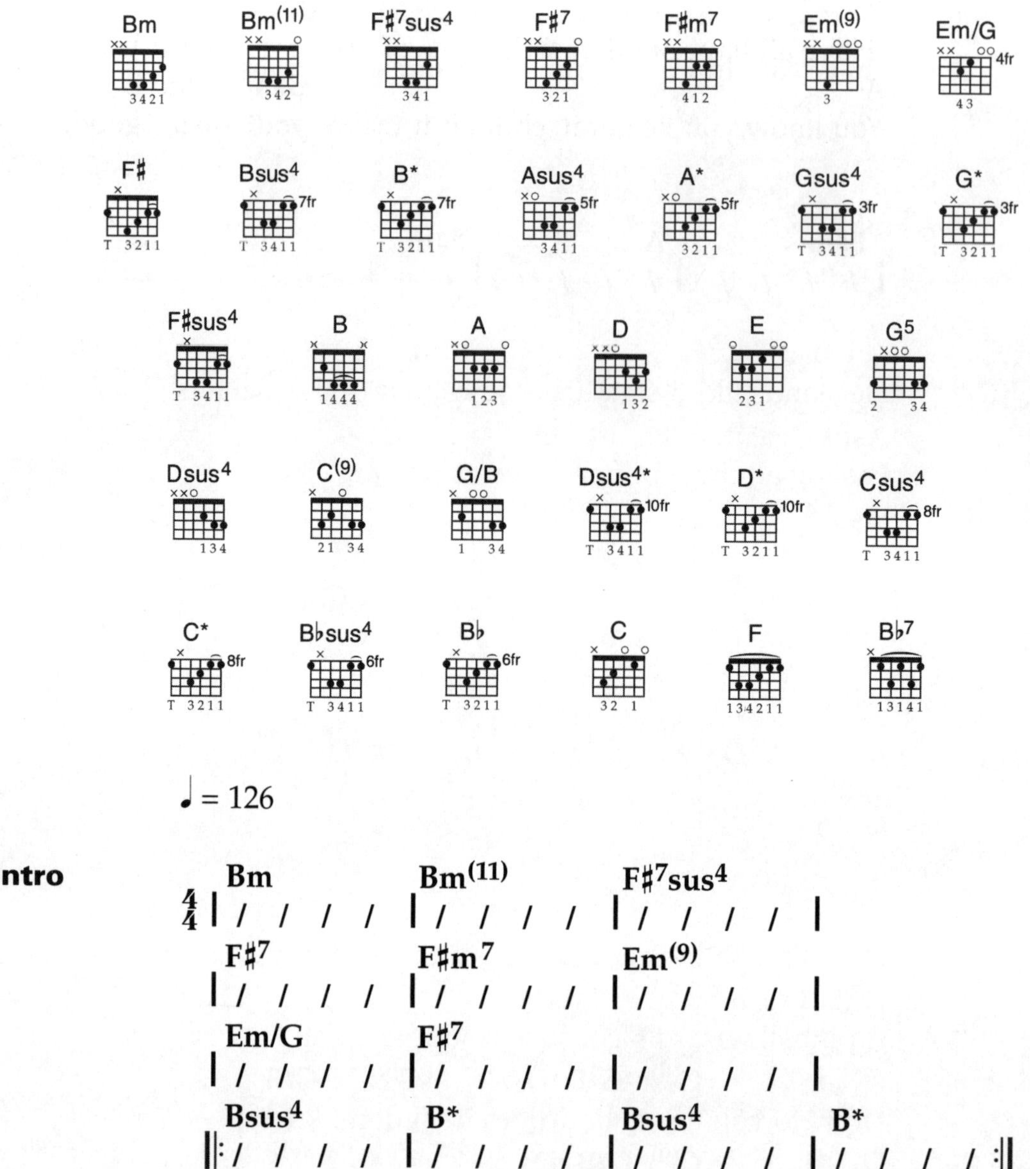

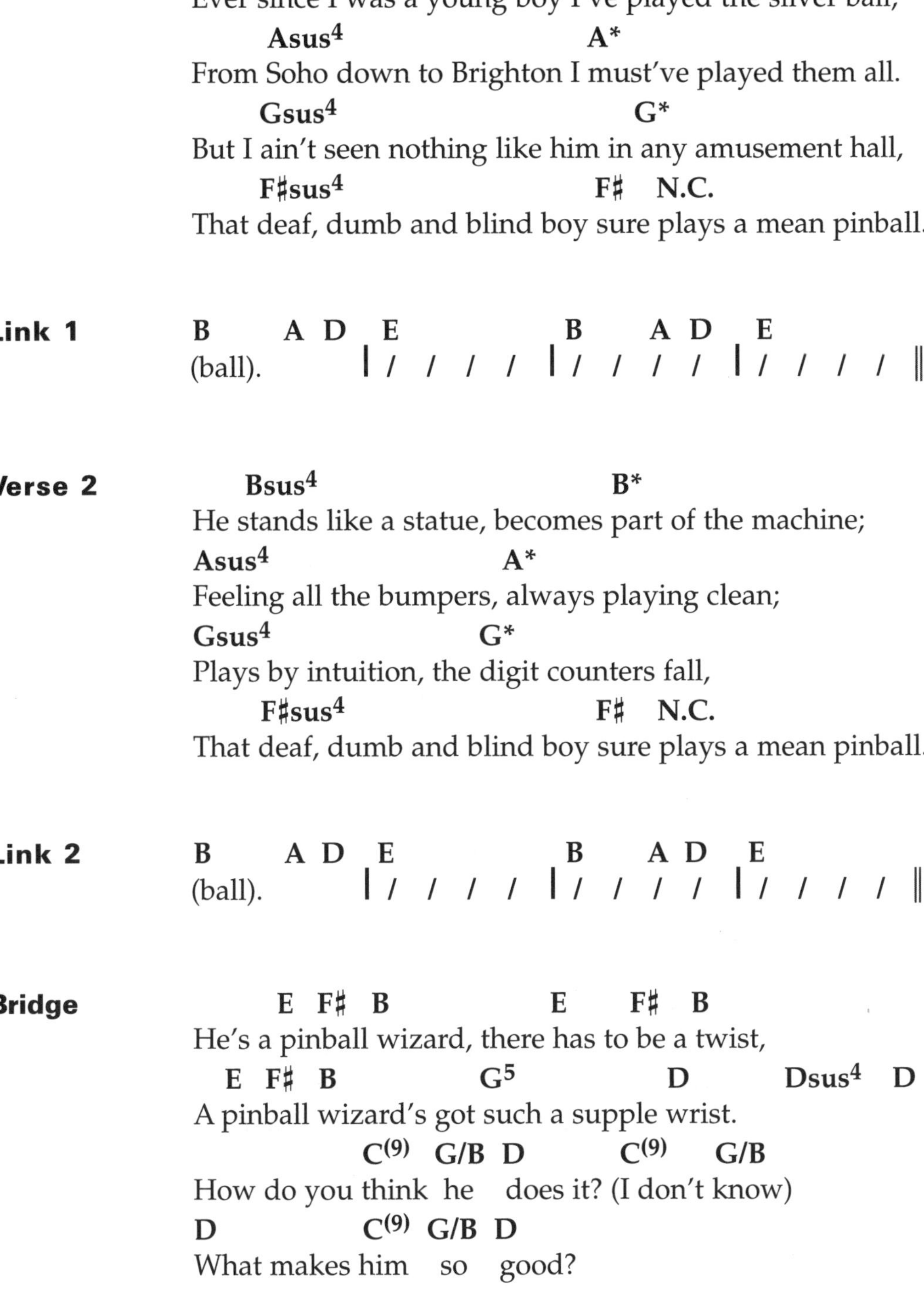

```
Verse 1        Bsus4                         B*
          Ever since I was a young boy I've played the silver ball,
               Asus4                     A*
          From Soho down to Brighton I must've played them all.
               Gsus4                          G*
          But I ain't seen nothing like him in any amusement hall,
               F#sus4                     F#   N.C.
          That deaf, dumb and blind boy sure plays a mean pinball.

Link 1    B        A  D   E               B      A  D   E
          (ball).        | / / / / | / / / / | / / / / ||

Verse 2       Bsus4                          B*
          He stands like a statue, becomes part of the machine;
          Asus4                  A*
          Feeling all the bumpers, always playing clean;
          Gsus4                G*
          Plays by intuition, the digit counters fall,
               F#sus4                     F#   N.C.
          That deaf, dumb and blind boy sure plays a mean pinball.

Link 2    B        A  D   E               B      A  D   E
          (ball).        | / / / / | / / / / | / / / / ||

Bridge          E  F#  B               E    F#   B
          He's a pinball wizard, there has to be a twist,
            E  F#  B             G5           D        Dsus4  D
          A pinball wizard's got such a supple wrist.
                          C(9)  G/B  D        C(9)   G/B
          How do you think  he    does it? (I don't know)
          D               C(9) G/B D
          What makes him    so    good?
```

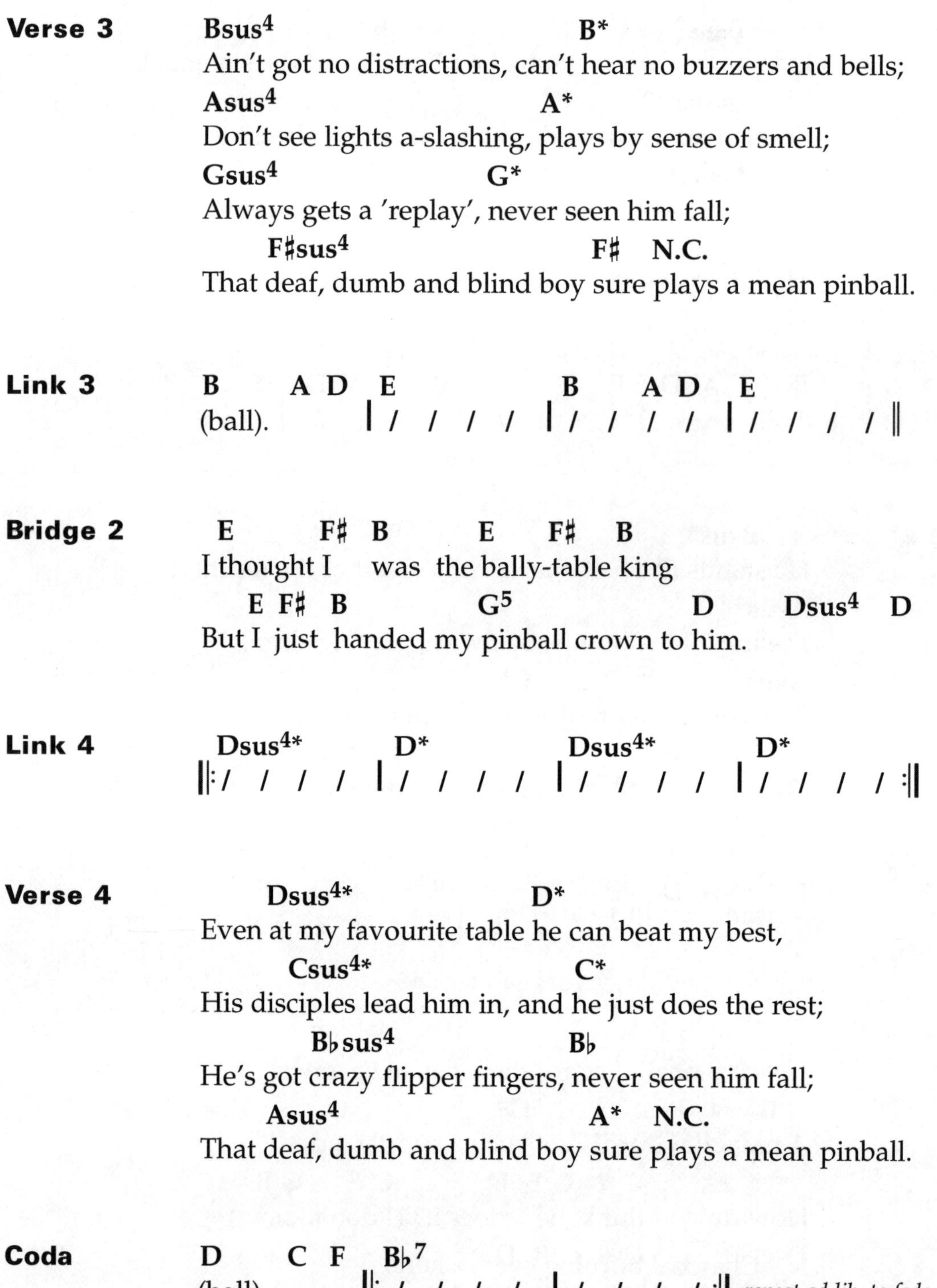

Verse 3

```
Bsus4                                B*
Ain't got no distractions, can't hear no buzzers and bells;
Asus4                               A*
Don't see lights a-slashing, plays by sense of smell;
Gsus4                        G*
Always gets a 'replay', never seen him fall;
      F♯sus4                         F♯    N.C.
That deaf, dumb and blind boy sure plays a mean pinball.
```

Link 3

```
B        A D   E                 B       A D    E
(ball).        | / / / / | / / / / | / / / / ||
```

Bridge 2

```
  E        F♯  B        E     F♯    B
I thought I    was  the bally-table king
     E F♯  B             G5                D       Dsus4   D
But I  just  handed my pinball crown to him.
```

Link 4

```
 Dsus4*         D*            Dsus4*         D*
||: / / / / | / / / / | / / / / | / / / / :||
```

Verse 4

```
      Dsus4*                 D*
Even at my favourite table he can beat my best,
        Csus4*                   C*
His disciples lead him in, and he just does the rest;
          B♭sus4                B♭
He's got crazy flipper fingers, never seen him fall;
      Asus4                          A*    N.C.
That deaf, dumb and blind boy sure plays a mean pinball.
```

Coda

```
D        C  F    B♭7
(ball).        ||: / / / / | / / / / :||
```
repeat ad lib. to fade

Pleasant Valley Sunday

Words and Music by
GERRY GOFFIN AND CAROLE KING

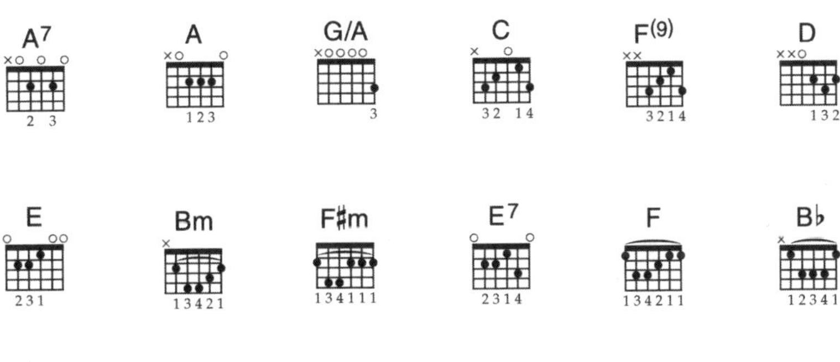

♩ = 176

Intro

```
     (A7)
4/4 | / / / / | / / / / |
      A         G/A         A         G/A
    | / / / / | / / / / | / / / / | / / / / |
```

Verse 1

```
A
     The local rock group down the street
                                      G/A
Is trying hard to learn their song,
A
     Serenade the weekend squire
                                         G/A
Who just came out to mow his lawn.
```

Chorus

```
C            F(9)          C        F(9)
     Another Pleasant Valley Sunday:_____
C            F(9)          C      D
     Charcoal burning everywhere;
E            A             D   A   E
     Rows of houses that are all  the same
    Bm  F♯m  D      A  E
And no - one   seems to  care.
```

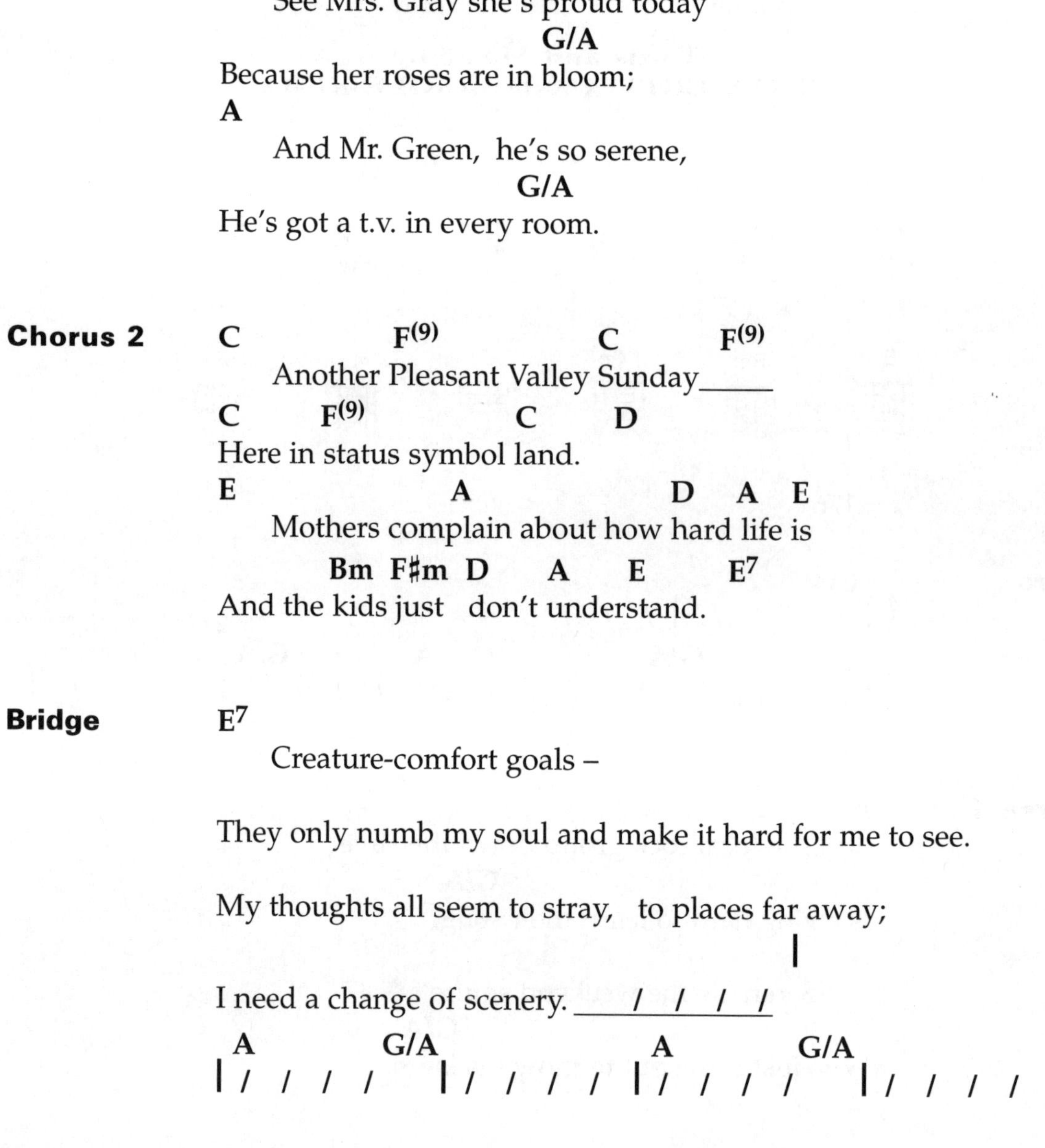

Verse 2

A
See Mrs. Gray she's proud today
G/A
Because her roses are in bloom;
A
And Mr. Green, he's so serene,
G/A
He's got a t.v. in every room.

Chorus 2

C F$^{(9)}$ C F$^{(9)}$
Another Pleasant Valley Sunday____
C F$^{(9)}$ C D
Here in status symbol land.
E A D A E
Mothers complain about how hard life is
Bm F♯m D A E E^7
And the kids just don't understand.

Bridge

E^7
Creature-comfort goals –

They only numb my soul and make it hard for me to see.

My thoughts all seem to stray, to places far away;

I need a change of scenery. | / / / /

A G/A A G/A
| / / / / | / / / / | / / / / | / / / / |

Instrumental

A G/A
||: Ta ta ta ta, ta ta ta ta, ta ta ta ta, ta ta ta ta. :||

Chorus 3

```
C              F(9)            C         F(9)
      Another Pleasant Valley Sunday:_____
C              F(9)            C
      Charcoal burning everywhere.
F              B♭              F         B♭
      Another Pleasant Valley Sunday______
F              B♭              F
      Here in status symbol land.______
  A           G/A           A          G/A
| / / / /    | / / / /    | / / / /    | / / / / |
```

Coda

```
 A7
||:    Another Pleasant Valley Sunday. :||  repeat to fade
```

Pretty In Pink

Words and Music by
RICHARD BUTLER, TIMOTHY BUTLER, JOHN ASHTON,
VINCENT DAVEY, ROGER MORRIS AND DUNCAN KILBURN

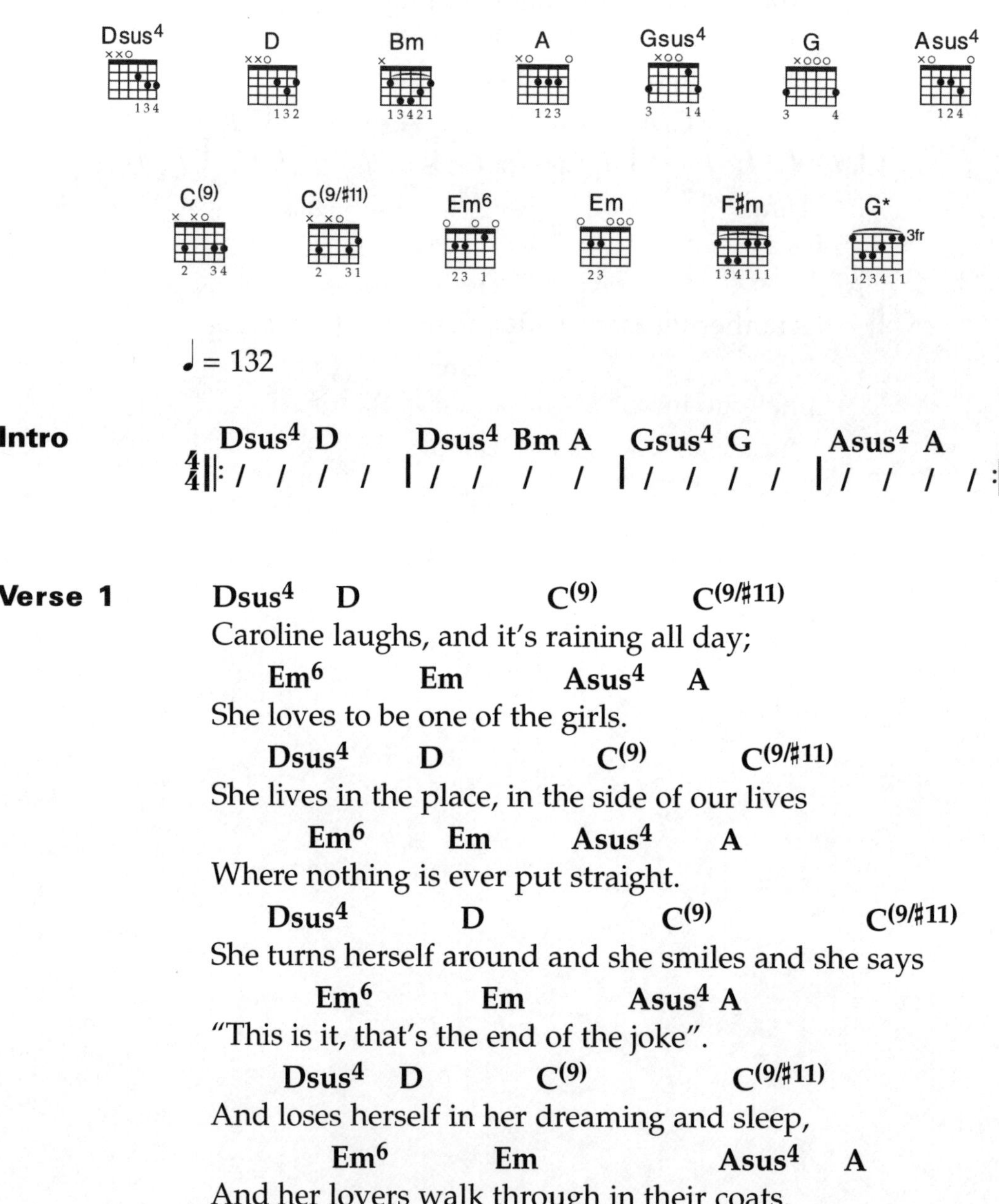

Chorus

```
    Em   F♯m       G*              F♯m       Em
Yes,     pretty in pink,           isn't she?____
F♯m       G*            F♯m
Pretty in pink,         isn't she?
```

Verse 2

```
Dsus4    D         C(9)        C(9/♯11)
All of her lovers all talk of the notes
           Em6          Em         Asus4    A
And the flowers that they never sent,
      Dsus4       D  C(9)  C(9/♯11)  Em6  Em
And wasn't she ea - - - - - - sy,__________
Asus4    A         Dsus4    D
Isn't she pretty in pink?
    C(9)          C(9/♯11)        Em6        Em
The one who insists he was first in the line
        Asus4   A              Dsus4    D
Is the last to remember her name:
     C(9)        C(9/♯11)       Em6           Em
He's walking around in this dress that she wore;
         Asus4        A                Em
She is gone but the joke's the same.____
```

Chorus 2

```
F♯m              G          F♯m        Em
Pretty in pink,___          isn't she?_____
F♯m              G          F♯m
Pretty in pink,___          isn't she?
```

Link

```
 Dsus4 D      Dsus4 Bm A    Gsus4 G       Asus4 A      x4
‖: / / / /  | / / / /     | / / / /     | / / / /    :‖
```

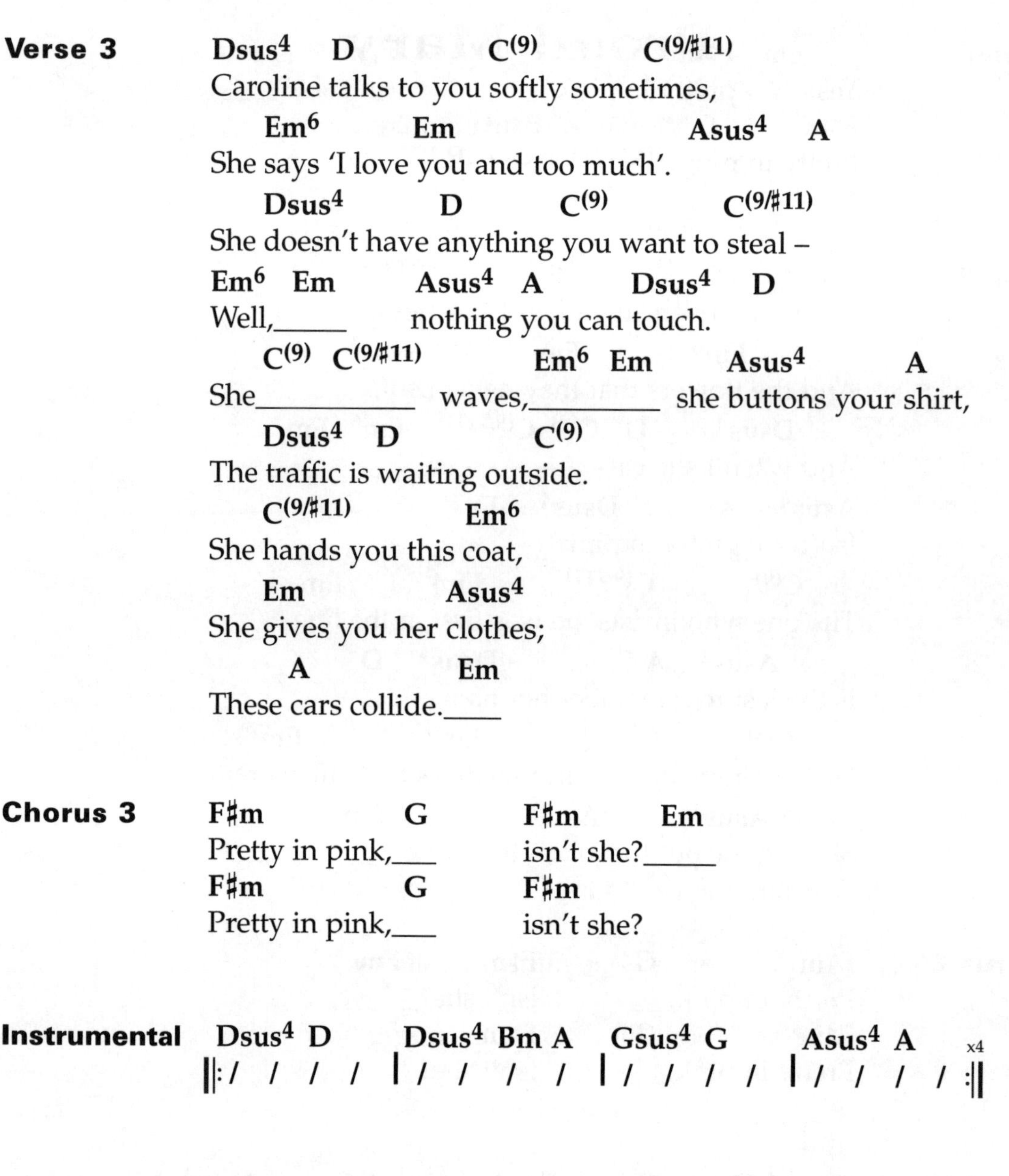

Verse 3

Dsus^4 D C$^{(9)}$ C$^{(9/\sharp11)}$
Caroline talks to you softly sometimes,
Em^6 Em Asus^4 A
She says 'I love you and too much'.
Dsus^4 D C$^{(9)}$ C$^{(9/\sharp11)}$
She doesn't have anything you want to steal –
Em^6 Em Asus^4 A Dsus^4 D
Well,_____ nothing you can touch.
C$^{(9)}$ C$^{(9/\sharp11)}$ Em^6 Em Asus^4 A
She___________ waves,_________ she buttons your shirt,
Dsus^4 D C$^{(9)}$
The traffic is waiting outside.
C$^{(9/\sharp11)}$ Em^6
She hands you this coat,
Em Asus^4
She gives you her clothes;
A Em
These cars collide.____

Chorus 3

F♯m G F♯m Em
Pretty in pink,___ isn't she?_____
F♯m G F♯m
Pretty in pink,___ isn't she?

Instrumental

Dsus^4 D | Dsus^4 Bm A | Gsus^4 G | Asus^4 A x4
‖: / / / / | / / / / | / / / / | / / / / :‖

Coda

Dsus^4 D | Dsus^4 Bm A | Gsus^4 G | Asus^4 A x4 | D
‖: / / / / | / / / / | / / / / | / / / / :‖ / ‖

Proud Mary

Words and Music by
JOHN FOGERTY

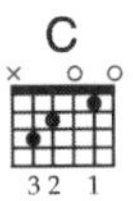

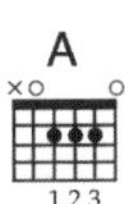

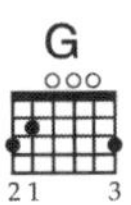

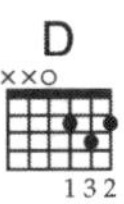

A^7

♩ = 118

Intro

```
    C      A      C      A      C      A G    F      D
4/4 | / / / / | / / / / | / / / / | / / / / |
    D
    | / / / / | / / / / ||
```

Verse 1

D
Left a good job in the city,

Workin' for The Man every night and day.

And I never lost one minute of sleepin',

Worryin' 'bout the way things might have been.
A⁷
Big wheel a-keep on turnin'.
Bm
Proud Mary keep on burnin'.

Chorus

D
Rollin', rollin', rollin' on a river.

Verse 2

D
Cleaned a lot of plates in Memphis,

Pumped a lot of pain down in New Orleans.

But I never saw the good side of the city

Till I hitched a ride on a river-boat queen.
A7
Big wheel keep on turnin',
Bm
Proud Mary keep on burnin'.

Chorus 2

D
Rollin', rollin', rollin' on a river.

Link 1

```
 C     A      C     A      C    A G    F       D
| / / / /  | / / / /  | / / / /  | / / / /  |
 D
| / / / /  | / / / /  |
```

Guitar solo

```
 D
||: / / / /  | / / / /  | / / / /  | / / / / :||
 A                        Bm
| / / / /  | / / / /  | / / / /  | / / / /  ||
```

Chorus 3

D
Rollin', rollin', rollin' on a river.

Link 2

```
 C     A      C     A      C    A G    F       D
| / / / /  | / / / /  | / / / /  | / / / /  |
 D
| / / / /  | / / / /  |
```

Verse 3 **D**
If you come down to the river

Bet you're gonna find some people who live.

You don't have to worry 'cause you have no money,

People on the river are happy to give.
A7
Big wheel keep on turnin',
Bm
Proud Mary keep on burnin'.

Chorus 3 ||: **D** :|| x4
Rollin', rollin', rollin' on a river. *(fade)*

The Red Telephone

Words and Music by
ARTHUR LEE

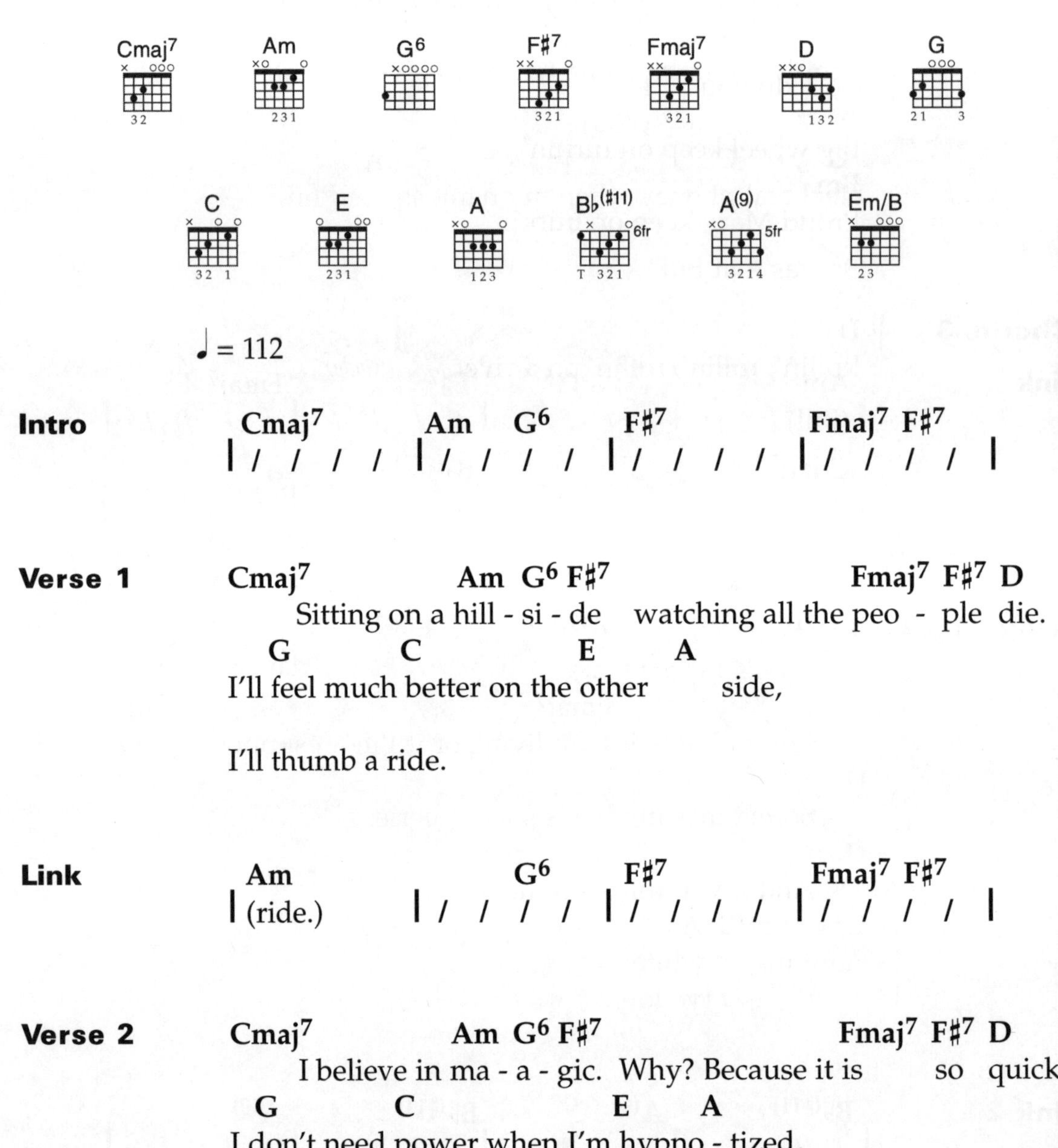

♩ = 112

Intro

Cmaj7 | Am G6 | F♯7 | Fmaj7 F♯7

| / / / / | / / / / | / / / / | / / / / |

Verse 1

Cmaj7 Am G6 F♯7 Fmaj7 F♯7 D
Sitting on a hill - si - de watching all the peo - ple die.
G C E A
I'll feel much better on the other side,

I'll thumb a ride.

Link

Am G6 F♯7 Fmaj7 F♯7
| (ride.) | / / / / | / / / / | / / / / |

Verse 2

Cmaj7 Am G6 F♯7 Fmaj7 F♯7 D
I believe in ma - a - gic. Why? Because it is so quick.
G C E A
I don't need power when I'm hypno - tized,

Look in my eyes.

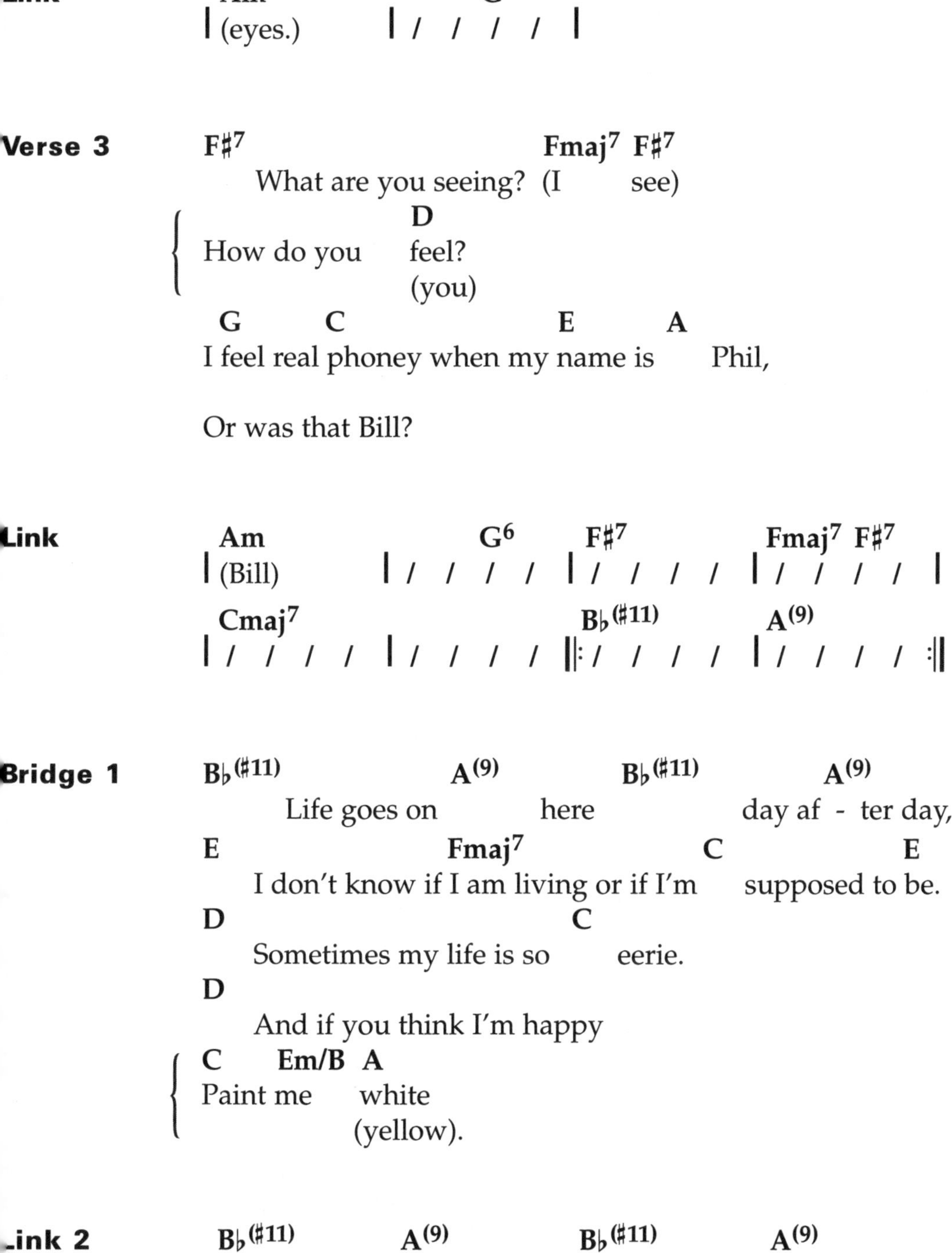
Link
Am G6
(eyes.) / / / /
Verse 3
F♯7 Fmaj7 F♯7
What are you seeing? (I see)
D
How do you feel?
(you)
G C E A
I feel real phoney when my name is Phil,
Or was that Bill?
Link
Am G6 F♯7 Fmaj7 F♯7
(Bill) / / / / / / / / / / / /
Cmaj7 B♭(♯11) A(9)
/ / / / / / / / / / / / / / / /
Bridge 1
B♭(♯11) A(9) B♭(♯11) A(9)
Life goes on here day af - ter day,
E Fmaj7 C E
I don't know if I am living or if I'm supposed to be.
D C
Sometimes my life is so eerie.
D
And if you think I'm happy
C Em/B A
Paint me white
(yellow).
Link 2
B♭(♯11) A(9) B♭(♯11) A(9)
/ / / / / / / / / / / / / / / /

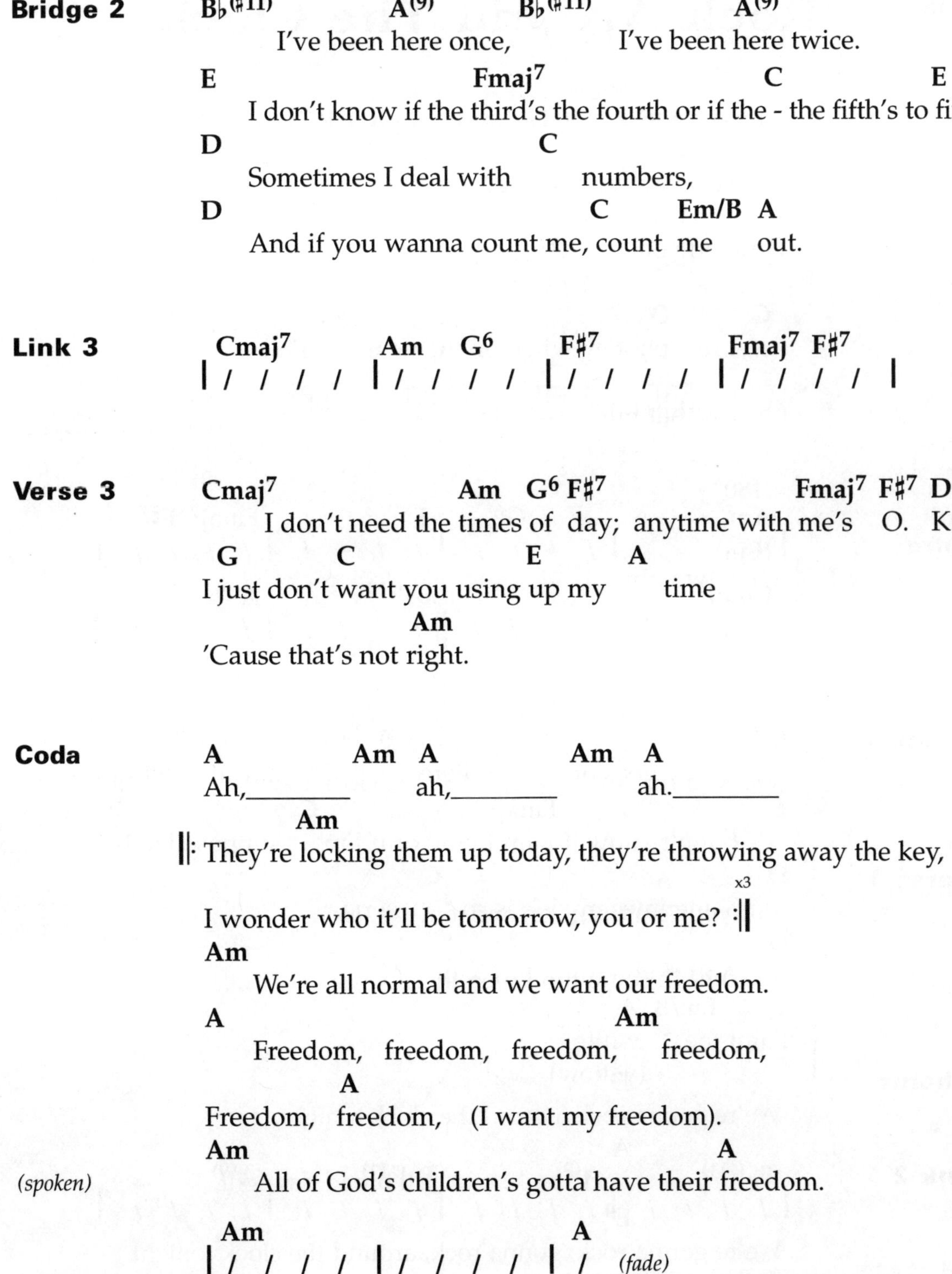
Bridge 2
B♭(♯11) A(9) B♭(♯11) A(9)
I've been here once, I've been here twice.
E Fmaj7 C E
I don't know if the third's the fourth or if the - the fifth's to fix.
D C
Sometimes I deal with numbers,
D C Em/B A
And if you wanna count me, count me out.
Link 3
Cmaj7 Am G6 F♯7 Fmaj7 F♯7
| / / / / | / / / / | / / / / | / / / / |
Verse 3
Cmaj7 Am G6 F♯7 Fmaj7 F♯7 D
I don't need the times of day; anytime with me's O. K.
G C E A
I just don't want you using up my time
Am
'Cause that's not right.
Coda
A Am A Am A
Ah,________ ah,________ ah.________
Am
‖: They're locking them up today, they're throwing away the key,
x3
I wonder who it'll be tomorrow, you or me? :‖
Am
We're all normal and we want our freedom.
A Am
Freedom, freedom, freedom, freedom,
A
Freedom, freedom, (I want my freedom).
(spoken)
Am A
All of God's children's gotta have their freedom.
Am A
| / / / / | / / / / | / (fade)

Rock Around The Clock

Words and Music by
JIMMY DE KNIGHT AND MAX FREEDMAN

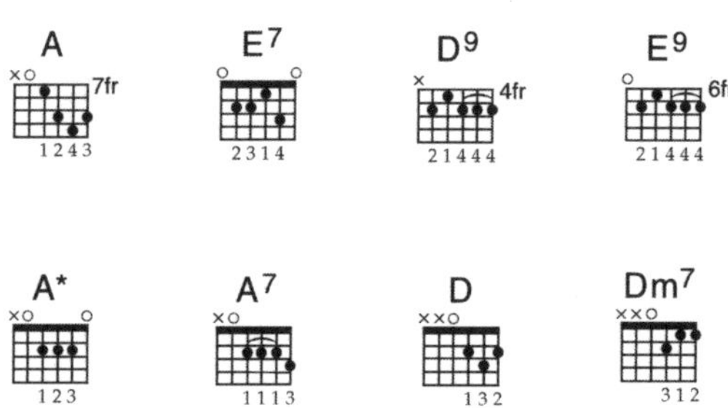

♩ = 180

Intro

4/4

N.C.
One, two, three o' clock, four'o'clock rock
A **N.C.**
Five, six, seven o'clock, eight'o'clock rock
A **N.C.**
Nine, ten, eleven o' clock, twelve o'clock rock
E7 N.C. E7 N.C. E7 N.C.
We're gonna rock around the clock tonight!

Verse 1

A
Put your glad rags on and join me, Hon'.

We'll have some fun when the clock strikes one,

Chorus

D9
We're gonna rock around the clock tonight,
A
We're gonna rock, rock, rock 'till broad daylight,
E9 **A**
We're gonna rock, gonna rock, around the clock tonight.

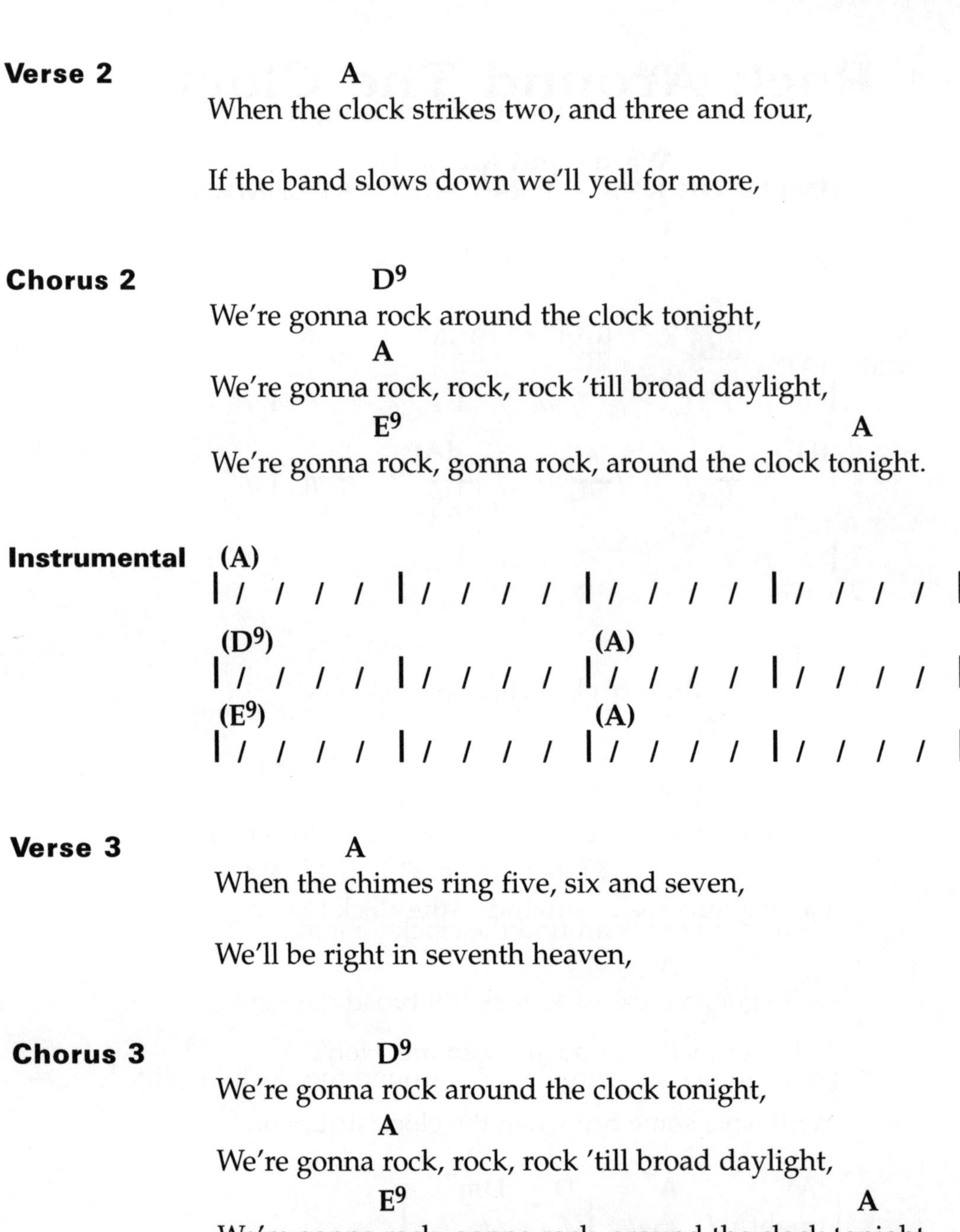

Verse 2

A
When the clock strikes two, and three and four,

If the band slows down we'll yell for more,

Chorus 2

D^9
We're gonna rock around the clock tonight,
A
We're gonna rock, rock, rock 'till broad daylight,
E^9 A
We're gonna rock, gonna rock, around the clock tonight.

Instrumental

(A)
| / / / / | / / / / | / / / / | / / / / |
(D^9) (A)
| / / / / | / / / / | / / / / | / / / / |
(E^9) (A)
| / / / / | / / / / | / / / / | / / / / |

Verse 3

A
When the chimes ring five, six and seven,

We'll be right in seventh heaven,

Chorus 3

D^9
We're gonna rock around the clock tonight,
A
We're gonna rock, rock, rock 'till broad daylight,
E^9 A
We're gonna rock, gonna rock, around the clock tonight.

Verse 4

A
When it's eight, nine, ten, eleven too,

I'll be goin' strong and so will you,

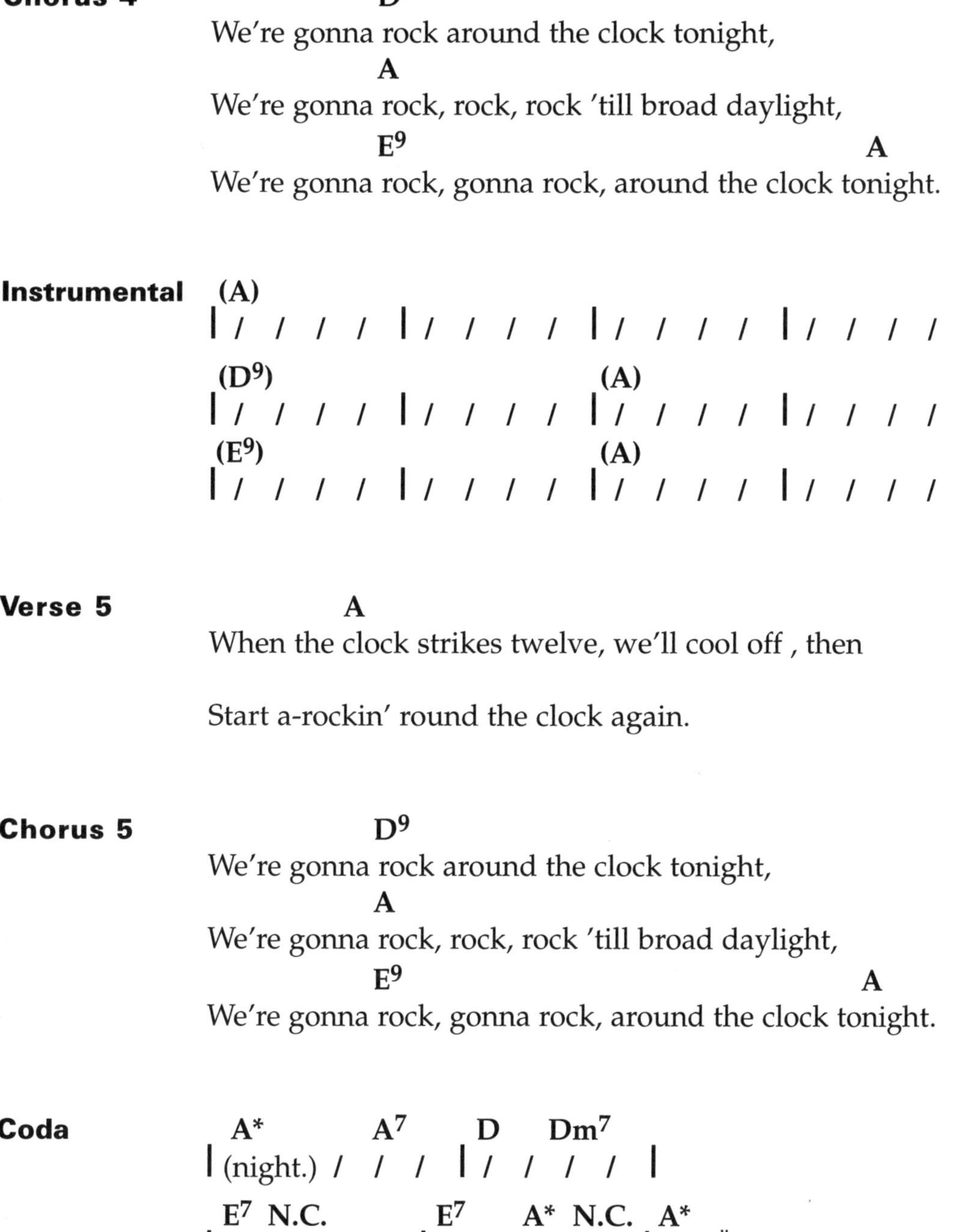

Chorus 4

D^9
We're gonna rock around the clock tonight,
A
We're gonna rock, rock, rock 'till broad daylight,
E^9 A
We're gonna rock, gonna rock, around the clock tonight.

Instrumental

(A)
| / / / / | / / / / | / / / / | / / / / |
(D^9) (A)
| / / / / | / / / / | / / / / | / / / / |
(E^9) (A)
| / / / / | / / / / | / / / / | / / / / |

Verse 5

A
When the clock strikes twelve, we'll cool off , then

Start a-rockin' round the clock again.

Chorus 5

D^9
We're gonna rock around the clock tonight,
A
We're gonna rock, rock, rock 'till broad daylight,
E^9 A
We're gonna rock, gonna rock, around the clock tonight.

Coda

A* A^7 D Dm^7
| (night.) / / / | / / / / |
E^7 N.C. E^7 A* N.C. A*
| / / / / | / / / / | / ‖

San Francisco (Be Sure To Wear Some Flowers In Your Hair)

Words and Music by
JOHN PHILLIPS

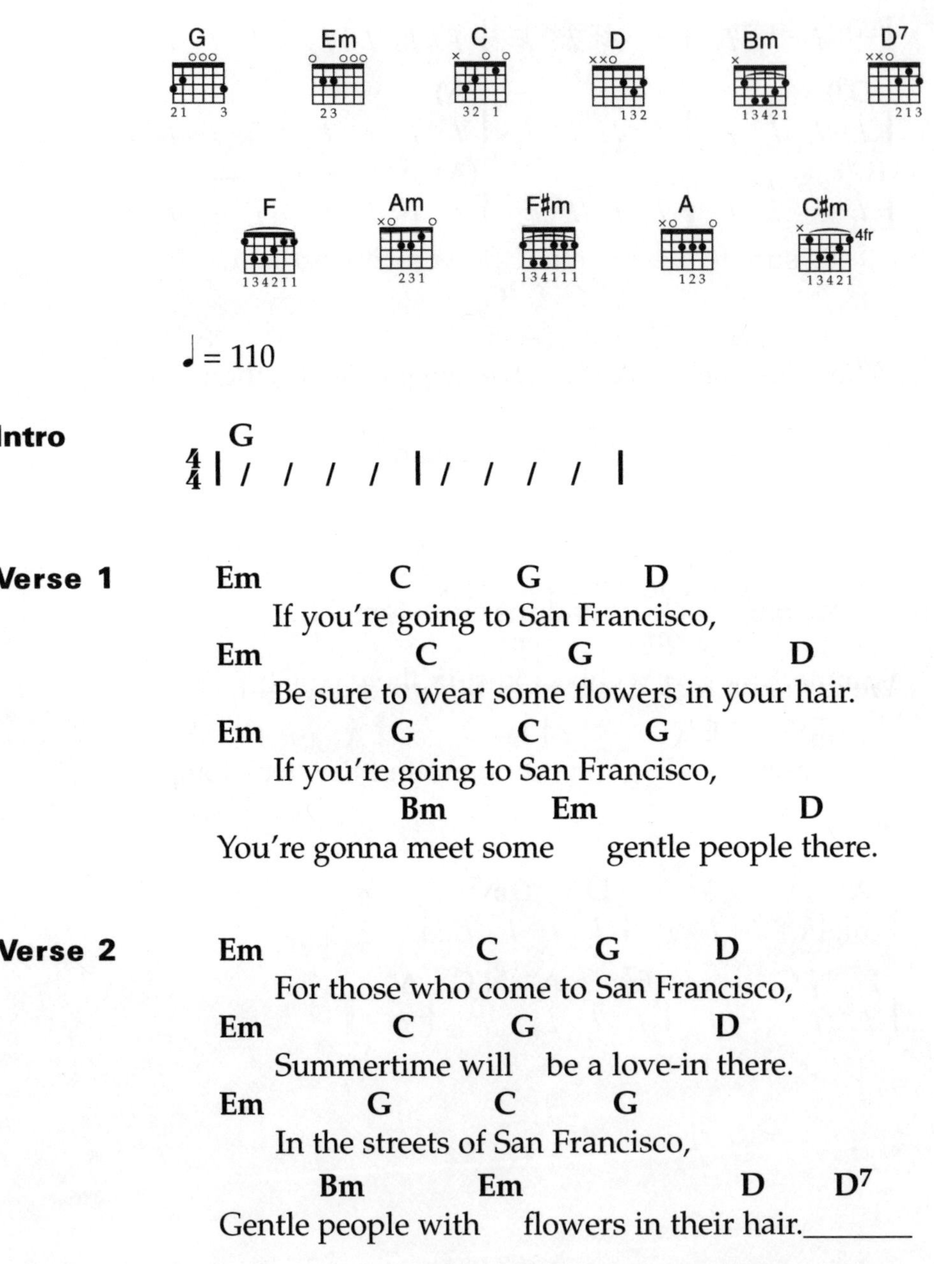

♩ = 110

Intro

G

Verse 1

```
Em                C          G           D
         If you're going to San Francisco,
Em                  C              G                D
         Be sure to wear some flowers in your hair.
Em                G          C           G
         If you're going to San Francisco,
                    Bm           Em                  D
You're gonna meet some      gentle people there.
```

Verse 2

```
Em                         C         G         D
         For those who come to San Francisco,
Em                C           G                D
         Summertime will     be a love-in there.
Em              G          C          G
         In the streets of San Francisco,
              Bm            Em                   D         D7
Gentle people with      flowers in their hair.________
```

Bridge

```
F
All across the nation, such a strange vibration.
   G
Mmm, people in motion.
F
There's a whole generation
                                     G
With a new explanation.____
                        D7
People in motion,     people in motion.
```

Verse 3

```
Em                 Am     C              G   Bm   D
   For those who come_______          to San Fran - cisco,
Em             C          G              D
   Be sure to wear some    flowers in your hair.
Em          G        C       G
   If you come to San Francisco,
      Bm  Em                   G       |        | (Em)      |
Summertime     will be a love-in there. ________   /  /  /  /
```

Coda

```
F♯m       A       D       A
   If you come to San Francisco,
      C♯m F♯m                   A      |        |
Summertime     will be a love-in there.__________
| F♯m      | A       | D       | A  (fade)
______
```

Say Hello Wave Goodbye

Words and Music by
DAVID BALL AND MARC ALMOND

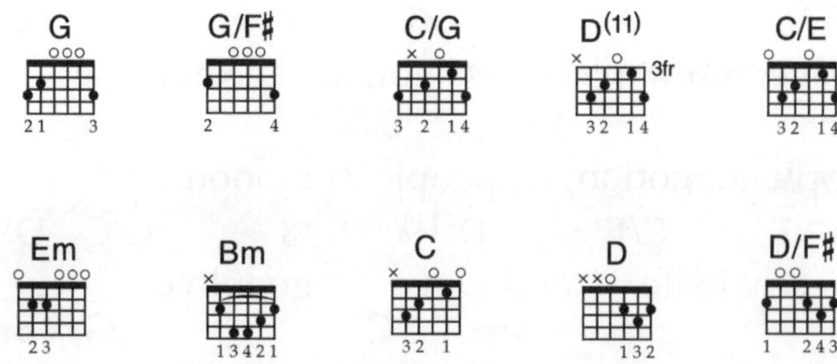

Capo 2nd fret

♩ = 78

```
Intro      G         G/F♯  C/G      D(11)       G         G/F♯  C/E      D(11)
       4/4 | / / / / | / / /          / | / / / / | / / /          / ||

Verse 1    G                                    C/E          D(11)
           Standing at the door of the Pink      Flamingo
                    G              C/G   D(11)
           Crying in the rain,
           G             C/E
           It was a kind of so - so love
           D(11)      G                                   C/G            D(11)
           And I'm going to make sure it doesn't happen again.
           G            C/E                D(11)
           You and I      had to be
                G                                C/G    D(11)
           The standing joke        of the year.
           G                          C/E            D(11)
           You were a run-around,             a lost and found,
           G                          C/G        D(11)
           And not for me, I fear.
```

```
Chorus      Em         G          Bm         C    D
            Take your hands   off me,____       hey,____
            Em        G     Bm      C     D/F♯
            I don't belong to you, you see.
            Em     G         Bm              C      D
            Take a look    in my face   for the last   time.
            Em                     G
            I never knew you,      you never knew me,
            Bm                  C     D/F♯
            Say hello, goodbye.____
            G          C/E       D(11)     G       C/G   D(11)
                Say hello   and wave    goodbye._________

Verse 2     G                        C/E             D(11)
            We tried to make it work: you in a cocktail     skirt
                 G                       C/G              D(11)
            And me in a suit     but it just     wasn't me.
            G                         C/E               D(11)
            You're used to wearing less, and now your life's a mess –
            G                   C/G   D(11)
            So insecure you see.
                 G                                C/E              D(11)
            Well  I've put up with all the scenes and this is one scene
                  G                              C/G     D(11)
            That's going to be played      my way.

Chorus 2    Em         G          Bm         C    D
            Take your hands   off me,____       hey,____
            Em        G     Bm      C     D/F♯
            I don't belong to you, you see.
            Em     G         Bm              C      D
            Take a look    in my face   for the last   time.
            Em                     G
            I never knew you,      you never knew me,
            Bm                  C     D/F♯
            Say hello, goodbye.____
            G          C/E       D(11)     G       C/G   D(11)
         ||:    Say hello   and wave    goodbye._________   :||
```

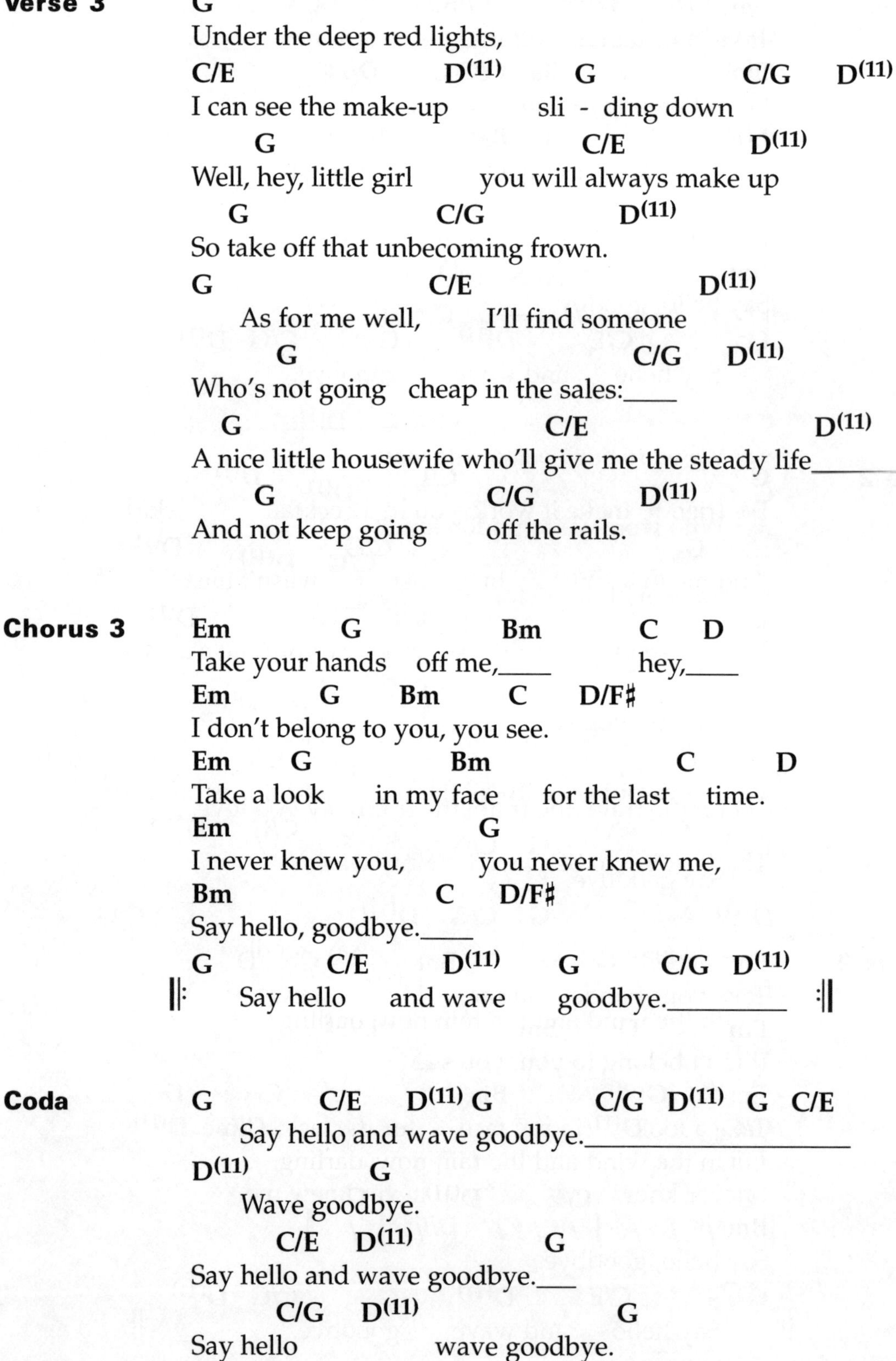

Verse 3

G
Under the deep red lights,
C/E D(11) G C/G D(11)
I can see the make-up sli - ding down
G C/E D(11)
Well, hey, little girl you will always make up
G C/G D(11)
So take off that unbecoming frown.
G C/E D(11)
As for me well, I'll find someone
G C/G D(11)
Who's not going cheap in the sales:____
G C/E D(11)
A nice little housewife who'll give me the steady life______
G C/G D(11)
And not keep going off the rails.

Chorus 3

Em G Bm C D
Take your hands off me,____ hey,____
Em G Bm C D/F♯
I don't belong to you, you see.
Em G Bm C D
Take a look in my face for the last time.
Em G
I never knew you, you never knew me,
Bm C D/F♯
Say hello, goodbye.____
G C/E D(11) G C/G D(11)
‖: Say hello and wave goodbye.________ :‖

Coda

G C/E D(11) G C/G D(11) G C/E
Say hello and wave goodbye.__________________
D(11) G
Wave goodbye.
C/E D(11) G
Say hello and wave goodbye.___
C/G D(11) G
Say hello wave goodbye.

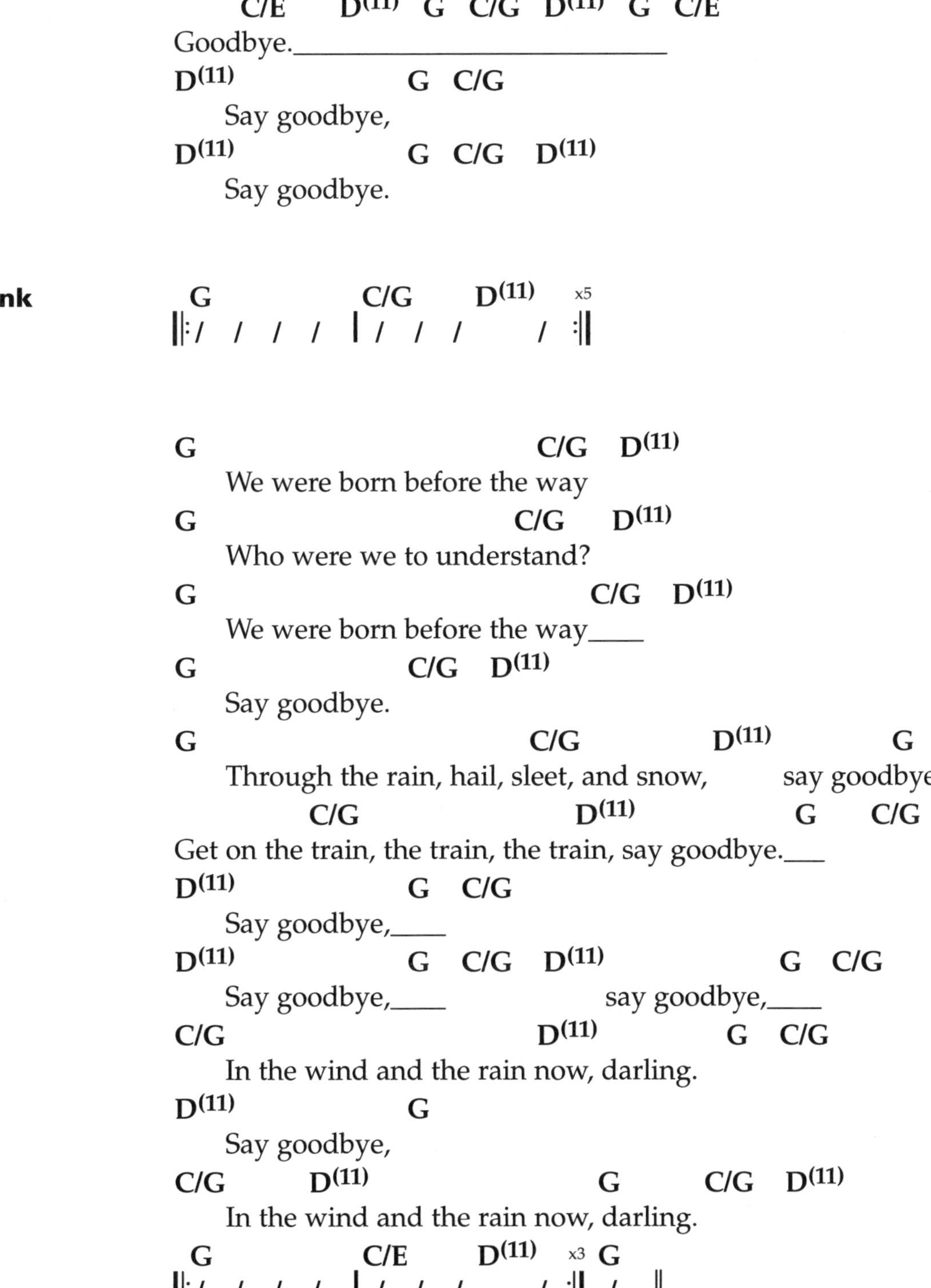

C/E D(11) G C/G D(11) G C/E
Goodbye.
D(11) G C/G
Say goodbye,
D(11) G C/G D(11)
Say goodbye.
Link
G C/G D(11) x5
G C/G D(11)
We were born before the way
G C/G D(11)
Who were we to understand?
G C/G D(11)
We were born before the way
G C/G D(11)
Say goodbye.
G C/G D(11) G
Through the rain, hail, sleet, and snow, say goodbye.
C/G D(11) G C/G
Get on the train, the train, the train, say goodbye.
D(11) G C/G
Say goodbye,
D(11) G C/G D(11) G C/G
Say goodbye, say goodbye,
C/G D(11) G C/G
In the wind and the rain now, darling.
D(11) G
Say goodbye,
C/G D(11) G C/G D(11)
In the wind and the rain now, darling.
G C/E D(11) x3 G

Senses Working Overtime

Words and Music by
ANDY PARTRIDGE

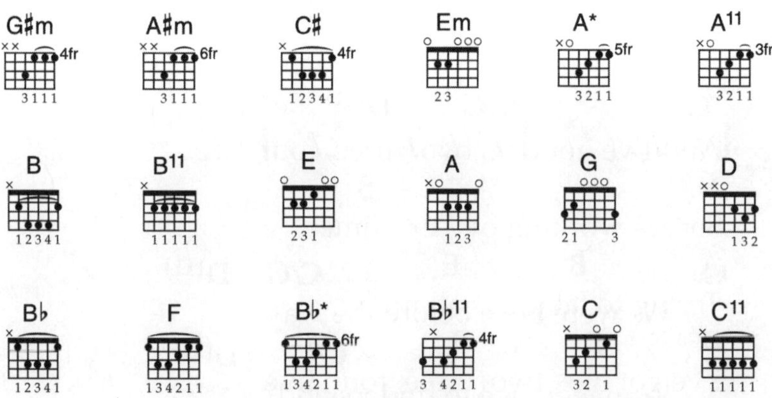

♩ = 128

Intro

G♯m A♯m | G♯m A♯m
4/4 ||: / / / / | / / / / :||

Verse 1

G♯m A♯m G♯m A♯m
Hey hey, the clouds are whey,
G♯m A♯m G♯m
There's straw for the donkeys, and the innocents
A♯m C♯ Em
Can all sleep safe-ly,
C♯ Em C♯ Em C♯ Em
All sleep safe - - ly.
G♯m A♯m G♯m A♯m
My, my, the sun is pie,
G♯m A♯m G♯m
There's fodder for the cannons, and the guilty ones
A♯m C♯ Em
Can all sleep safe-ly,
C♯ Em C♯ Em C♯ Em
All sleep safe - - ly.

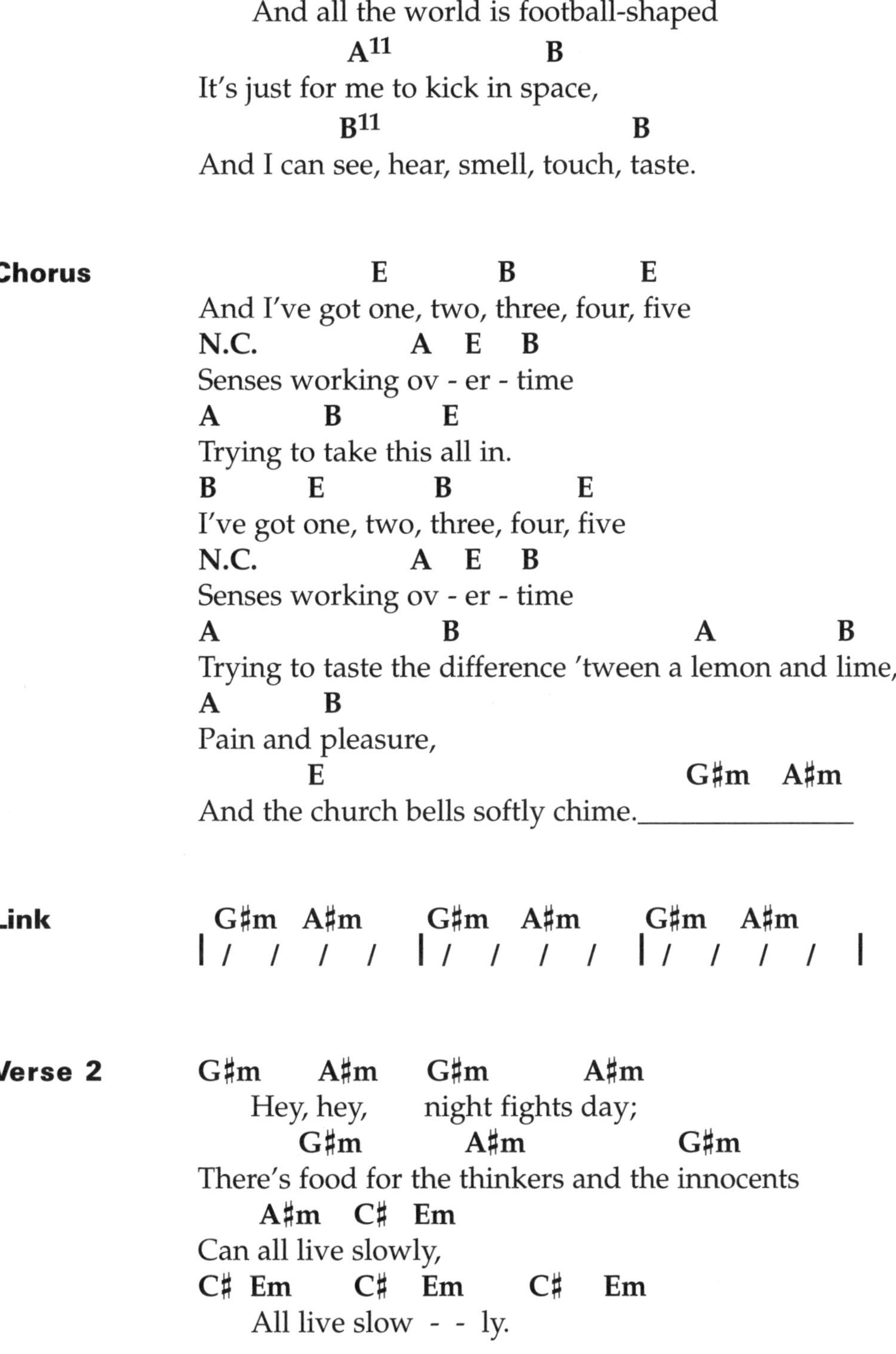

Prechorus

A* A^{11} A*
And all the world is football-shaped
A^{11} B
It's just for me to kick in space,
B^{11} B
And I can see, hear, smell, touch, taste.

Chorus

E B E
And I've got one, two, three, four, five
N.C. A E B
Senses working ov - er - time
A B E
Trying to take this all in.
B E B E
I've got one, two, three, four, five
N.C. A E B
Senses working ov - er - time
A B A B
Trying to taste the difference 'tween a lemon and lime,
A B
Pain and pleasure,
E G♯m A♯m
And the church bells softly chime.______________

Link

G♯m A♯m G♯m A♯m G♯m A♯m
| / / / / | / / / / | / / / / |

Verse 2

G♯m A♯m G♯m A♯m
Hey, hey, night fights day;
G♯m A♯m G♯m
There's food for the thinkers and the innocents
A♯m C♯ Em
Can all live slowly,
C♯ Em C♯ Em C♯ Em
All live slow - - ly.

G♯m A♯m G♯m A♯m
My, my, the sky will cry
G♯m A♯m G♯m
Jewels for the thirsty and the guilty ones
A♯m C♯ Em
Can all die slowly,
C♯ Em C♯ Em C♯ Em
All die slow - - ly.

Prechorus 2

A A^{11} A
And all the world is biscuit-shaped,
A^{11} B
It's just for me to feed my face
B^{11} B
And I can see, hear, smell, touch, taste.

Chorus 2

E B E
And I've got one, two, three, four, five
N.C. A E B
Senses working ov - er - time
A B E
Trying to take this all in.
B E B E
I've got one, two, three, four, five
N.C. A E B
Senses working ov - er - time
A B A B
Trying to taste the difference 'tween a lemon and lime,
A B
Pain and pleasure,
E
And the church bells softly chime.

Link/solo

A G A G A G A G
| / / / / | / / / / | / / / / | / / / / ||

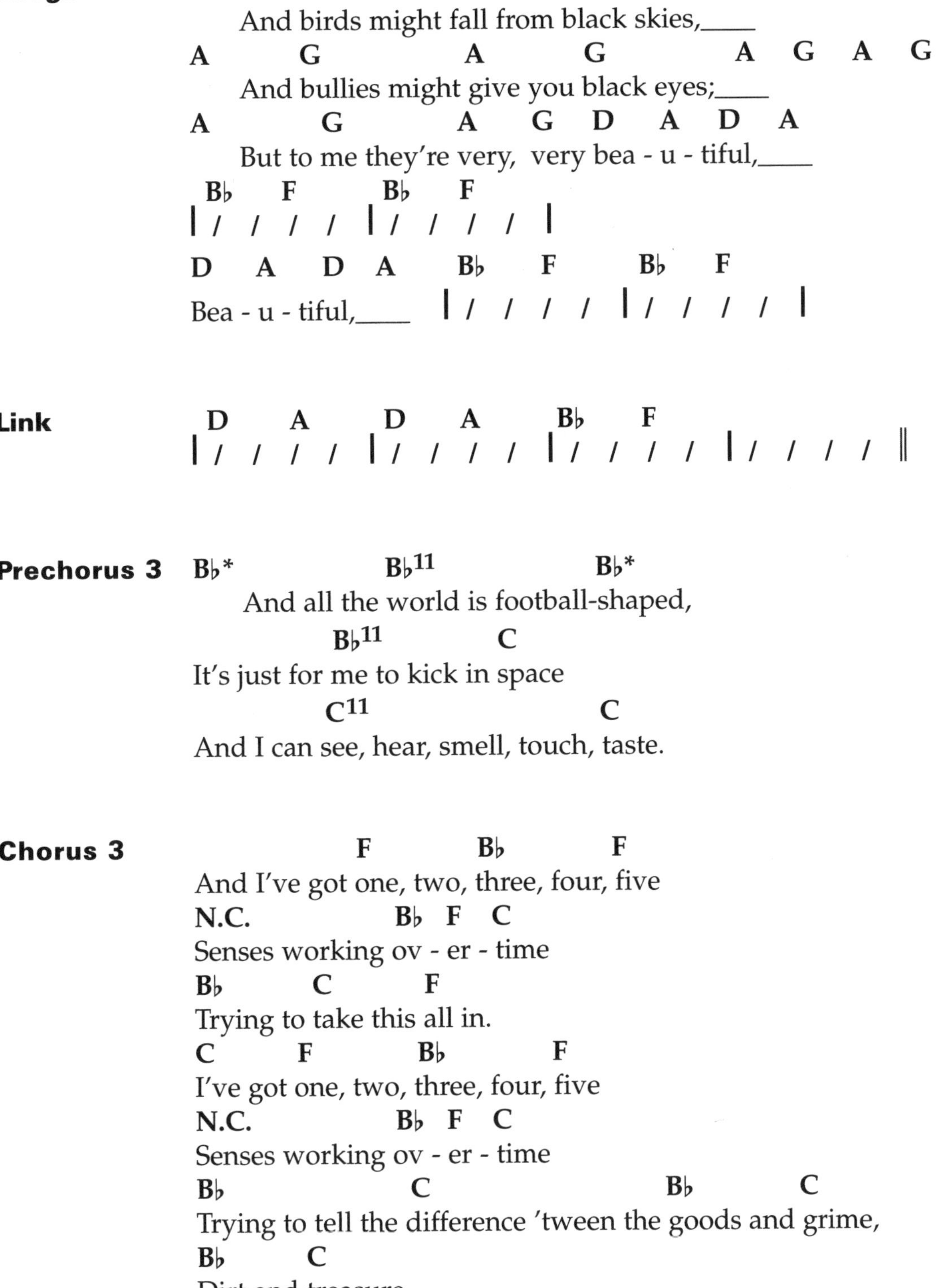

Bridge

A G A G A G A G
And birds might fall from black skies,____
A G A G A G A G
And bullies might give you black eyes;____
A G A G D A D A
But to me they're very, very bea - u - tiful,____
B♭ F B♭ F
| / / / / | / / / / |

D A D A B♭ F B♭ F
Bea - u - tiful,____ | / / / / | / / / / |

Link

D A D A B♭ F
| / / / / | / / / / | / / / / | / / / / ||

Prechorus 3

B♭* B♭11 B♭*
And all the world is football-shaped,
B♭11 C
It's just for me to kick in space
C11 C
And I can see, hear, smell, touch, taste.

Chorus 3

F B♭ F
And I've got one, two, three, four, five
N.C. B♭ F C
Senses working ov - er - time
B♭ C F
Trying to take this all in.
C F B♭ F
I've got one, two, three, four, five
N.C. B♭ F C
Senses working ov - er - time
B♭ C B♭ C
Trying to tell the difference 'tween the goods and grime,
B♭ C
Dirt and treasure,

Chorus 4

```
                F          B♭        F
And there's one, two, three, four, five
N.C.                B♭  F  C
Senses working ov - er - time
B♭       C       F
Trying to take this all in.
C        F          B♭        F
I've got one, two, three, four, five
N.C.                B♭  F  C
Senses working ov - er - time
B♭                 C                    B♭           C
Trying to taste the difference 'tween a lemon and a lime,
B♭          C                 F                N.C.
Pain and pleasure, and the church bells softly chime._______ ||
```

She's Not There

Words and Music by
ROD ARGENT

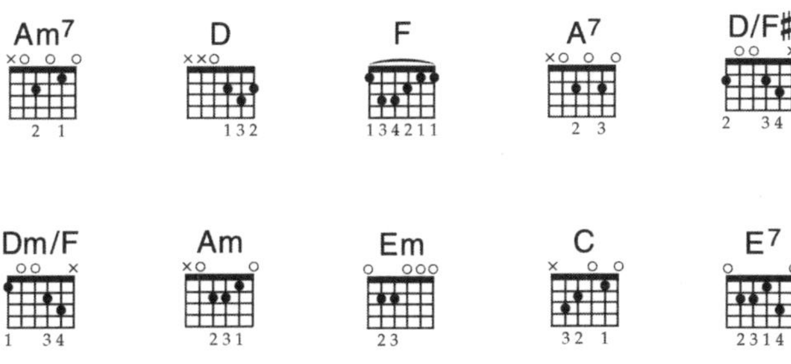

♩ = 126

Intro

```
Am7  D       Am7  D       Am7  D       Am7  D
| / / / /  | / / / /  | / / / /  | / / / /  ||
```

Verse 1

```
Am7                D          Am7  D
        Well no-one told me about  her,
Am7      F                Am7  D
        The way she lied.
Am7                D          Am7  D
        Well no-one told me about  her,
Am7                F              A7
        How many people cried.
```

Prechorus

```
                 D/F♯   Dm/F      Am
But it's too late to say you're sorry
                   Em                     Am
How would I know? Why should I care?
                    D/F♯   Dm/F     C
Please don't bother trying to find her –
                E7
She's not there.
```

Chorus

Am
Well let me tell you 'bout the way she looked:
D Am F Am
The way she acted, the colour of her hair,
D Am
Her voice was soft and cool,
F Am D
Her eyes were clear and bright,
A^7 N.C.
But she's not there.

Link

Am^7 D | Am^7 D | Am^7 D | Am^7 D
| / / / / | / / / / | / / / / | / / / / ||

Verse 2

Am^7 D Am^7 D
Well no-one told me about her,
Am^7 F Am^7 D
What could I do?
Am^7 D Am^7 D
Well no-one told me about her,
Am^7 F A^7
Though they all knew.

Prechorus 2

D/F♯ Dm/F Am
But it's too late to say you're sorry
Em Am
How would I know? Why should I care?
D/F♯ Dm/F C
Please don't bother trying to find her –
E^7
She's not there.

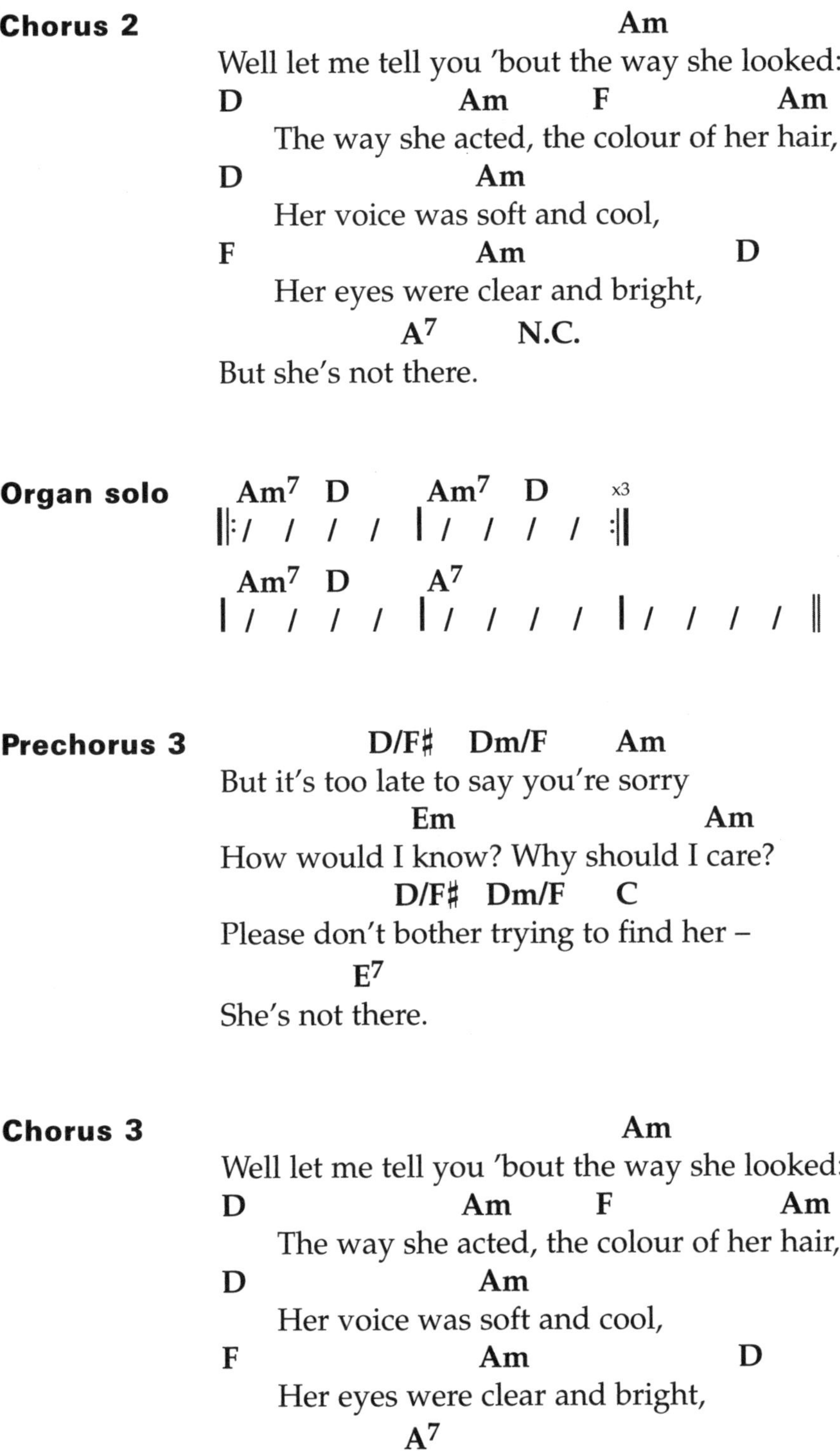

Chorus 2

Am
Well let me tell you 'bout the way she looked:
D Am F Am
The way she acted, the colour of her hair,
D Am
Her voice was soft and cool,
F Am D
Her eyes were clear and bright,
A^7 N.C.
But she's not there.

Organ solo

Am^7 D | Am^7 D x3
‖: / / / / | / / / / :‖

Am^7 D | A^7 |
| / / / / | / / / / | / / / / ‖

Prechorus 3

D/F♯ Dm/F Am
But it's too late to say you're sorry
Em Am
How would I know? Why should I care?
D/F♯ Dm/F C
Please don't bother trying to find her –
E^7
She's not there.

Chorus 3

Am
Well let me tell you 'bout the way she looked:
D Am F Am
The way she acted, the colour of her hair,
D Am
Her voice was soft and cool,
F Am D
Her eyes were clear and bright,
A^7
But she's not there.

Somewhere In My Heart

Words and Music by
RODDY FRAME

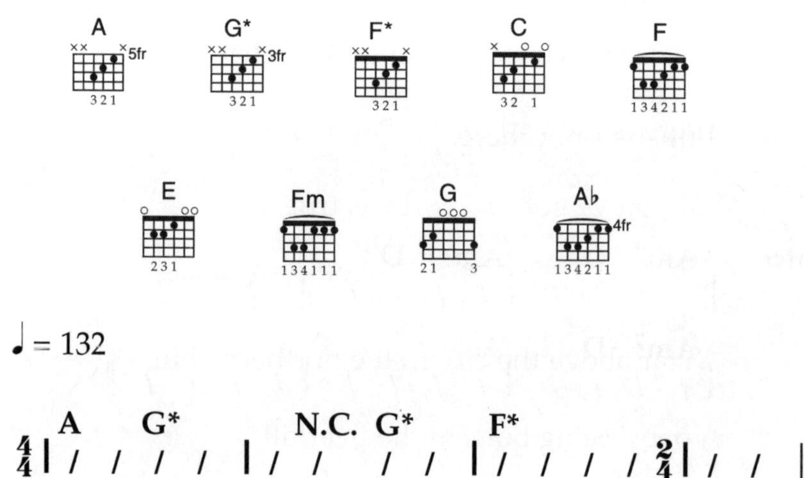

Verse 1

C
Summer in the city where the air is still,

A baby being born to the overkill.
F
Well, who cares what people say;

We walk down love's motorway.
C
Ambition and love wearing boxing gloves

And singing hearts and flowers.

Chorus

F
But somewhere in my heart
            E
There is a star that shines for you.
F   C
Silver splits the blue,   love will see it through.
     F
And somewhere in my heart
              E
There is the will to set you free.
F   Fm   C
All you've got to   be is true.

Verse 2

   C
A star above the city in the northern chill,

A baby being born to the overkill.
F
    No say, no place to go,

A T.V. and a radio.
     C
Ambition and love wearing boxing gloves

And singing hearts and flowers.

Chorus 2

F
But somewhere in my heart
            E
There is a star that shines for you.
F   C
Silver splits the blue,   love will see it through.
     F
And somewhere in my heart
              E
There is the will to set you free.
F   Fm   C
All you've got to   be is true.

Bridge

G
Who could heal what's never been as one?
Fm
And our hearts have been torn

Since the day we were born
E
Just like anyone.

Verse 3

A♭
From Westwood to Hollywood

The one thing that's understood
G
Is that you can't buy time

But you can sell your soul,

And the closest thing to heaven is to rock and roll.

Guitar solo

F C
| / / / / | / / / / | / / / / | / / / / |
F E
| / / / / | / / / / | / / / / | / / / / ||

Chorus 3

F
But somewhere in my heart
E
There is a star that shines for you.
F C
Silver splits the blue, love will see it through.
F
And somewhere in my heart
E
There is the will to set you free.
F Fm C
All you've got to be is true.

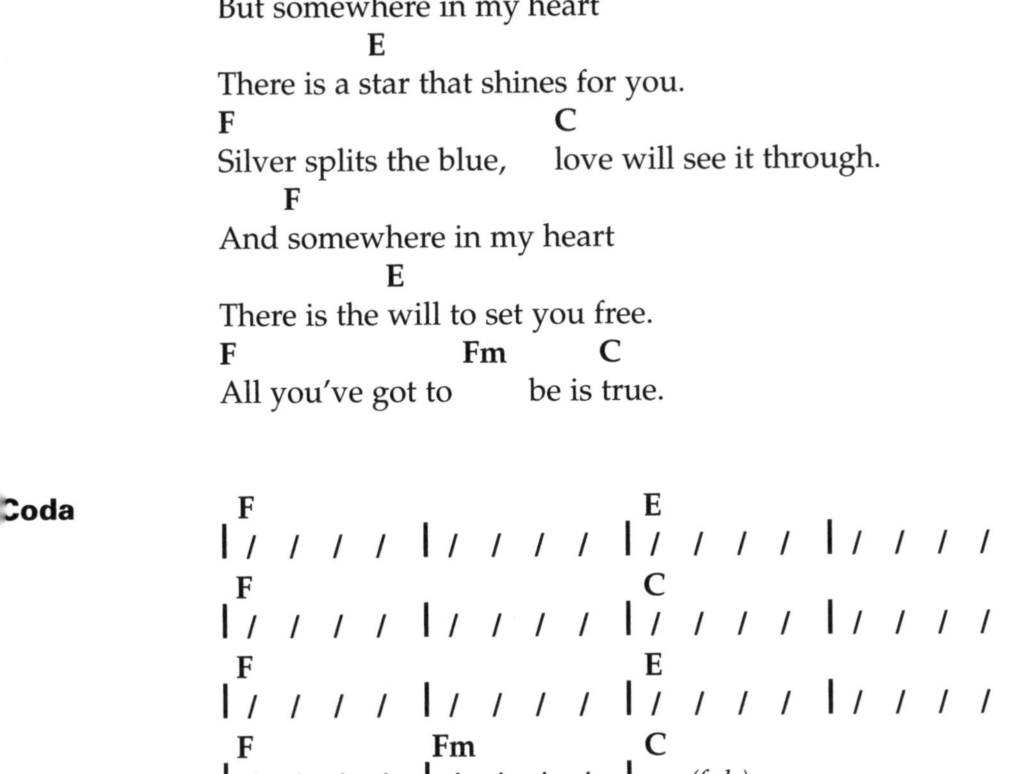

Chorus 4

F
But somewhere in my heart
E
There is a star that shines for you.
F C
Silver splits the blue, love will see it through.
F
And somewhere in my heart
E
There is the will to set you free.
F Fm C
All you've got to be is true.

Coda

F / / / /	/ / / /	E / / / /	/ / / /
F / / / /	/ / / /	C / / / /	/ / / /
F / / / /	/ / / /	E / / / /	/ / / /
F / / / /	Fm / / / /	C *(fade)*

Sorrow

Words and Music by
BOB FELDMAN, JERRY GOLDSTEIN
AND RICHARD GOTTEHRER

G C/G C D F

♩ = 118

Intro

4/4 | (G) / / / / | (C/G) / / / / | (G) / / / / | (C/G) / / / / |
| G / / / / | / / / / ||

Verse 1

G
With your long blonde hair and your eyes of blue
C G
The only thing I ever got from you was sorrow, sorrow.

Verse 2

G
You acted funny trying to spend my money,
C G
You're out there playing your high class games of sorrow, sorrow.

Verse 3

G
You never do what you know you oughta,
C G
Something tells me you're the devil's daughter. Sorrow, sorrow.
D C G
Ah,____ ah,____ ah.

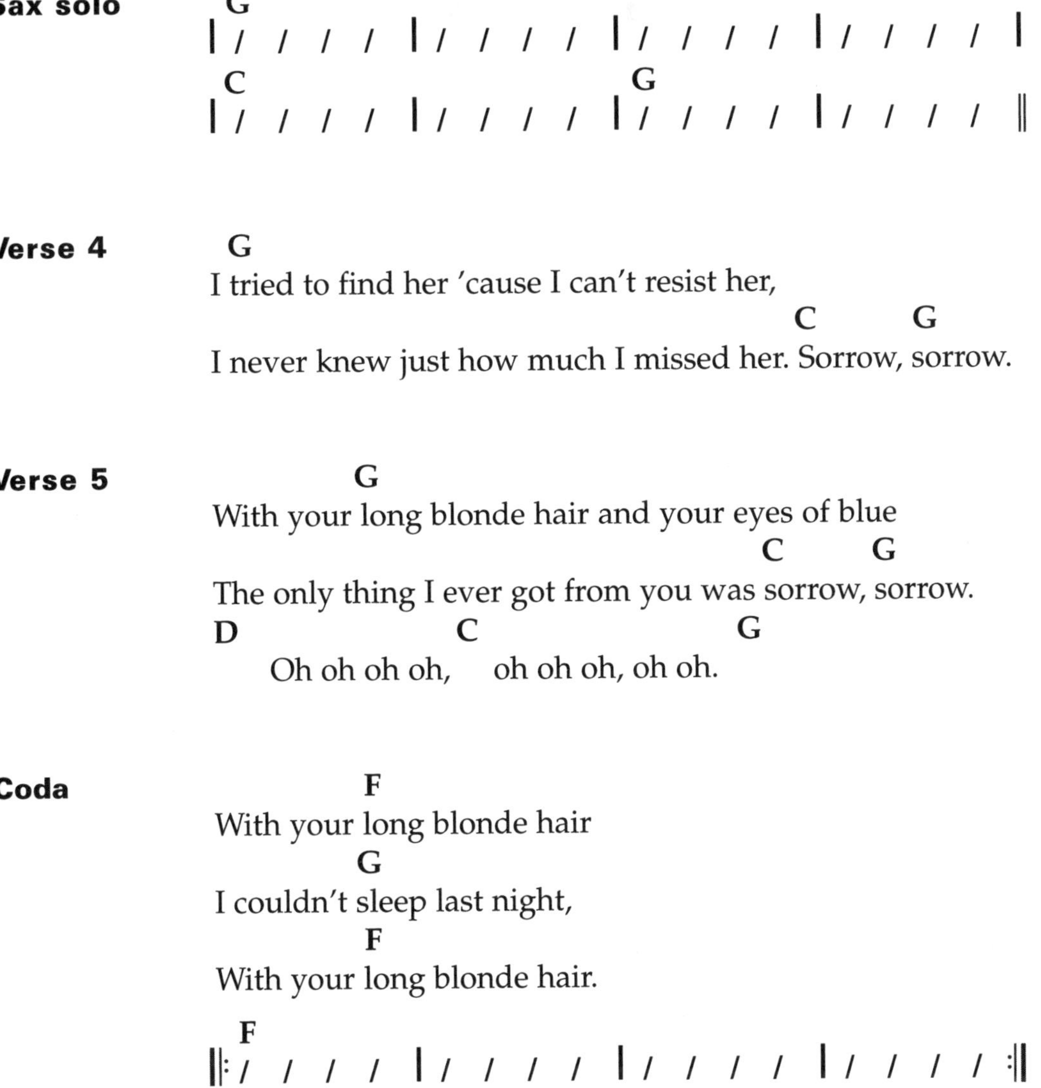

Sax solo

```
 G
| / / / / | / / / / | / / / / | / / / / |
 C                   G
| / / / / | / / / / | / / / / | / / / / ||
```

Verse 4

G
I tried to find her 'cause I can't resist her,
C G
I never knew just how much I missed her. Sorrow, sorrow.

Verse 5

G
With your long blonde hair and your eyes of blue
C G
The only thing I ever got from you was sorrow, sorrow.
D C G
Oh oh oh oh, oh oh oh, oh oh.

Coda

F
With your long blonde hair
G
I couldn't sleep last night,
F
With your long blonde hair.

```
  F
||: / / / / | / / / / | / / / / | / / / / :||
```

repeat to fade

Starman

Words and Music by
DAVID BOWIE

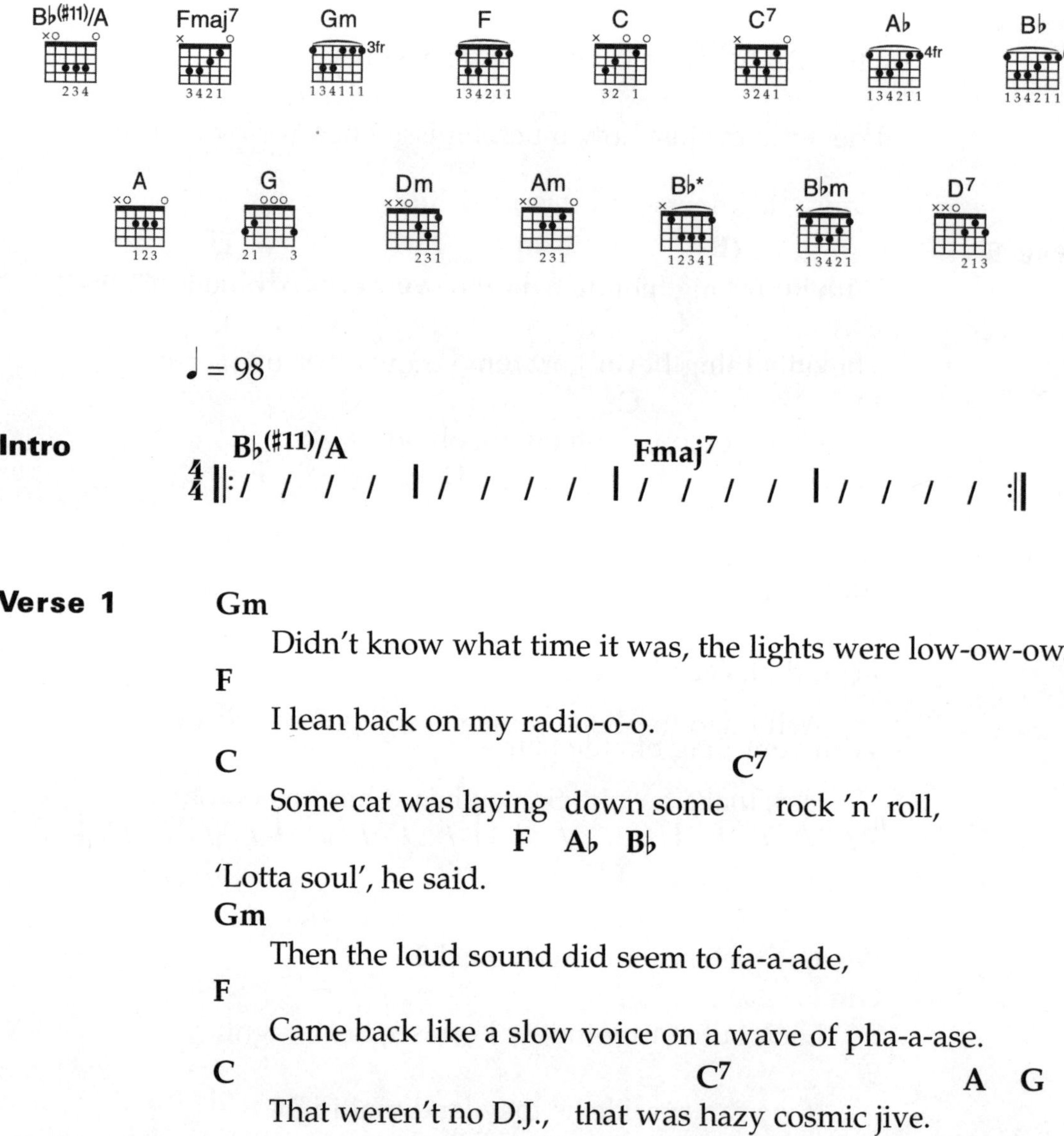

♩ = 98

Intro

B♭(♯11)/A | Fmaj7
4/4 ‖: / / / / | / / / / | / / / / | / / / / :‖

Verse 1

Gm
Didn't know what time it was, the lights were low-ow-ow.
F
I lean back on my radio-o-o.
C C7
Some cat was laying down some rock 'n' roll,
F A♭ B♭
'Lotta soul', he said.
Gm
Then the loud sound did seem to fa-a-ade,
F
Came back like a slow voice on a wave of pha-a-ase.
C C7 A G
That weren't no D.J., that was hazy cosmic jive.

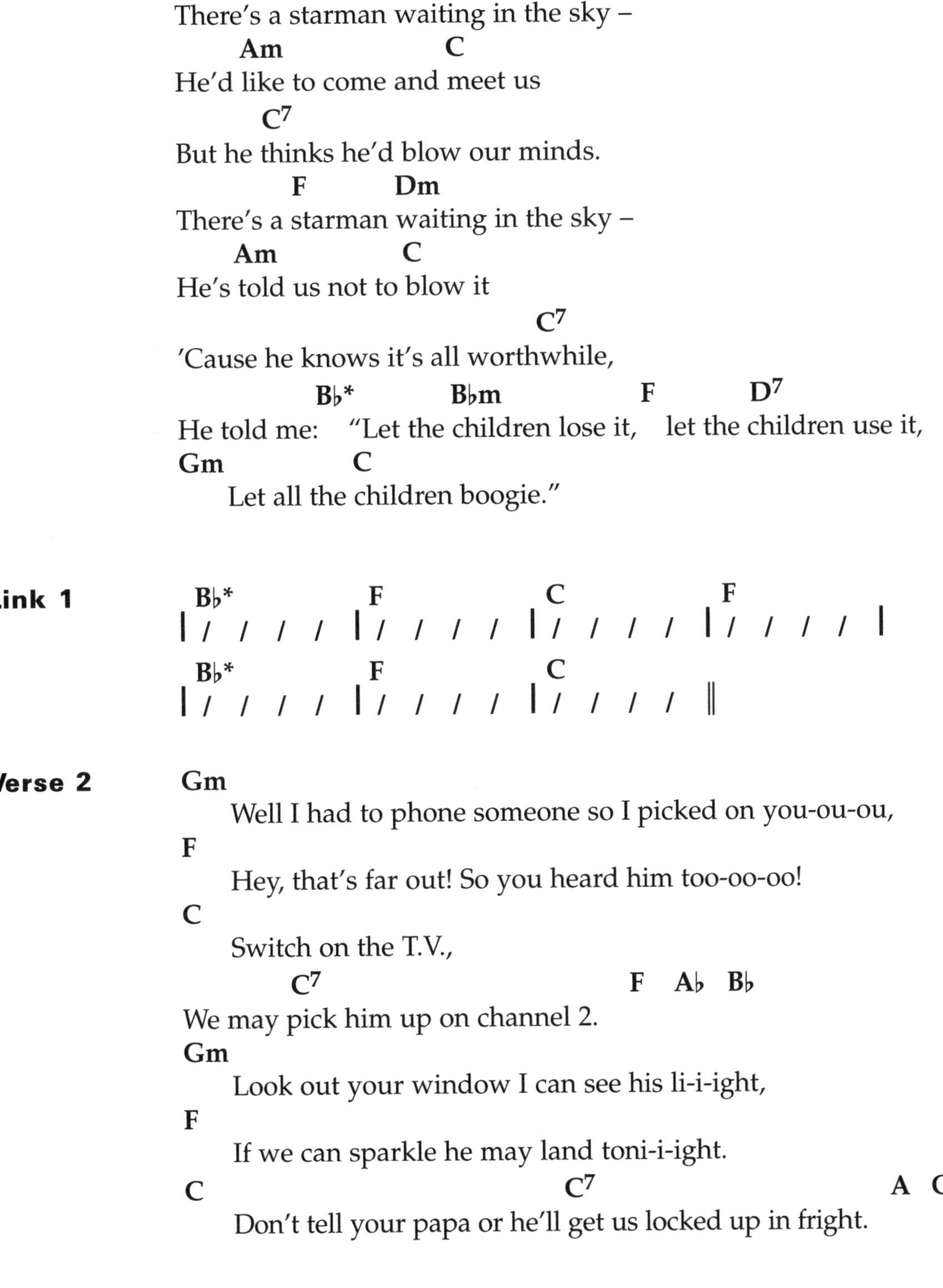

Chorus

F Dm
There's a starman waiting in the sky –
Am C
He'd like to come and meet us
C7
But he thinks he'd blow our minds.
F Dm
There's a starman waiting in the sky –
Am C
He's told us not to blow it
C7
'Cause he knows it's all worthwhile,
B♭* B♭m F D7
He told me: "Let the children lose it, let the children use it,
Gm C
Let all the children boogie."

Link 1

| B♭* / / / / | F / / / / | C / / / / | F / / / / |
| B♭* / / / / | F / / / / | C / / / / ||

Verse 2

Gm
Well I had to phone someone so I picked on you-ou-ou,
F
Hey, that's far out! So you heard him too-oo-oo!
C
Switch on the T.V.,
C7 F A♭ B♭
We may pick him up on channel 2.
Gm
Look out your window I can see his li-i-ight,
F
If we can sparkle he may land toni-i-ight.
C C7 A G
Don't tell your papa or he'll get us locked up in fright.

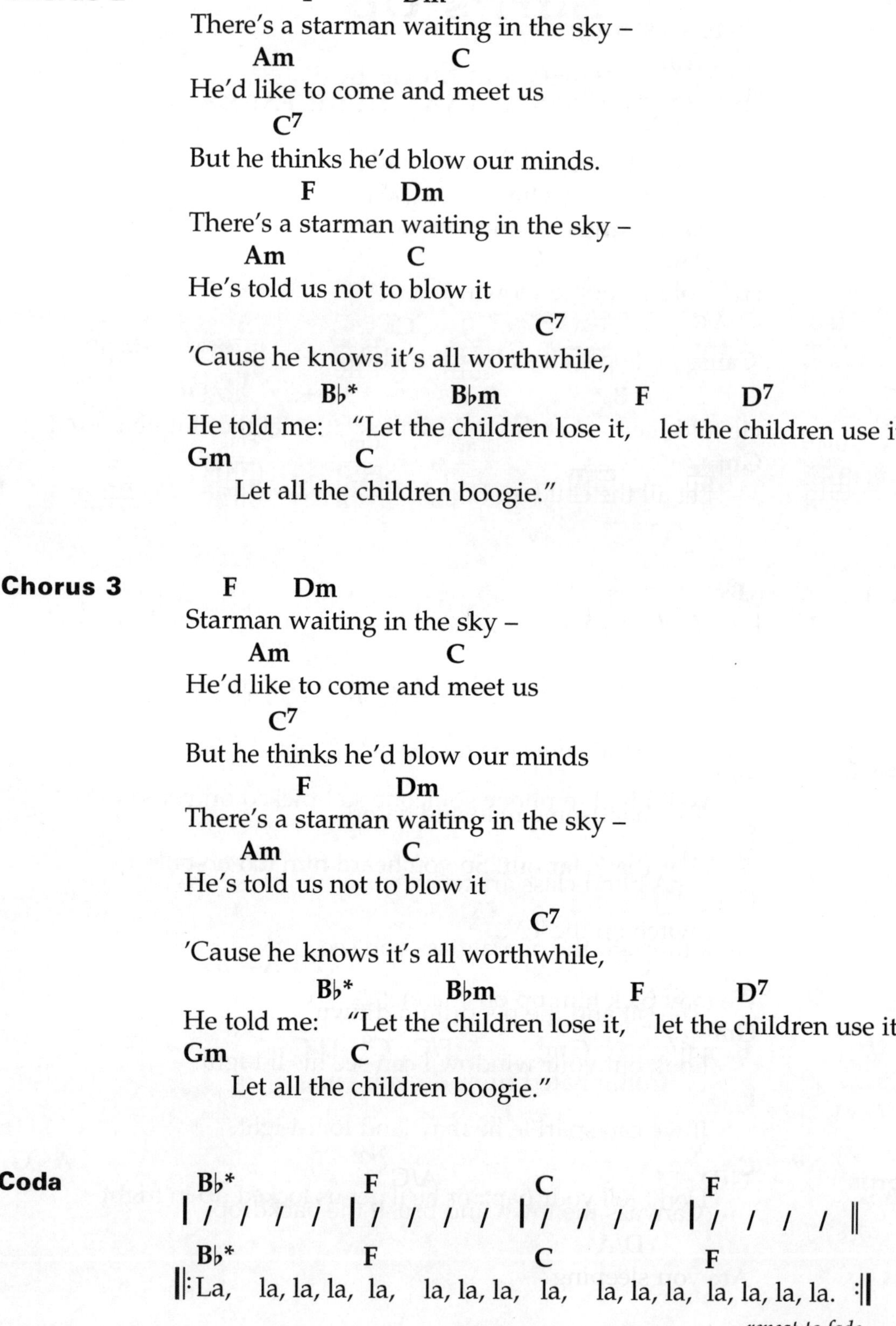

Chorus 2

F Dm
There's a starman waiting in the sky –
Am C
He'd like to come and meet us
C⁷
But he thinks he'd blow our minds.
F Dm
There's a starman waiting in the sky –
Am C
He's told us not to blow it
C⁷
'Cause he knows it's all worthwhile,
B♭* B♭m F D⁷
He told me: "Let the children lose it, let the children use it,
Gm C
Let all the children boogie."

Chorus 3

F Dm
Starman waiting in the sky –
Am C
He'd like to come and meet us
C⁷
But he thinks he'd blow our minds
F Dm
There's a starman waiting in the sky –
Am C
He's told us not to blow it
C⁷
'Cause he knows it's all worthwhile,
B♭* B♭m F D⁷
He told me: "Let the children lose it, let the children use it,
Gm C
Let all the children boogie."

Coda

B♭* F C F
| / / / / | / / / / | / / / / | / / / / ||
B♭* F C F
||: La, la, la, la, la, la, la, la, la, la, la, la, la, la, la, la. :||

repeat to fade

Surf's Up

Words and Music by
BRIAN WILSON AND VAN DYKE PARKS

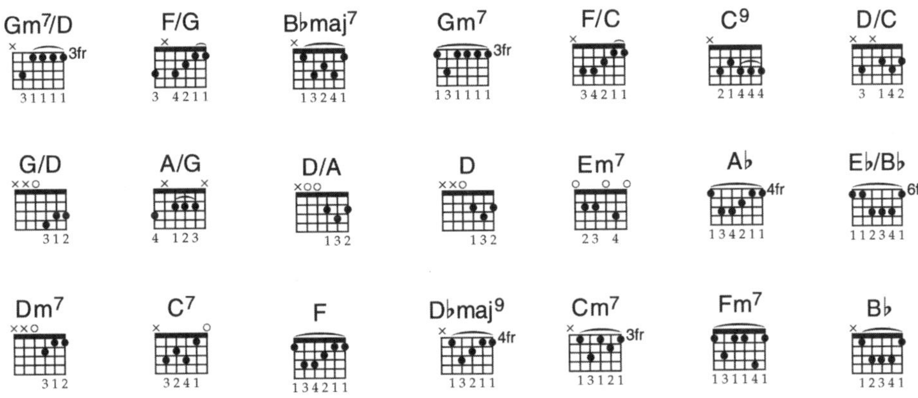

♩ = 84

Verse 1

4/4 **Gm7/D**
A diamond necklace played the pawn,

Hand in hand some drummed along, oh,
F/G
To a handsome man and baton.
Gm7/D
A blind class aristocracy

Back through the opera glass you see
F/G
The pit and the pendulum drawn.
B♭maj7 Gm7 F/C C9 D/C
Columnated ruins do - mi - no.

Chorus

G/D A/G
Canvass the town and brush the backdrop,
D/A
Are you sleeping?

Verse 2

Gm⁷/D
Hung velvet overtaken me,

Dim chandelier awaken me
F/G
To a song dissolved in the dawn.
Gm⁷/D
The music hall a costly bow,

The music all is lost for now
F/G
To a muted trumpeter swan.
B♭maj⁷ Gm⁷ F/C C⁹ D/C
Columnated ruins do - mi - no.

Chorus 2

G/D A/G
Canvass the town and brush the backdrop,
D/A D Em⁷ Gm⁷ D
Are you sleeping, Brother John?____________

♩ = 49

Bridge

A♭
Dove-nested towers, the hour was
E♭/B♭
Strike the street quicksilver moon.
A♭
Carriage across the fog
E♭/B♭
Two-step to lamp-light's cellar tune.
Dm⁷ C⁹ C⁷ F
The laughs come hard in 'Auld Lang Syne'.

Verse 4

Dm⁷
The glass was raised, the fire had rose,
C⁹ C⁷
The fullness of the wine,
C⁹ F
The dim last toasting

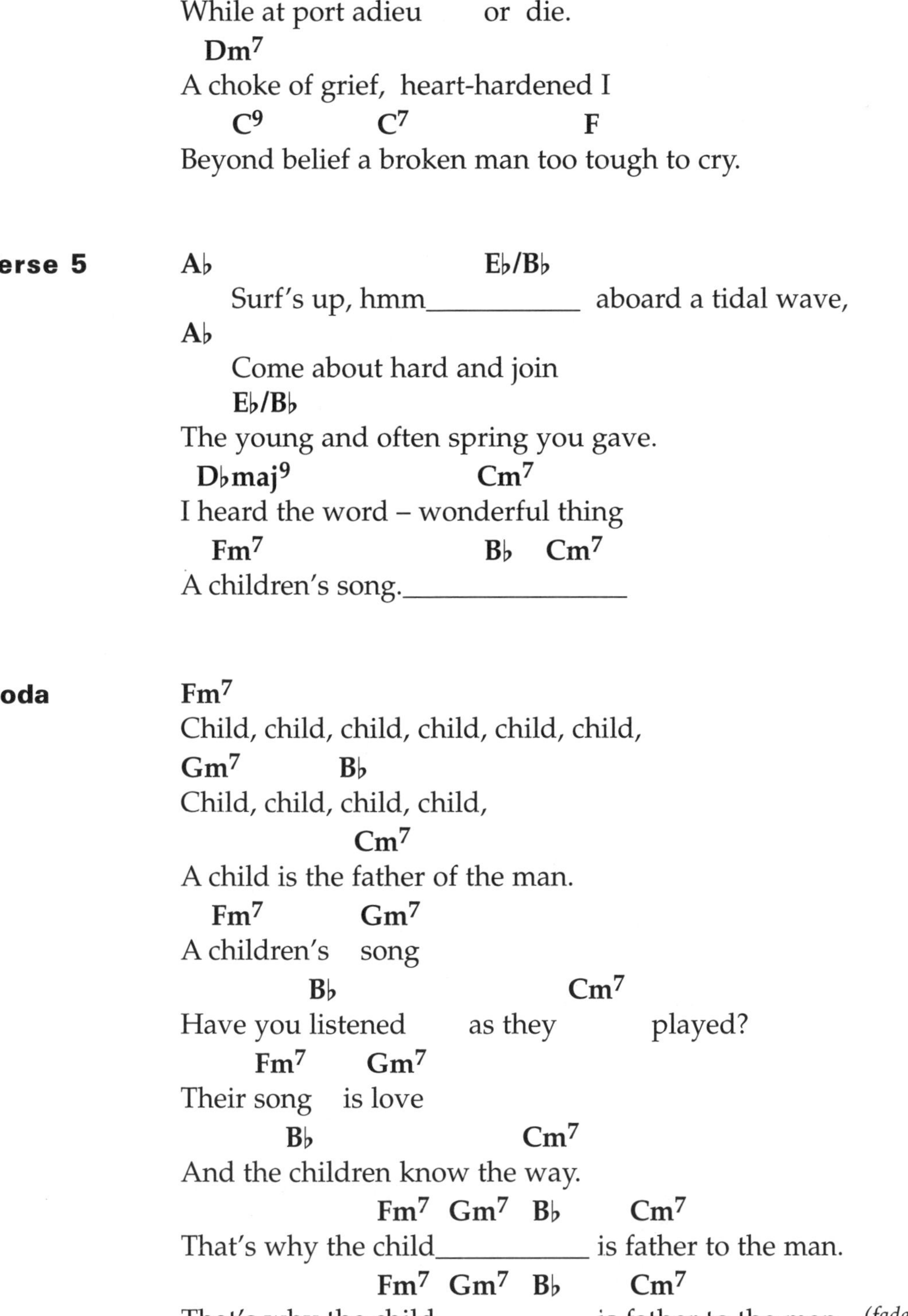

Dm7 C9 C7 F
While at port adieu or die.
Dm7
A choke of grief, heart-hardened I
C9 C7 F
Beyond belief a broken man too tough to cry.

Verse 5

A♭ E♭/B♭
Surf's up, hmm__________ aboard a tidal wave,
A♭
Come about hard and join
E♭/B♭
The young and often spring you gave.
D♭maj9 Cm7
I heard the word – wonderful thing
Fm7 B♭ Cm7
A children's song.______________

Coda

Fm7
Child, child, child, child, child, child,
Gm7 B♭
Child, child, child, child,
Cm7
A child is the father of the man.
Fm7 Gm7
A children's song
B♭ Cm7
Have you listened as they played?
Fm7 Gm7
Their song is love
B♭ Cm7
And the children know the way.
Fm7 Gm7 B♭ Cm7
That's why the child__________ is father to the man.
Fm7 Gm7 B♭ Cm7
That's why the child__________ is father to the man. *(fade)*

Stay With Me

Words and Music by
ROD STEWART AND RONALD WOOD

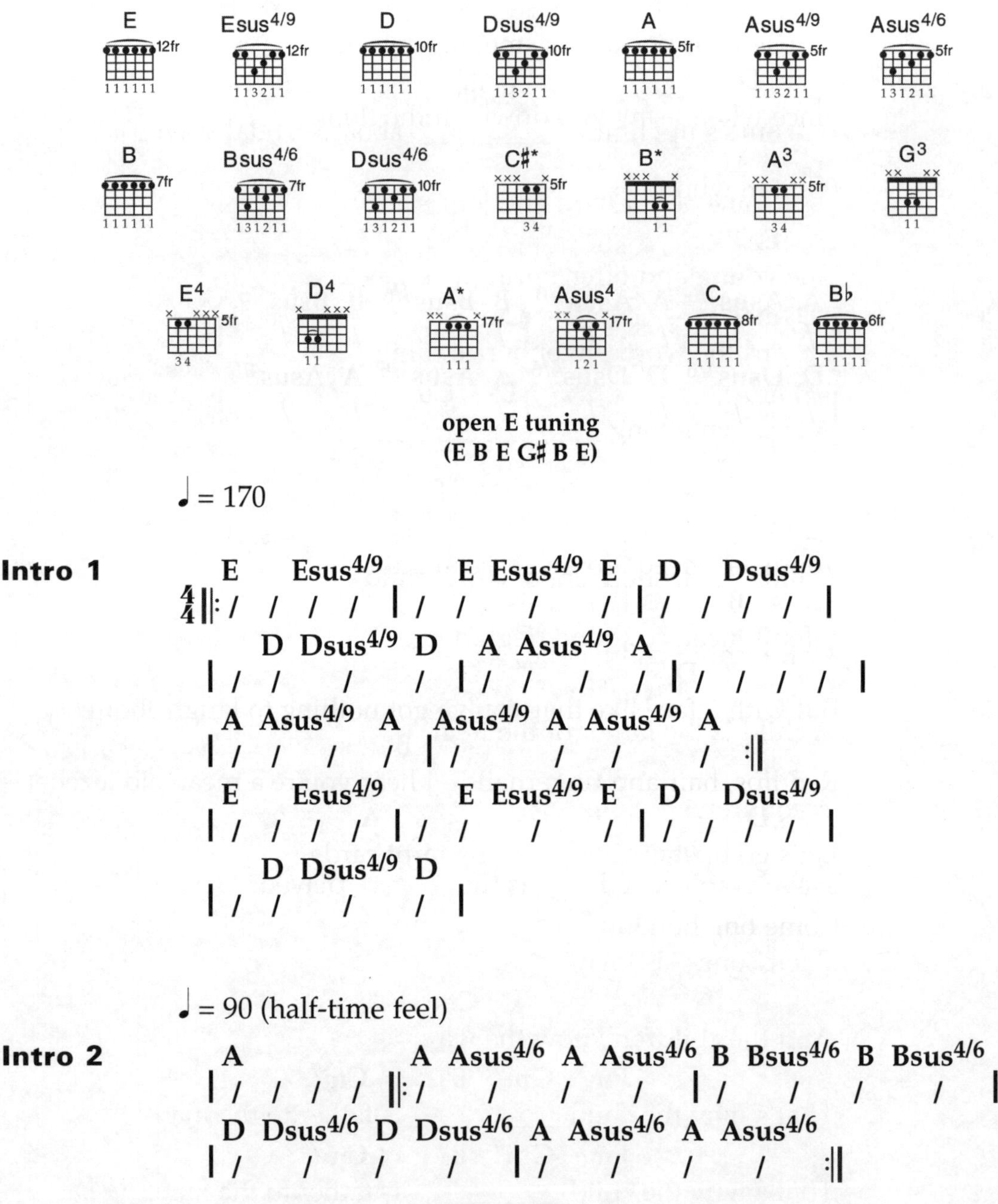

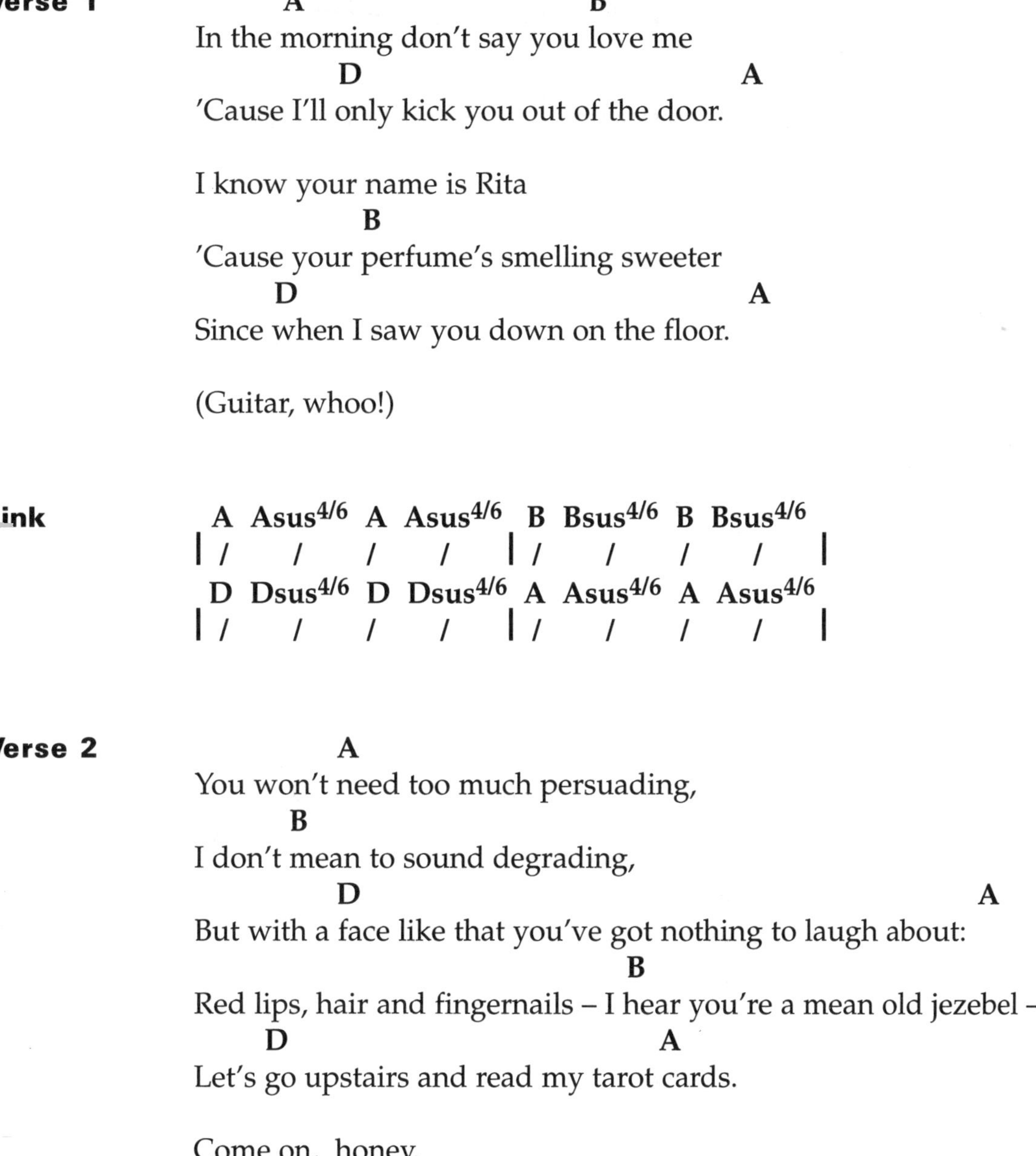

Verse 1

A B
In the morning don't say you love me
D A
'Cause I'll only kick you out of the door.

I know your name is Rita
B
'Cause your perfume's smelling sweeter
D A
Since when I saw you down on the floor.

(Guitar, whoo!)

Link

A Asus$^{4/6}$ A Asus$^{4/6}$ B Bsus$^{4/6}$ B Bsus$^{4/6}$
| / / / / | / / / / |
D Dsus$^{4/6}$ D Dsus$^{4/6}$ A Asus$^{4/6}$ A Asus$^{4/6}$
| / / / / | / / / / |

Verse 2

A
You won't need too much persuading,
B
I don't mean to sound degrading,
D A
But with a face like that you've got nothing to laugh about:
B
Red lips, hair and fingernails – I hear you're a mean old jezebel –
D A
Let's go upstairs and read my tarot cards.

Come on, honey.

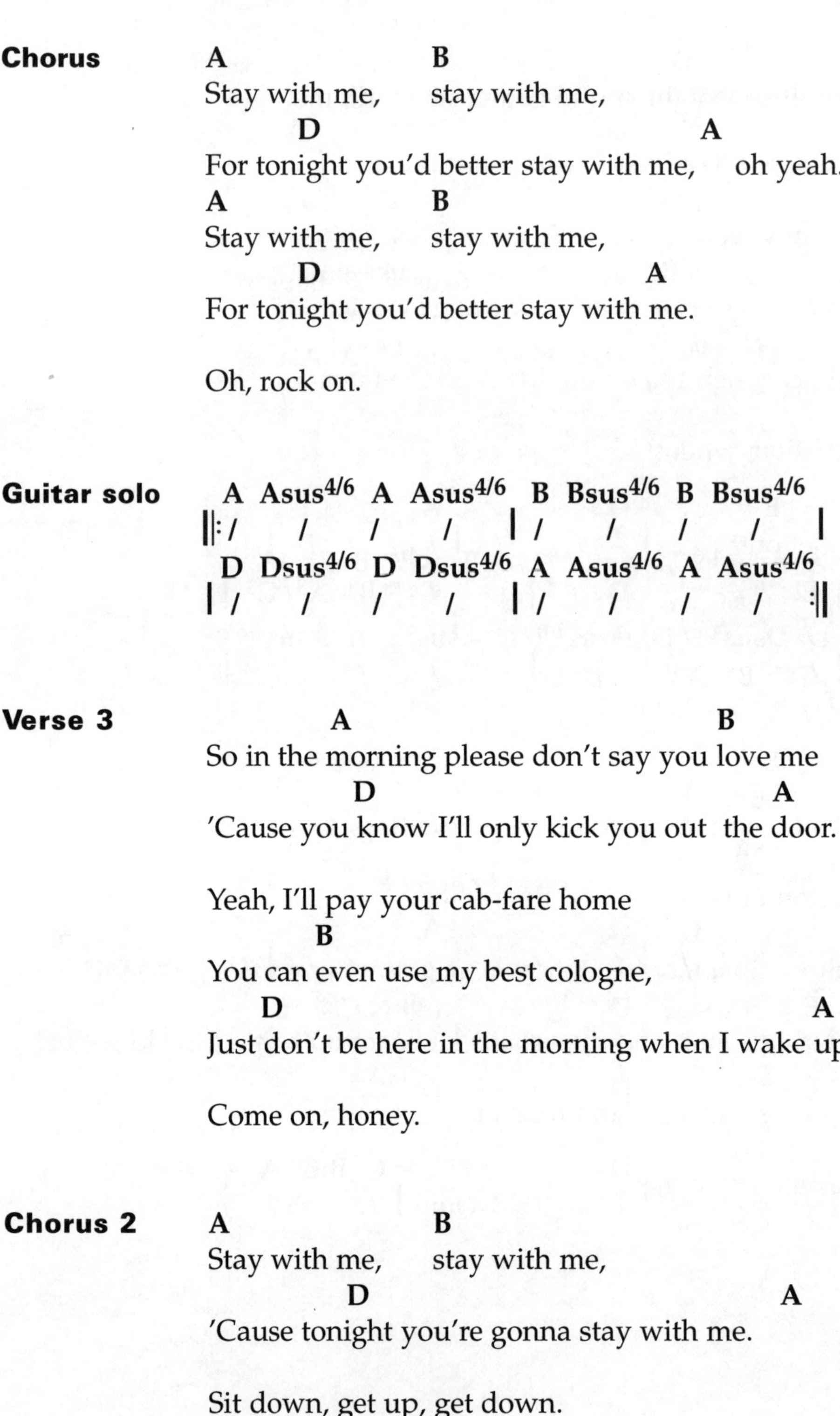

Chorus

A B
Stay with me, stay with me,
D A
For tonight you'd better stay with me, oh yeah.
A B
Stay with me, stay with me,
D A
For tonight you'd better stay with me.

Oh, rock on.

Guitar solo

A Asus$^{4/6}$ A Asus$^{4/6}$ B Bsus$^{4/6}$ B Bsus$^{4/6}$
||: / / / / | / / / / |
D Dsus$^{4/6}$ D Dsus$^{4/6}$ A Asus$^{4/6}$ A Asus$^{4/6}$
| / / / / | / / / / :||

Verse 3

A B
So in the morning please don't say you love me
D A
'Cause you know I'll only kick you out the door.

Yeah, I'll pay your cab-fare home
B
You can even use my best cologne,
D A
Just don't be here in the morning when I wake up.

Come on, honey.

Chorus 2

A B
Stay with me, stay with me,
D A
'Cause tonight you're gonna stay with me.

Sit down, get up, get down.
B
Stay with me, stay with me,

```
        D                          A
'Cause tonight you're gonna stay with me.

Hey, what's your name again?
```

Link

```
 A  Asus4/6  A  Asus4/6   B  Bsus4/6  B  Bsus4/6
| /    /     /    /     | /    /      /    /     |
 D  Dsus4/6  D  Dsus4/6  A  Asus4/6  A  Asus4/6
| /    /     /    /     | /    /      /    /     |
```

Coda

```
   E             D              A
Get out!      | / / / /    | / / / /  | / / / / |
 E              D             C#*  B*  A3  G3  E4 D4
| / / / /     | / / / /    | /      /    /   /       |
 C#*  B*  A3  G3  E4 D4
| /      /    /   /      |

   E             D              A*  Asus4     A*
Get out!      | / / / /    | /     /    /    /    |
    Asus4       A*
|              Get yourself home! |
 E              D              A
| / / / /     | / / / /    | / / / /  | / / / / |
 E              D              (A) N.C.
| / / / /     | / / / /    |   [drums 2 bars]   |
 E              D              A
| / / / /     | / / / /    | / / / /  | Slow down there! |
 E              D                   C  B Bb A  C  B Bb A
| / / / /     | / / / / Quit! | /        /  /       /  ||
```

Substitute

Words and Music by
PETER TOWNSHEND

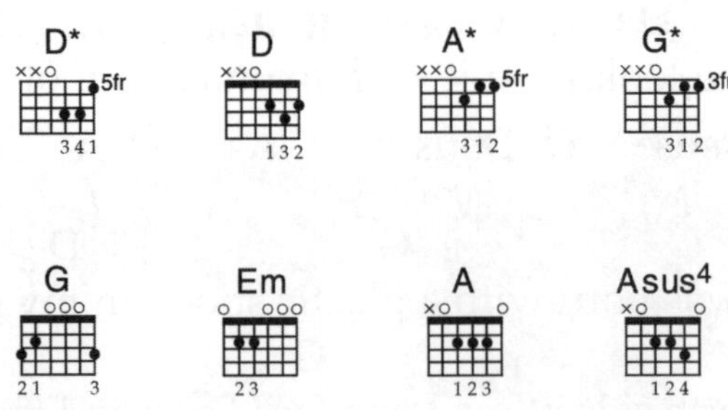

♩ = 140

Intro

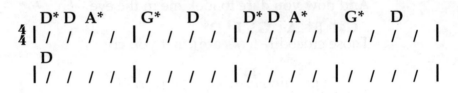

```
     D* D  A*     G*    D      D* D  A*     G*    D
4/4 | /  /  /  /  | /  /  /  /  | /  /  /  /  | /  /  /  /  |
     D
    | /  /  /  /  | /  /  /  /  | /  /  /  /  | /  /  /  /  |
```

Verse 1

```
D                G                 D
You think we look pretty good together,
                 G                 D
You think my shoes are made of leather.
```

Pre-chorus 1

```
                Em
But I'm a substitute for another guy

I look pretty tall but my heels are high.

The simple things you see are all complicated.
                                           A    Asus4  A
I look pretty young but I'm just back-dated, yeah.
```

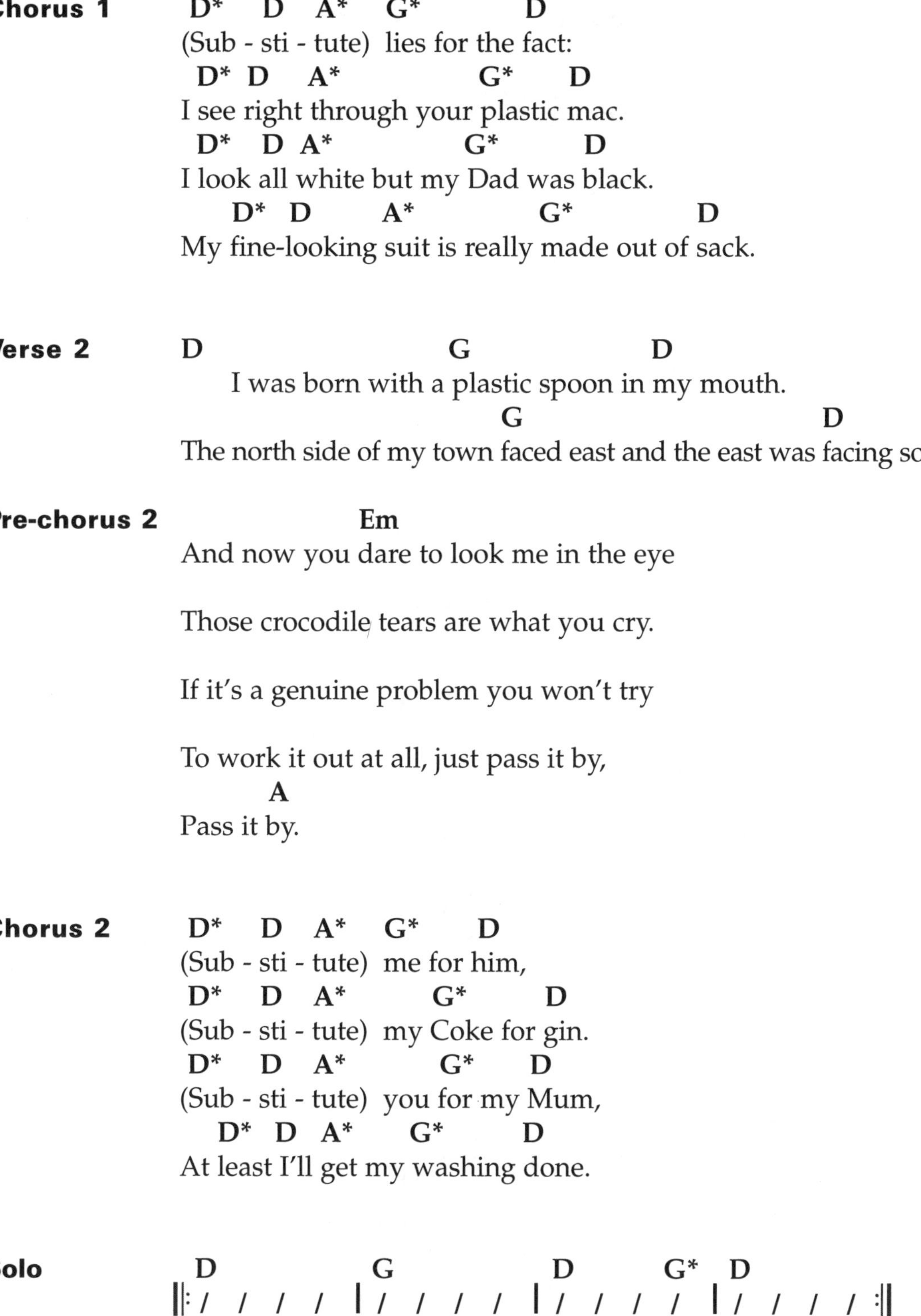

Chorus 1

```
 D*    D   A*    G*          D
(Sub - sti - tute)  lies for the fact:
 D*  D    A*             G*      D
I see right through your plastic mac.
 D*   D  A*              G*        D
I look all white but my Dad was black.
    D*  D      A*             G*            D
My fine-looking suit is really made out of sack.
```

Verse 2

```
D                          G                   D
     I was born with a plastic spoon in my mouth.
                                 G                              D
The north side of my town faced east and the east was facing south.
```

Pre-chorus 2

```
                Em
And now you dare to look me in the eye

Those crocodile tears are what you cry.

If it's a genuine problem you won't try

To work it out at all, just pass it by,
        A
Pass it by.
```

Chorus 2

```
 D*    D   A*    G*      D
(Sub - sti - tute)  me for him,
 D*    D   A*       G*       D
(Sub - sti - tute)  my Coke for gin.
 D*    D   A*        G*     D
(Sub - sti - tute)  you for my Mum,
   D*  D  A*     G*       D
At least I'll get my washing done.
```

Solo

```
 D               G                D          G*   D
||: /  /  /  /  | /  /  /  /  | /  /  /  /  | /  /  /  / :||
```

Pre-chorus 3

```
                Em
But I'm a substitute for another guy

I look pretty tall but my heels are high.

The simple things you see are all complicated.
                                                 A    Asus4   A
I look pretty young but I'm just back-dated, yeah.
```

Link

```
   D* D  A*       G*     D        D* D  A*       G*      D
||: /  /  /  /  | /  /  /  /  | /  /  /  /  | /  /  /  /  :||
```

Verse 3

```
D                    G                   D
    I was born with a plastic spoon in my mouth.
                               G                            D
The north side of my town faced east and the east was facing south.
```

Pre-chorus 4

```
                     Em                   G  D  Em          G  D
And now you dare to look me                  in the eye
         Em                 G  D   Em
Those crocodile tears        are what you cry.
G  D    Em       G    D     Em                   G  D
If  it's a genuine problem you won't try
     Em                 G  D   Em
To work it out at all, just pass it by,
G          D  A    Asus4   A
    Pass it   by.
```

Chorus 3

```
D*     D    A*    G*       D
(Sub - sti - tute)  me for him,
D*     D    A*        G*       D
(Sub - sti - tute)  my Coke for gin.
D*     D    A*           G*      D
(Sub - sti - tute)  you for my Mum,
   D*  D  A*       G*        D
At least I'll get my washing done.
```

Chorus 4

```
 D*    D   A*          G*          D
(Sub - sti - tute) your lies for the fact:
 D* D    A*               G*      D
I see right through your plastic mac.
 D*   D A*               G*        D
I look all white but my Dad was black.
    D*  D       A*            G*             D
My fine-looking suit is really made out of sack.
```

2-4-6-8 Motorway

Words and Music by
TOM ROBINSON

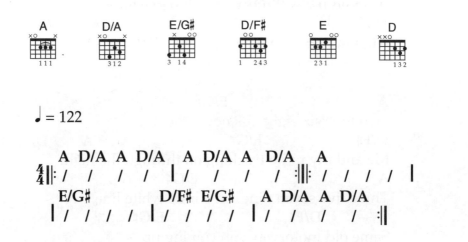

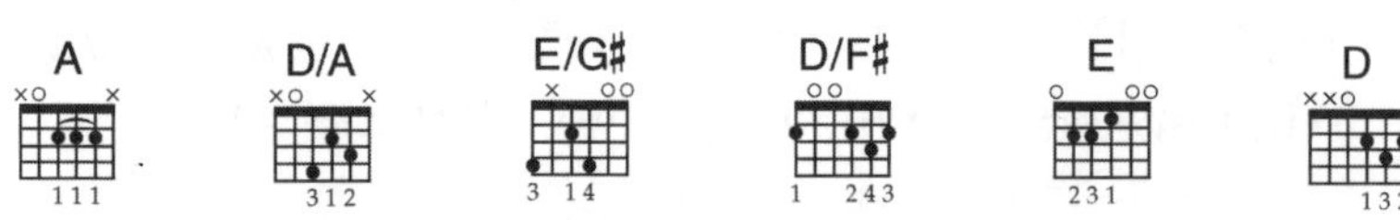

♩ = 122

Intro

```
   A D/A  A D/A    A D/A  A  D/A     A
4/4 ||: /   /    /   /  | /   /    /    /  :||: /  /  /  /  |

   E/G♯            D/F♯ E/G♯      A D/A A D/A
| /  /  /  /  | /   /   /   /  | /  /   /   /  :||
```

Verse 1

```
A                                         E/G♯
Drive my truck midway to the motorway station,
D/F♯                     E
Fair-lane cruiser coming up
                 A     D/A  A  D/A
On the left-hand side.
                                       E/G♯
Headlights shining, driving rain on the window frame,
D/F♯              E                  A     D/A  A
Little young lady stardust hitching a ride.
```

Chorus

```
     D/A  A                        E/G♯
And it's   two four six eight, it's never too late,
D/F♯              E/G♯                    A     D/A  A  D/A
Me and my radio trucking on through the night.
A                         E/G♯
Three five seven nine  on a little white line,
D/F♯                   E/G♯
Motorway sun coming up
                   A     D/A  A  D/A
With the morning light.
```

Verse 2

```
A                                             E/G♯
Whizz-kid sitting pretty on your two-wheel stallion,
D/F♯                E                  A     D/A  A  D/A
This old ten-ton lorry got a bead on you.
A                                              E/G♯
Ain't no use setting off with a bad companion.
D/F♯                      E                   A     D/A  A  D/A
Ain't nobody got the better of you know who.
```

Chorus 2

```
A                            E/G♯
Two four six eight, it's never too late,
D/F♯                  E/G♯                      A       D/A  A  D/A
Me and my radio trucking on through the night.
A                                 E/G♯
Three five seven nine  on a little white line,
            D/F♯                        E/G♯
Same old motorway sun coming up
                        A       D/A  A  D/A
With the morning light.
```

Guitar solo

```
  A                E/G♯              D/F♯   E       A
||: /  /  /  /  | /  /  /  /  | /  /  /  /  | /  /  /  / :||
```

Verse 3

```
A                                             E/G♯
Well, there ain't no route you can choose to lose the two of us,
D/F♯                E                  A
Ain't nobody know when you're acting right or wrong.
A                                             E/G♯
No-one knows if a roadway's leading nowhere.
D/F♯                      E                   A  D/A  A
Gonna keep on driving on the road I'm on.
```

Chorus 3

```
       D/A  A                    E/G♯
And it's    two four six eight, it's never too late,
D/F♯                 E/G♯                     A       D/A  A  D/A
Me and my radio trucking on through the night.
A                                E/G♯
Three five seven nine  on a little white line,
D/F♯                     E/G♯
Motorway sun coming up
                      A       D/A  A  D/A
With the morning light.
```

Chorus 4

```
A                          E/G♯
Two four six eight, it's never too late,
D/F♯                 E/G♯                     A     D/A  A  D/A
Me and my radio trucking on through the night.
A                                E/G♯
Three five seven nine  on a little white line,
         D/F♯                    E/G♯
Same old motorway sun coming up
                      A       D/A  A  D/A
With the morning light.
                         E                  A
Motorway sun coming up with the morning light.
                                    E                   D
That same old motorway sun coming up with the morning light.
```

Guitar solo

```
  A           E/G♯           D/F♯  E    [1. A
|:/  /  /  /  |/  /  /  /  |/  /  /  /  |/  /  /  /  :|

[2.
 A
 Yeah, yeah, yeah, said it's
```

Chorus 5

```
A                                   E/G♯
Two four six eight, it's never too late,
D/F♯                E/G♯                    A      D/A  A  D/A
Me and my radio trucking on through the night.
A                                   E/G♯
Three five seven nine  on a little white line,
        D/F♯                         E/G♯
Same old motorway sun coming up
                    A      D/A  A  D/A
With the morning light.
```

repeat Chorus to fade

Take It Easy

Words and Music by
GLENN FREY AND JACKSON BROWNE

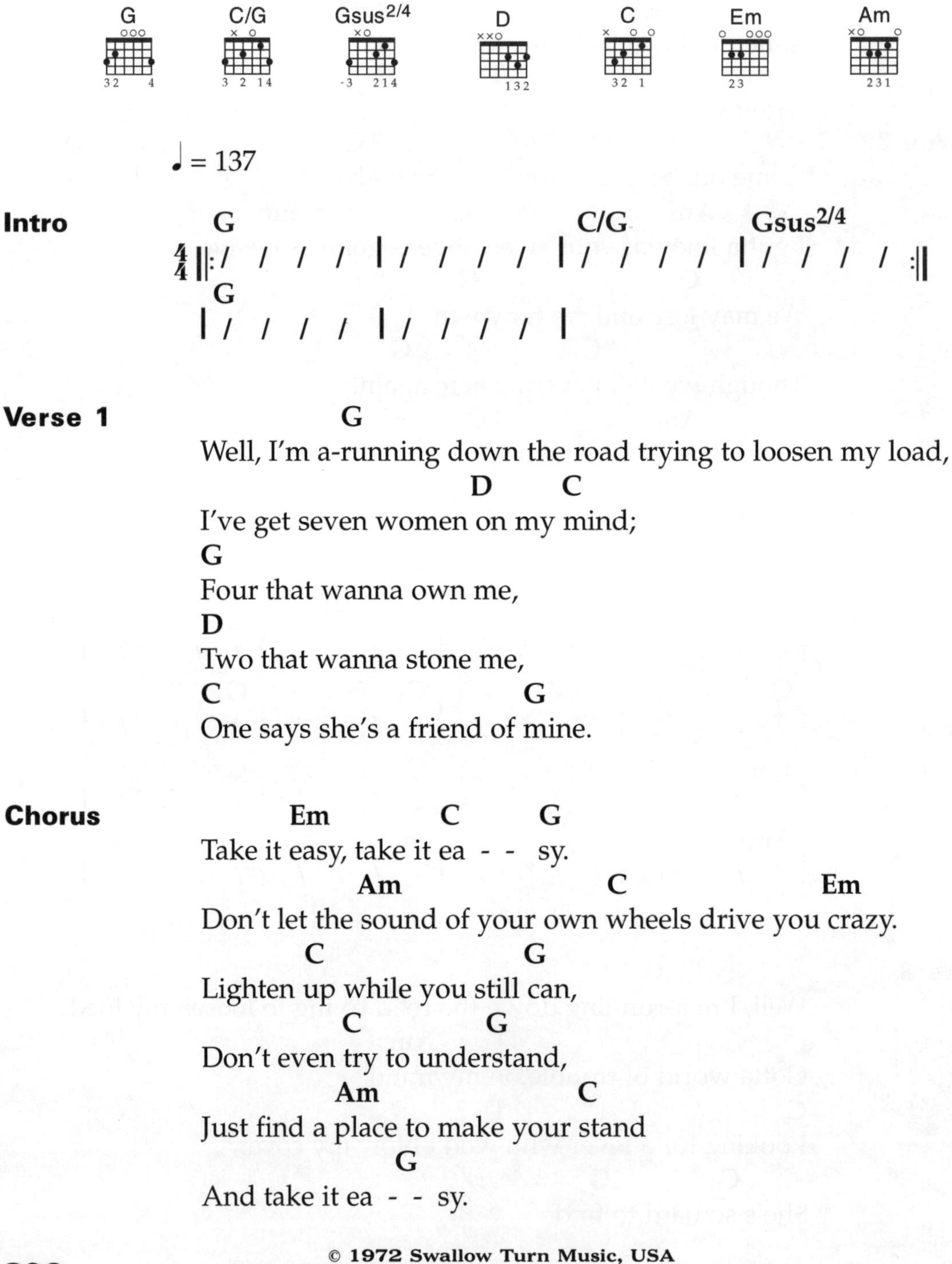

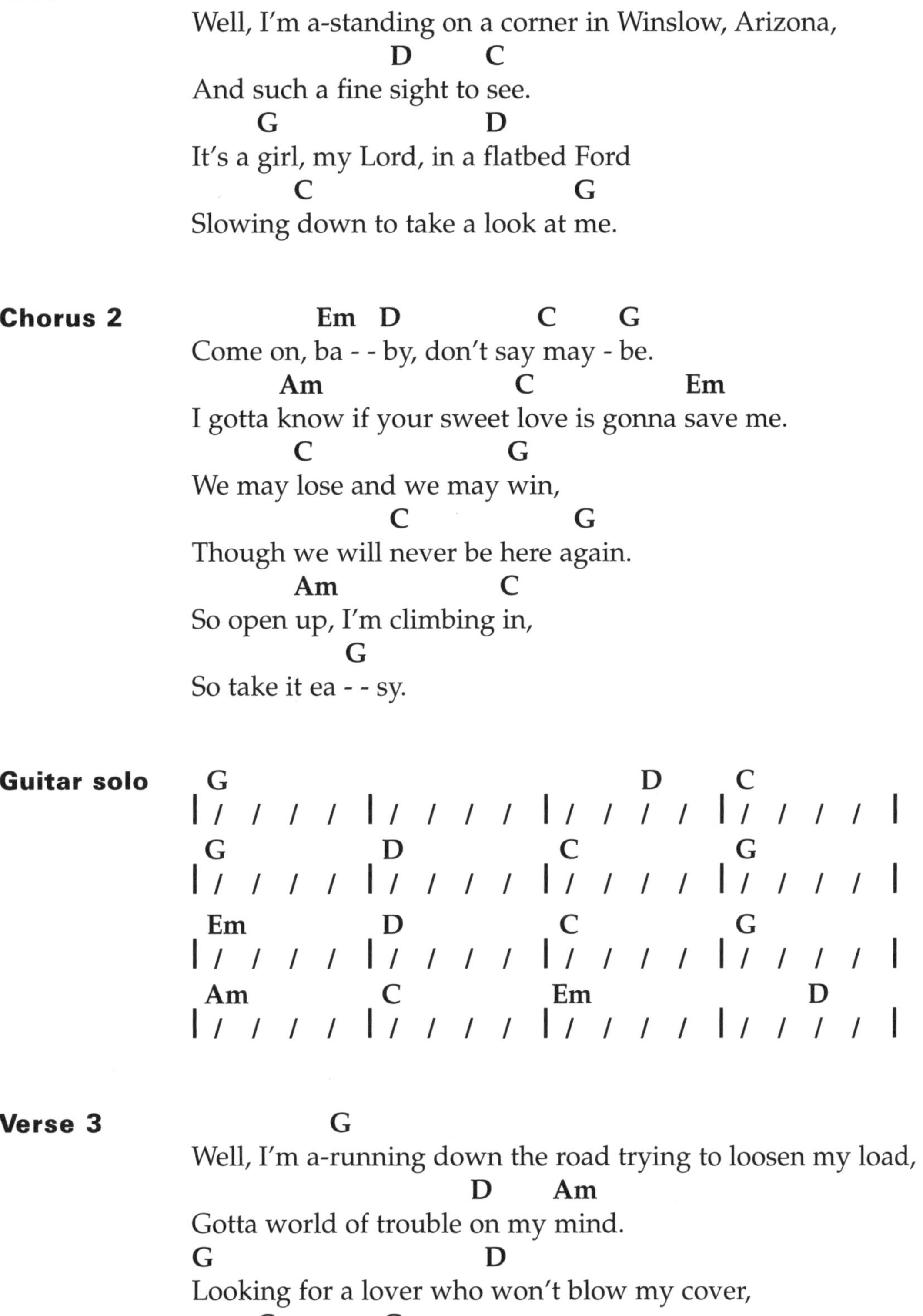

Verse 2

```
                G
Well, I'm a-standing on a corner in Winslow, Arizona,
                     D      C
And such a fine sight to see.
      G                     D
It's a girl, my Lord, in a flatbed Ford
         C                       G
Slowing down to take a look at me.
```

Chorus 2

```
            Em  D           C     G
Come on, ba - - by, don't say may - be.
        Am                C               Em
I gotta know if your sweet love is gonna save me.
         C                 G
We may lose and we may win,
                  C           G
Though we will never be here again.
          Am              C
So open up, I'm climbing in,
              G
So take it ea - - sy.
```

Guitar solo

```
 G                                   D       C
| /  /  /  /  | /  /  /  /  | /  /  /  /  | /  /  /  /  |
 G              D              C              G
| /  /  /  /  | /  /  /  /  | /  /  /  /  | /  /  /  /  |
 Em             D              C              G
| /  /  /  /  | /  /  /  /  | /  /  /  /  | /  /  /  /  |
 Am             C              Em                   D
| /  /  /  /  | /  /  /  /  | /  /  /  /  | /  /  /  /  |
```

Verse 3

```
                G
Well, I'm a-running down the road trying to loosen my load,
                            D     Am
Gotta world of trouble on my mind.
G                         D
Looking for a lover who won't blow my cover,
     C         G
She's so hard to find.
```

Chorus 3

```
           Em          C       G
Take it easy, take it ea  - -  sy.
                Am                     C                 Em
Don't let the sound of your own wheels make you crazy.
          C   G              C    G
Come on, ba - by, don't say may - be.
        Am                      C              G    N.C.
I gotta know if your sweet love is gonna save me.
```

Coda

```
C          G
Ooh, ooh, ooh, ooh.
C          G
Ooh, ooh, ooh, ooh.
C                          G  Gsus2/4 C
Ooh, ooh, oh, we got it ea  - - - -  sy.
                       G  Gsus2/4
We ought to take it ea  - - - -
 C                                  Em
| / / / / | / / / / | /  ||
(-sy.)
```

Tin Soldier

Words and Music by
STEVE MARRIOTT AND RONNIE LANE

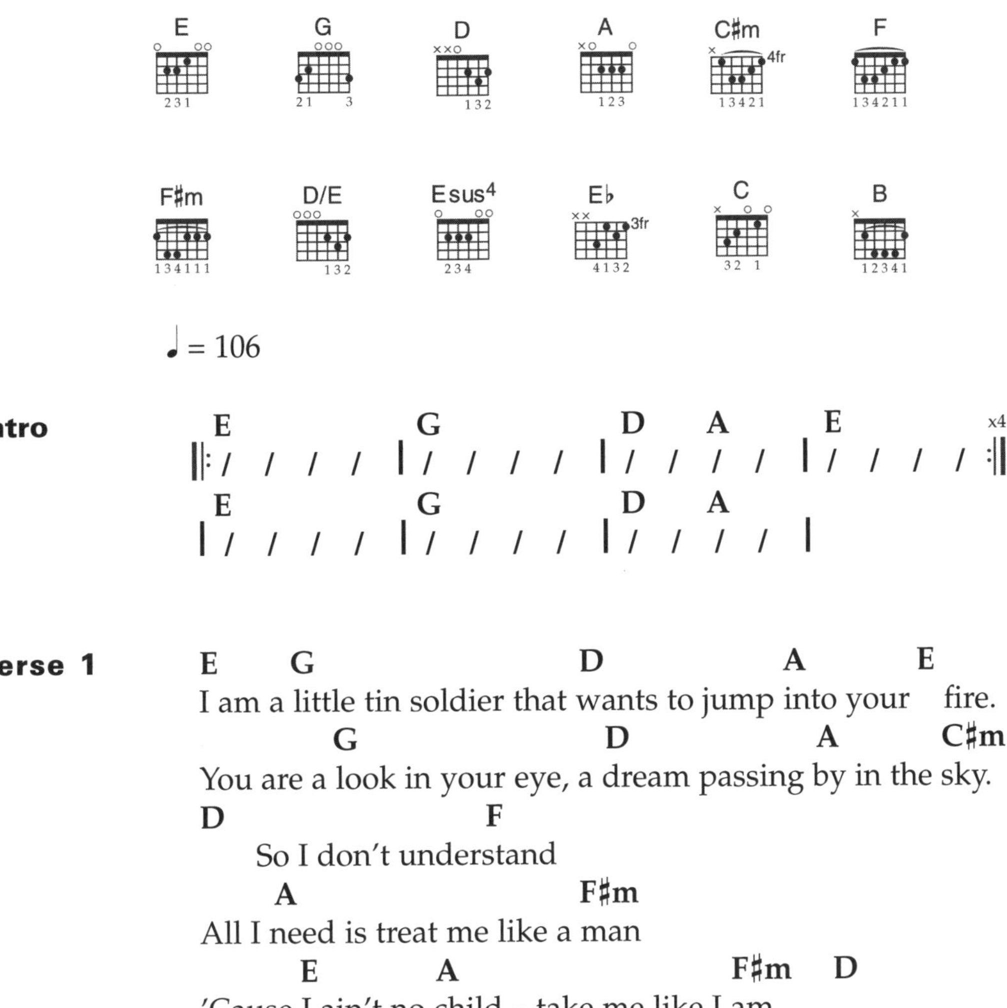

Chorus

E D/E Esus4 E
I gotta know I belong to you,
D/E Esus4 E
Do anything that you want me to
D/E Esus4 E
Sing any song that you want me to
E♭ D C B
Sing to you. | / / / / |

Link

E G A G E G A G
| / / / / | / / / / | / / / / | / / / / ‖

Verse 2

E G A G E G A G
I don't need no aggravation___
E G A G
I just got to make you – I said, listen,
E G A G (E)
I just got to make you my occup(ation).

Chorus 2

E D/E Esus4 E
I gotta know I belong to you,
D/E Esus4 E
Do anything that you want me to
D/E Esus4 E
Sing any song that you want me to
E♭ D C B
Sing to you. | / / / / |

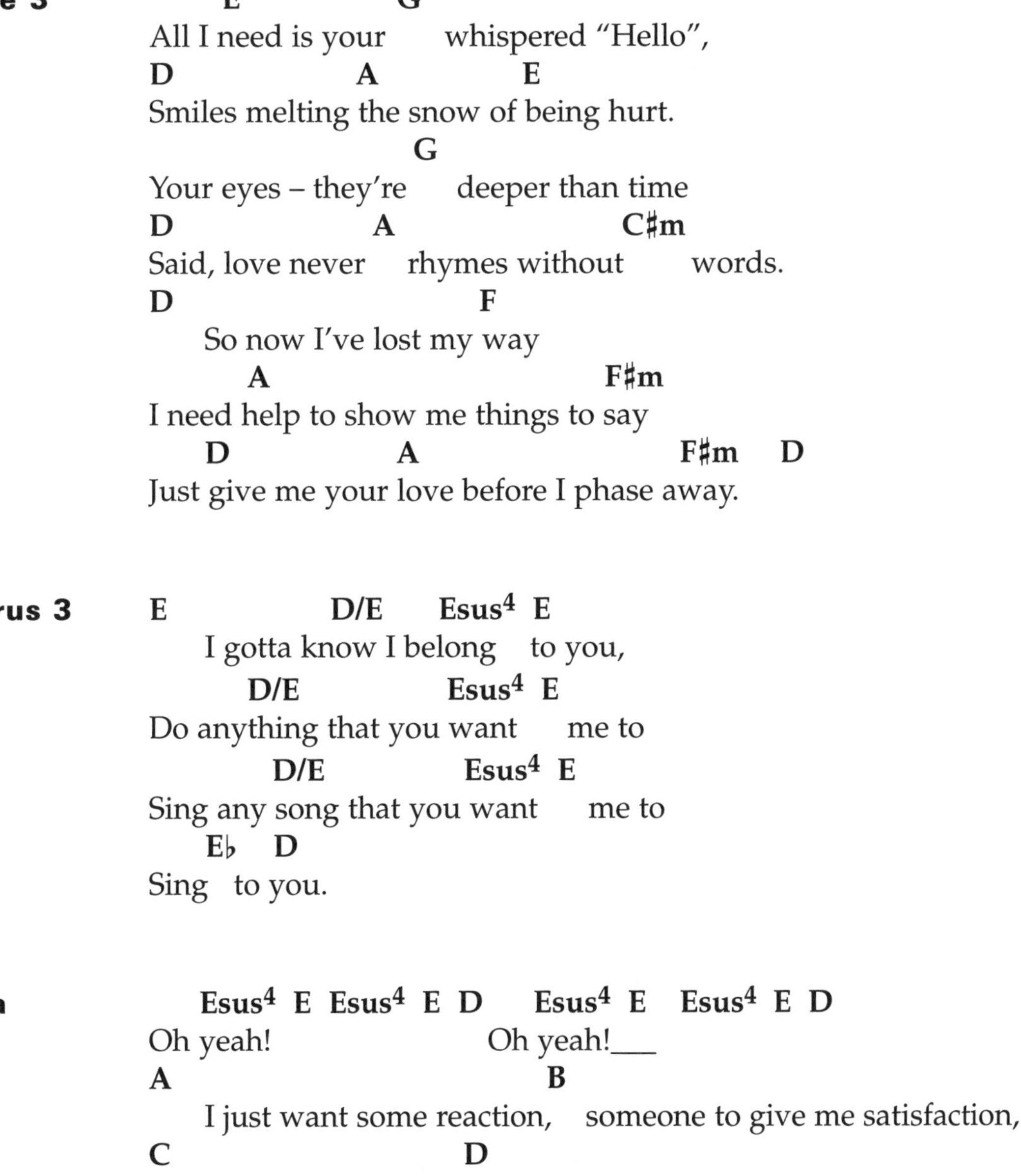

Verse 3

```
      E             G
All I need is your     whispered "Hello",
D                A            E
Smiles melting the snow of being hurt.
                      G
Your eyes – they're     deeper than time
D                  A                   C♯m
Said, love never    rhymes without       words.
D                          F
    So now I've lost my way
        A                          F♯m
I need help to show me things to say
    D              A                 F♯m    D
Just give me your love before I phase away.
```

Chorus 3

```
E              D/E       Esus⁴  E
    I gotta know I belong    to you,
        D/E             Esus⁴  E
Do anything that you want      me to
          D/E              Esus⁴  E
Sing any song that you want      me to
    E♭   D
Sing   to you.
```

Coda

```
    Esus⁴  E  Esus⁴  E  D     Esus⁴  E   Esus⁴  E  D
Oh yeah!                   Oh yeah!___
A                              B
    I just want some reaction,    someone to give me satisfaction,
C                         D
    All I want to do is sit with you
        Esus⁴  E
'Cause I love_____  you.
```

Tired Of Waiting

Words and Music by
RAYMOND DAVIES

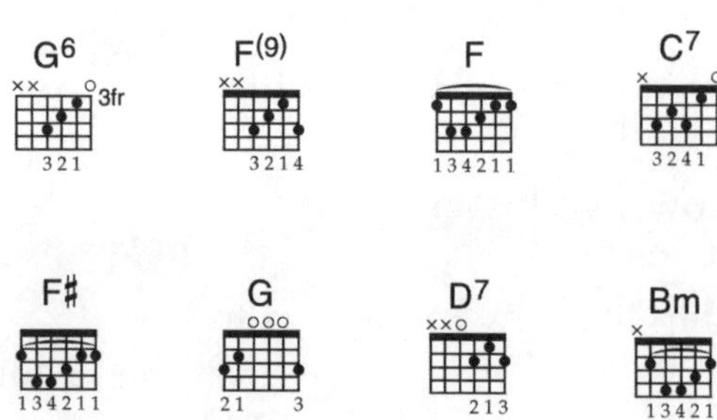

♩ = 120

Intro

G6 F(9) G6 F(9)
4/4 ||: / / / / | / / / / :||

Chorus

G6 F(9) G6 F(9)
So tired, tired of wait - ing,
G6 F(9) G6 F(9) G6 F(9)
Tired of waiting for you.________
G6 F(9) G6 F(9)
So tired, tired of wait - ing,
G6 F(9) G6 F(9) G6 F(9)
Tired of waiting for you.________

Verse 1

F C7 F C7 F C7 F
I was a lonely soul, I had nobody till I met you.
F# G D7 G D7 G D7 G D7
But you keep-a me waiting all of the time, what can I do?

Bridge 1

G Bm F D7
It's your life and you can do what you want.
G Bm F D7
Do what you like but please don't keep-a me waiting,
F D7
Please don't keep-a me waiting.

Chorus 2

G^6 $F^{(9)}$ G^6 $F^{(9)}$
So tired, tired of wait - ing,
G^6 $F^{(9)}$ G^6 $F^{(9)}$ G^6 $F^{(9)}$
Tired of waiting for you.________
G^6 $F^{(9)}$ G^6 $F^{(9)}$
So tired, tired of wait - ing,
G^6 $F^{(9)}$ G^6 $F^{(9)}$ G^6 $F^{(9)}$
Tired of waiting for you.________

Verse 2

F C^7 F C^7 F C^7 F
I was a lonely soul, I had nobody till I met you.
F♯ G D^7 G D^7 G D^7 G
But you keep-a me waiting all of the time, what can I do?

Bridge 2

G Bm F D^7
It's your life and you can do what you want.
G Bm F D^7
Do what you like but please don't keep-a me waiting,
F D^7
Please don't keep-a me waiting.

Chorus 3

G^6 $F^{(9)}$
'Cause I'm so tired, tired of waiting,
G^6 $F^{(9)}$ G^6 $F^{(9)}$ G^6 $F^{(9)}$
Tired of waiting for you.________
G^6 $F^{(9)}$ G^6 $F^{(9)}$
So tired, tired of wait - ing,
G^6 $F^{(9)}$ G^6 $F^{(9)}$ G^6 $F^{(9)}$
Tired of waiting for you.________
G^6 $F^{(9)}$ G^6 $F^{(9)}$
For you,__________
G^6 $F^{(9)}$ G^6 $F^{(9)}$ G ‖
For you.________

The Whole Of The Moon

Words and Music by
MICHAEL SCOTT

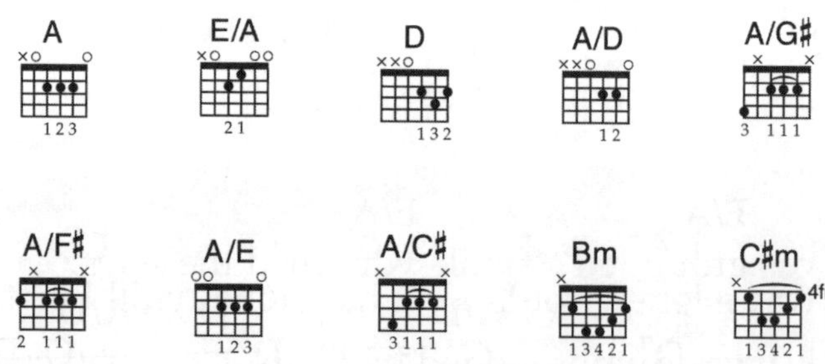

Capo 3rd fret

♩ = 102

Intro

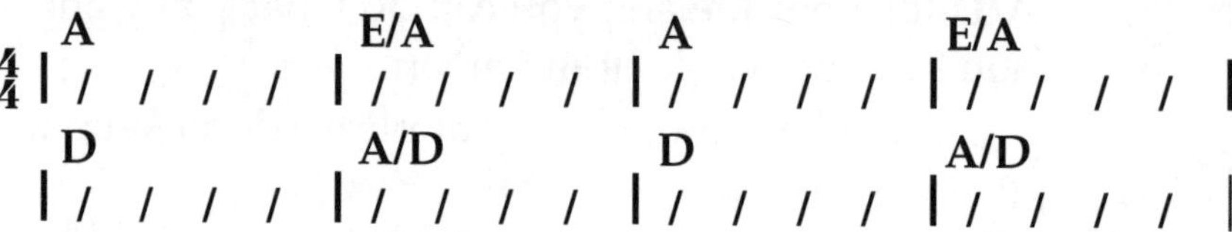

Verse 1

```
A                         E/A         A          E/A
      I pictured a rainbow,           you held it in your hands;
D            A/D         D        A/D
      I had flashes            but you saw the plan.
A                              E/A
I wandered out in the world for years
A            E/A                          D
      While you just stayed in your room.
                   A/D    D     A/D                              A        E/A
I saw the crescent,            you saw the whole of the moon.
                         D          A/D
The whole of the moon.
```

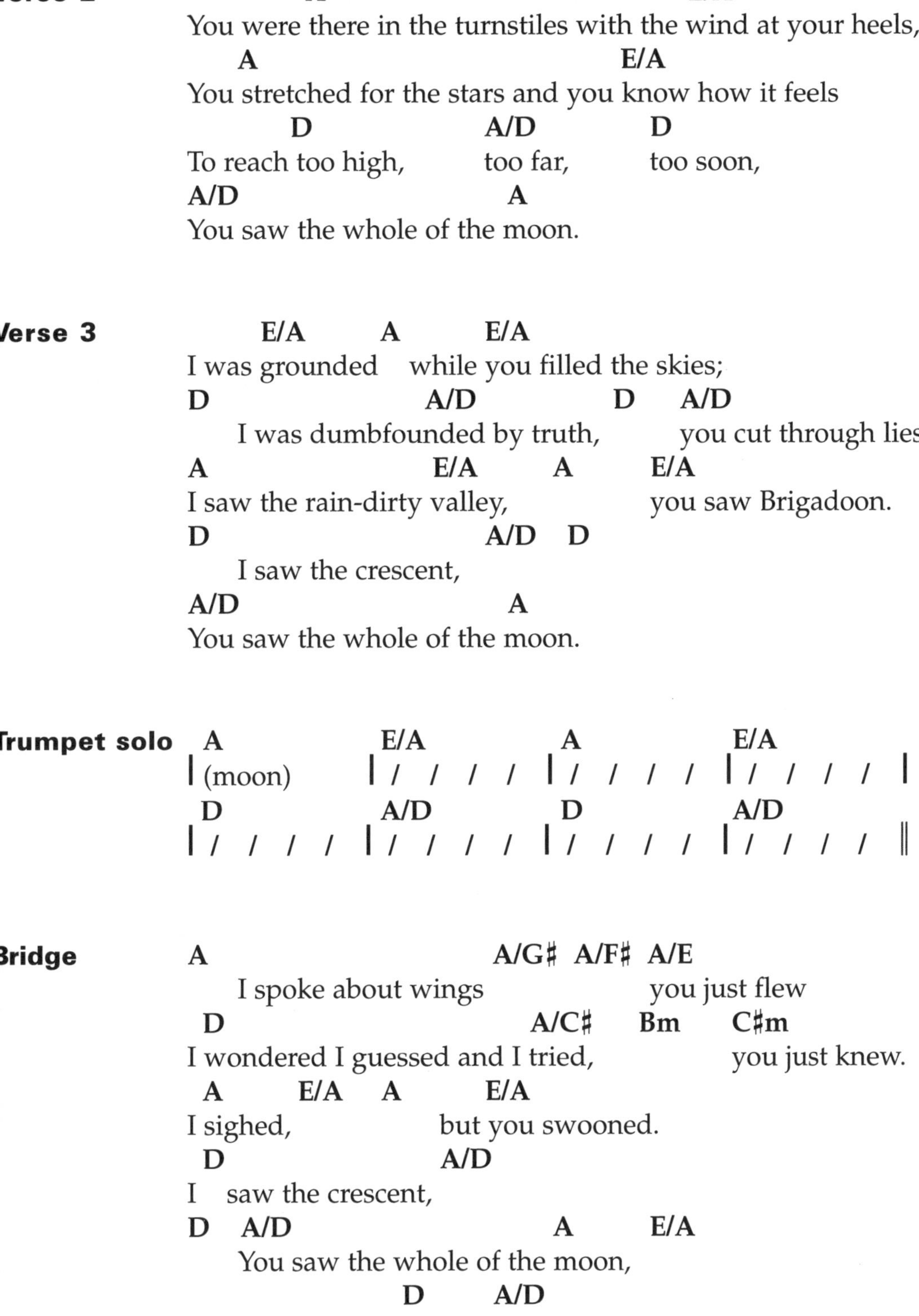

```
Verse 2          A                                   E/A
            You were there in the turnstiles with the wind at your heels,
                A                                E/A
            You stretched for the stars and you know how it feels
                   D                  A/D           D
            To reach too high,        too far,      too soon,
            A/D                        A
            You saw the whole of the moon.


Verse 3           E/A       A        E/A
            I was grounded    while you filled the skies;
            D                    A/D             D    A/D
                I was dumbfounded by truth,           you cut through lies.
            A                    E/A      A       E/A
            I saw the rain-dirty valley,          you saw Brigadoon.
            D                        A/D  D
                I saw the crescent,
            A/D                        A
            You saw the whole of the moon.


Trumpet solo  A              E/A            A              E/A
            | (moon)        | / / / /      | / / / /      | / / / /  |
              D              A/D            D              A/D
            | / / / /       | / / / /      | / / / /      | / / / /  ||


Bridge      A                          A/G♯  A/F♯  A/E
                I spoke about wings                  you just flew
              D                          A/C♯    Bm     C♯m
            I wondered I guessed and I tried,            you just knew.
              A      E/A    A      E/A
            I sighed,            but you swooned.
              D                  A/D
            I   saw the crescent,
            D   A/D                      A       E/A
                You saw the whole of the moon,
                          D      A/D
            The whole of the moon.
```

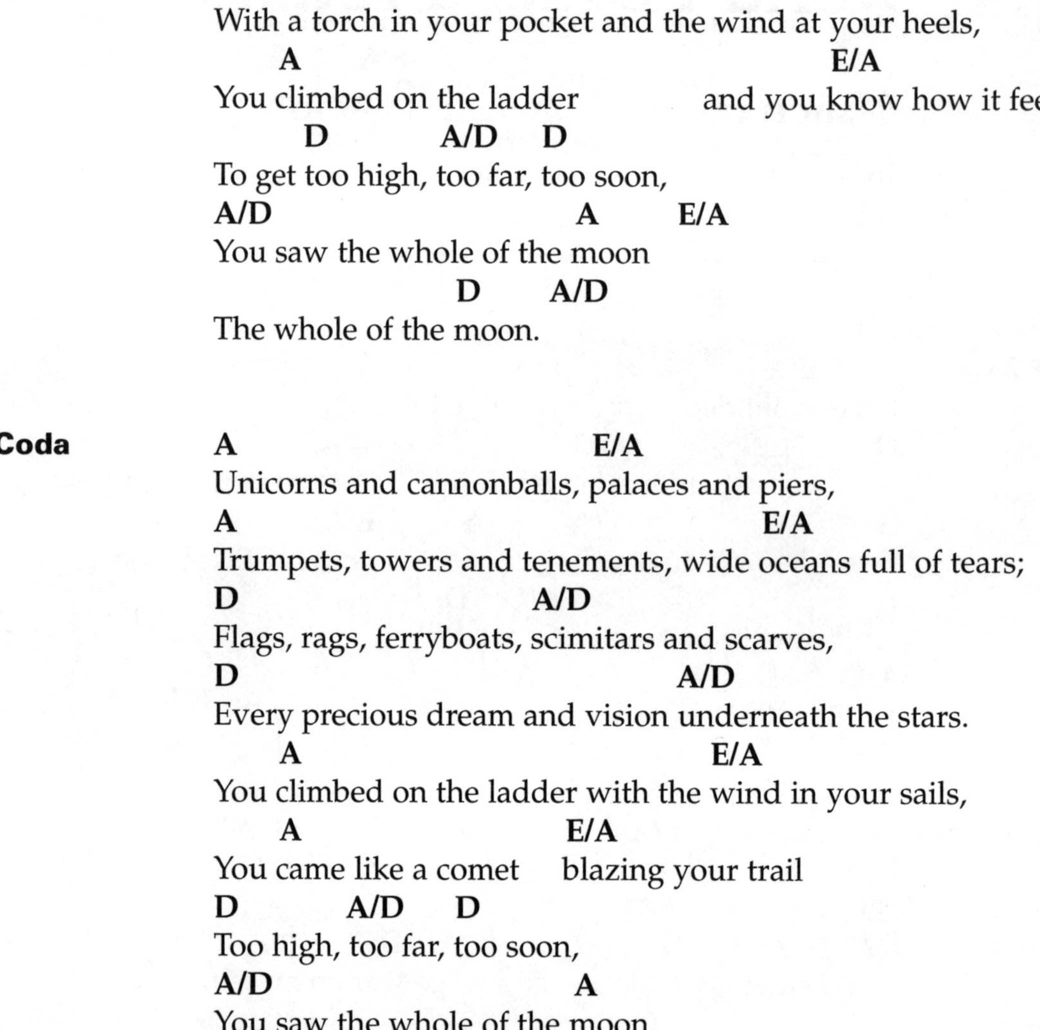

Verse 5

A E/A
With a torch in your pocket and the wind at your heels,
A E/A
You climbed on the ladder and you know how it feels
D A/D D
To get too high, too far, too soon,
A/D A E/A
You saw the whole of the moon
D A/D
The whole of the moon.

Coda

A E/A
Unicorns and cannonballs, palaces and piers,
A E/A
Trumpets, towers and tenements, wide oceans full of tears;
D A/D
Flags, rags, ferryboats, scimitars and scarves,
D A/D
Every precious dream and vision underneath the stars.
A E/A
You climbed on the ladder with the wind in your sails,
A E/A
You came like a comet blazing your trail
D A/D D
Too high, too far, too soon,
A/D A
You saw the whole of the moon.

A E/A A E/A x5
||: (moon) | / / / / | / / / / | / / / / :||
A E/A A A
| / / / / | / / / / | / / / / | / ||

World Leader Pretend

Words and Music by
MICHAEL MILLS, WILLIAM BERRY,
PETER BUCK AND MICHAEL STIPE

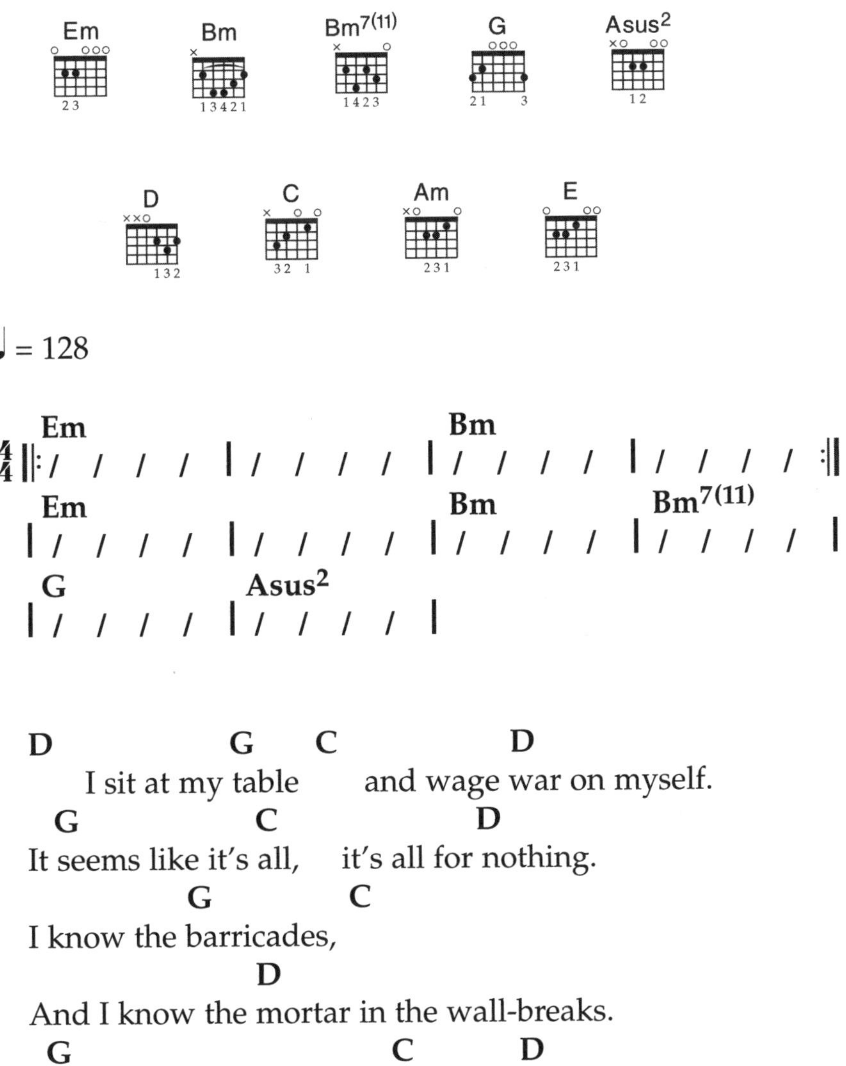

Intro

```
     Em                                  Bm
4/4 ||: / / / / | / / / / | / / / / | / / / / :||
     Em                    Bm          Bm7(11)
    | / / / / | / / / / | / / / / | / / / / |
     G          Asus2
    | / / / / | / / / / |
```

Verse 1

```
D                 G      C                 D
      I sit at my table       and wage war on myself.
  G                C                D
It seems like it's all,     it's all for nothing.
             G             C
I know the barricades,
                       D
And I know the mortar in the wall-breaks.
  G                              C          D
I recognize the weapons,           I've used them well.
```

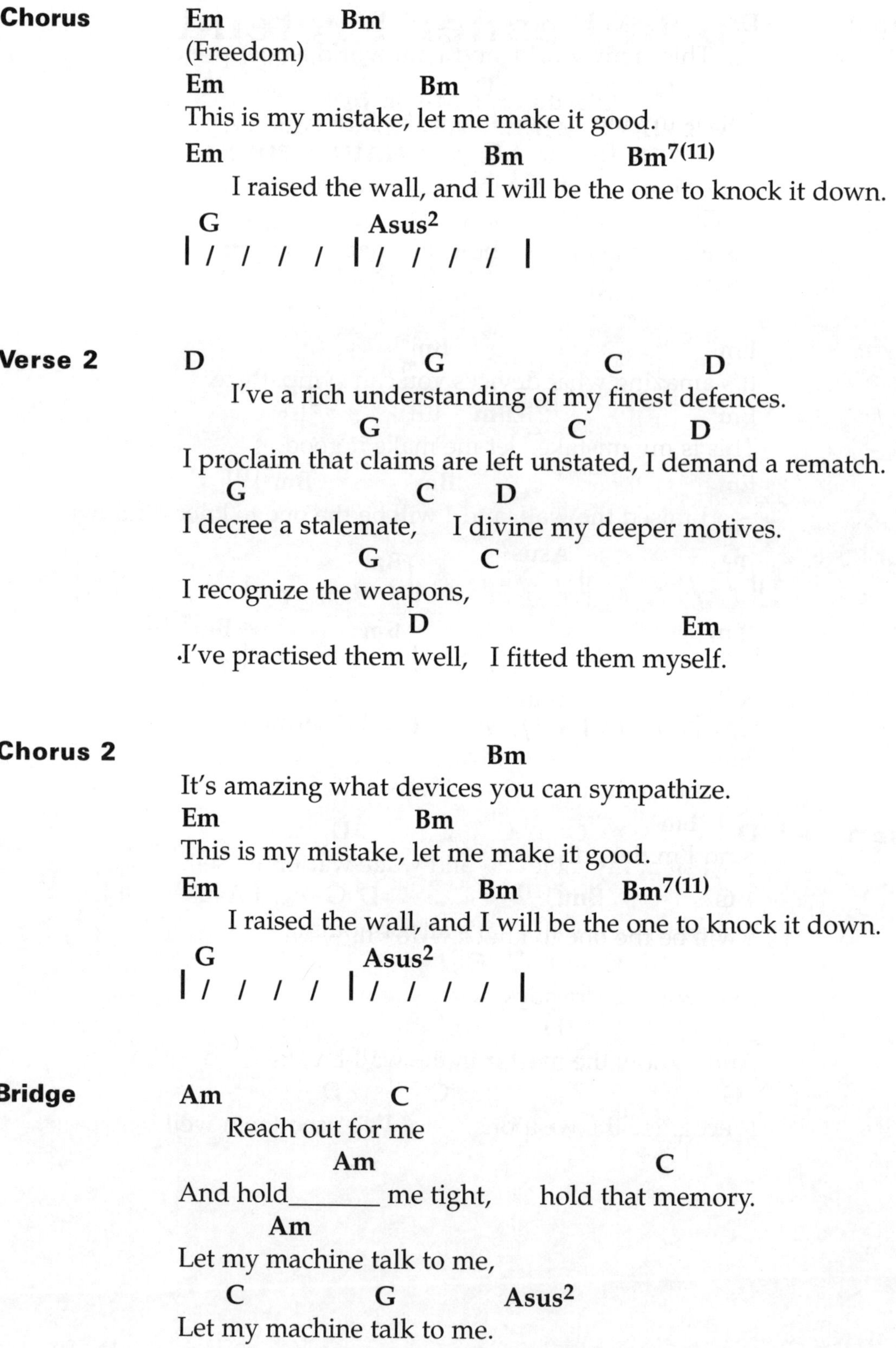

Chorus

Em Bm
(Freedom)
Em Bm
This is my mistake, let me make it good.
Em Bm Bm$^{7(11)}$
I raised the wall, and I will be the one to knock it down.
G Asus^2
| / / / / | / / / / |

Verse 2

D G C D
I've a rich understanding of my finest defences.
G C D
I proclaim that claims are left unstated, I demand a rematch.
G C D
I decree a stalemate, I divine my deeper motives.
G C
I recognize the weapons,
D Em
I've practised them well, I fitted them myself.

Chorus 2

Bm
It's amazing what devices you can sympathize.
Em Bm
This is my mistake, let me make it good.
Em Bm Bm$^{7(11)}$
I raised the wall, and I will be the one to knock it down.
G Asus^2
| / / / / | / / / / |

Bridge

Am C
Reach out for me
Am C
And hold_______ me tight, hold that memory.
Am
Let my machine talk to me,
C G Asus^2
Let my machine talk to me.

Verse 3

D G C D
This is my world, and I am world leader pretend.
G C D
This is my life and this is my time.
G C D
I have been given the freedom to do as I see fit.
G C D
It's high time I razed the walls that I've constructed.

Chorus 3

Em Bm
It's amazing what devices you can sympathize.
Em Bm
This is my mistake, let me make it good.
Em Bm Bm$^{7(11)}$
I raised the wall, and I will be the one to knock it down.
G Asus^2
| / / / / | / / / / |

Chorus 4

Em Bm
You fill in the mortar, you fill in the harmony.
Em Bm
You fill in the mortar. I raised the wall
Em
And I'm the only one,
Bm Bm$^{7(11)}$ G | Asus^2 | E ||
I will be the one to knock it down.___

Will You Love Me Tomorrow?

Words and Music by
GERRY GOFFIN AND CAROLE KING

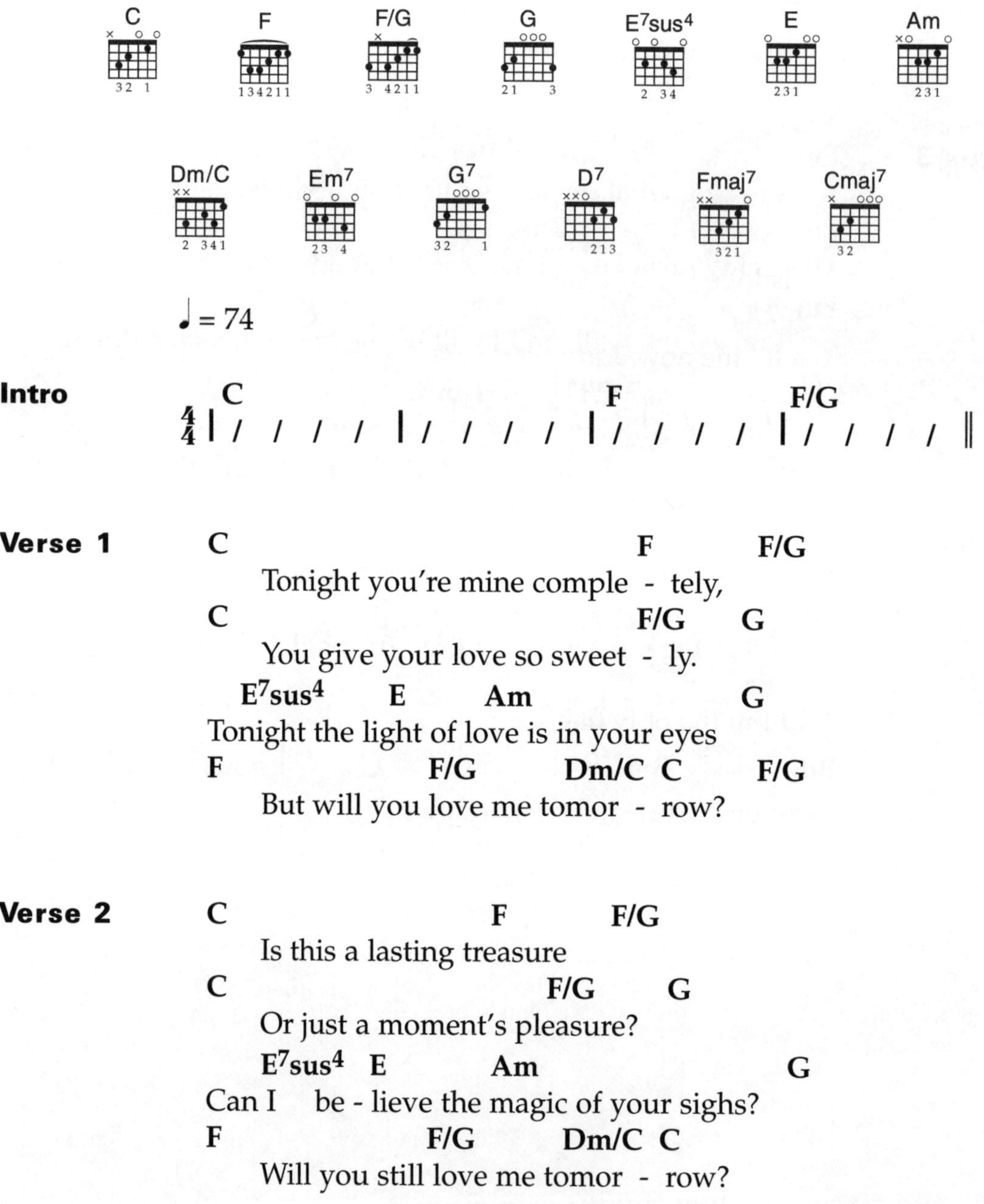

Intro

C | F | F/G

4/4 | / / / / | / / / / | / / / / | / / / / ||

Verse 1

C F F/G
Tonight you're mine comple - tely,
C F/G G
You give your love so sweet - ly.
E7sus4 E Am G
Tonight the light of love is in your eyes
F F/G Dm/C C F/G
But will you love me tomor - row?

Verse 2

C F F/G
Is this a lasting treasure
C F/G G
Or just a moment's pleasure?
E7sus4 E Am G
Can I be - lieve the magic of your sighs?
F F/G Dm/C C
Will you still love me tomor - row?

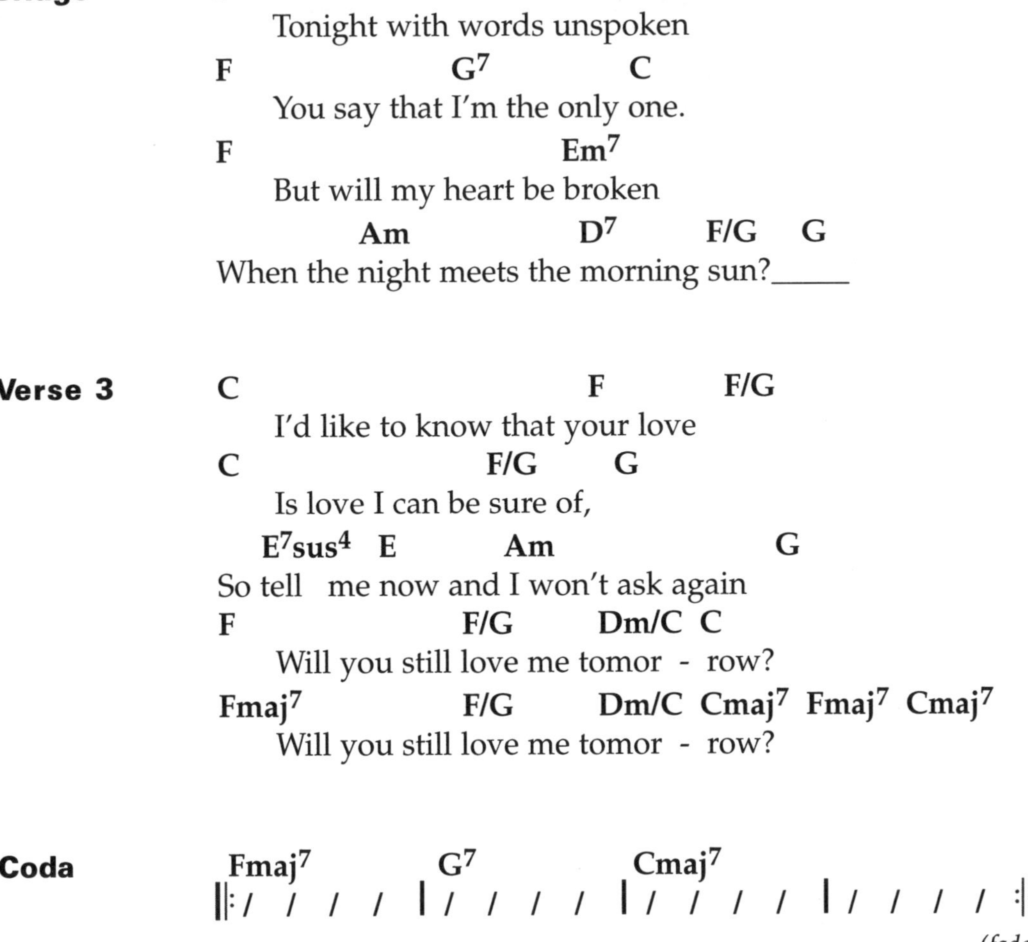

Bridge

F Em7
Tonight with words unspoken
F G7 C
You say that I'm the only one.
F Em7
But will my heart be broken
Am D7 F/G G
When the night meets the morning sun?_____

Verse 3

C F F/G
I'd like to know that your love
C F/G G
Is love I can be sure of,
E7sus4 E Am G
So tell me now and I won't ask again
F F/G Dm/C C
Will you still love me tomor - row?
Fmaj7 F/G Dm/C Cmaj7 Fmaj7 Cmaj7
Will you still love me tomor - row?

Coda

Fmaj7 G7 Cmaj7
𝄆 / / / / | / / / / | / / / / | / / / / 𝄇
(fade)

Wish You Were Here

Words and Music by
GEORGE ROGER WATERS AND DAVID GILMOUR

Em7 G A7sus4 C D/F♯ Am

♩ = 60

Intro

Em7	G	Em7	G
4/4 ‖: / / / /	/ / / /	/ / / /	/ / / /
Em7	**A7sus4**	**Em7**	**A7sus4**
/ / / /	/ / / /	/ / / /	/ / / /
1. **G**		2. **G**	
/ / / /	/ / / / :‖	/ / / /	

Verse 1

C D/F♯
So, so you think you can tell_____
Am G
Heaven from Hell, blue skies from pain?
D/F♯ C
Can you tell a green field from a cold steel rail?
Am G
A smile from a veil? Do you think you can tell?

Verse 2

C D/F♯
And did they get you to trade your heroes for ghosts?
Am G
Hot ashes for trees? Hot air for a cool breeze?
D C
Cold comfort for change? And did you exchange
Am G
A walk on part in the war for a lead role in a cage?

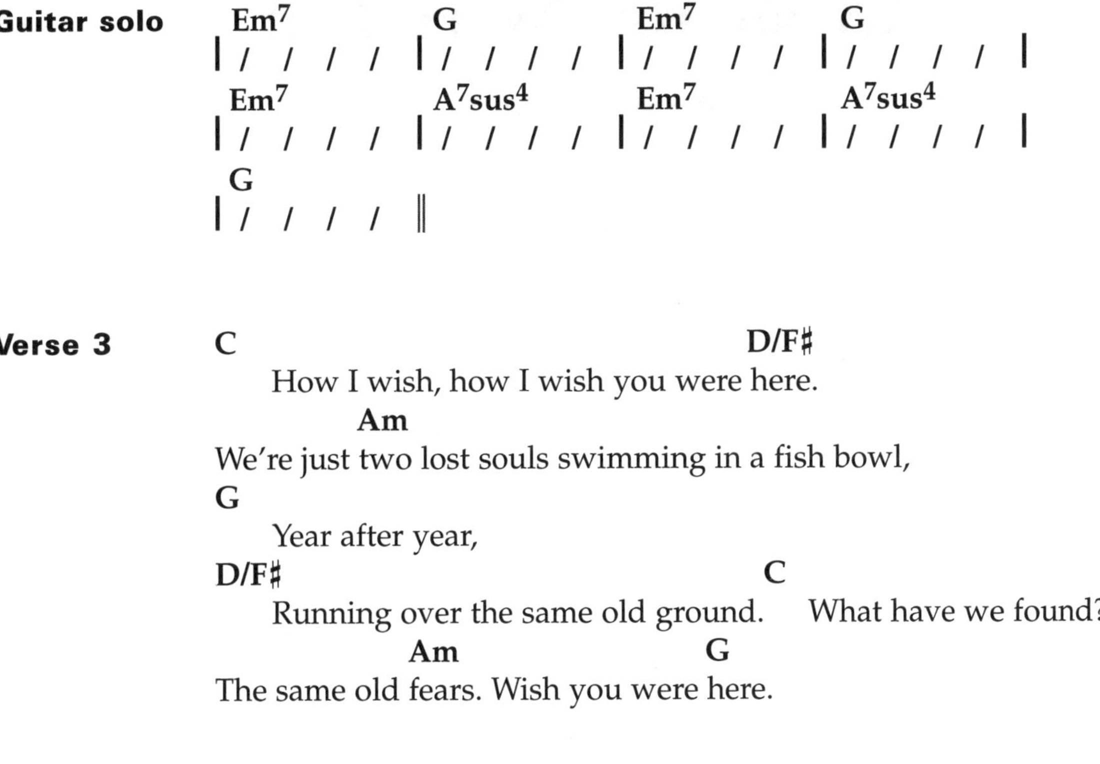

Guitar solo

```
 Em7            G              Em7            G
| /  /  /  /  | /  /  /  /  | /  /  /  /  | /  /  /  /  |
 Em7            A7sus4         Em7            A7sus4
| /  /  /  /  | /  /  /  /  | /  /  /  /  | /  /  /  /  |
 G
| /  /  /  /  ||
```

Verse 3

```
C                                         D/F♯
     How I wish, how I wish you were here.
            Am
We're just two lost souls swimming in a fish bowl,
G
     Year after year,
D/F♯                                        C
     Running over the same old ground.     What have we found?
                 Am                      G
The same old fears. Wish you were here.
```

Coda

```
  Em7            G              Em7            G
||: /  /  /  /  | /  /  /  /  | /  /  /  /  | /  /  /  /  |
 Em7            A7sus4         Em7            A7sus4
| /  /  /  /  | /  /  /  /  | /  /  /  /  | /  /  /  /  |
 G
| /  /  /  /  | /  /  /  /  :||  repeat to fade
```

Songs guitars were meant to play

Essential Acoustic Playlist 2

9854A VC ISBN: 1-84328-411-1

A Minha Meninha (The Bees) – Ain't That Enough (Teenage Fanclub) – All Together Now (The Farm) – Alright (Supergrass) – Am I Wrong (Mull Historical Society) – American English (Idlewild) – Average Man (Turin Brakes) – Beetlebum (Blur) – Breakfast at Tiffany's (Deep Blue Something) – Buy It In Bottles (Richard Ashcroft) – Can You Dig It? (The Mock Turtles) – Caught By The River (Doves) – Coffee & TV (Blur) – Come Away With Me (Norah Jones) – Come Back To What You Know (Embrace) – Common People (Pulp) – Crazy Beat (Blur) – Creep (Radiohead) – A Design For Life (Manic Street Preachers) – Distant Sun (Crowded House) – Don't Let Me Down Gently (The Wonderstuff) – Don't Think You're The First (The Coral) – Everlong (Foo Fighters) – Fallen Angel (Elbow) – Fastboy (The Bluetones) – The Final Arrears (Mull Historical Society) – Forget About Tomorrow (Feeder) – Getting Away With It (Electronic) – Go To Sleep (Radiohead) – Grace (Supergrass) – Here's Where The Story Ends (The Sundays) – High And Dry (Radiohead) – History (The Verve) – Hooligan (Embrace) – I Need Direction (Teenage Fanclub) – I Will (Radiohead) – (I'm Gonna) Cry Myself Blind (Primal Scream) – In A Room (Dodgy) – It's True That We Love One Another (The White Stripes) – Just When You're Thinkin' Things Over (The Charlatans) – La Breeze (Simian) – Lilac Wine (Jeff Buckley) – A Little Like You (Grand Drive) – Live In A Hiding Place (Idlewild) – Lucky (Radiohead) – A Man Needs To Be Told (The Charlatans) – No Surprises (Radiohead) – Only Happy When It Rains (Garbage) – Out Of Time (Blur) – Painkiller (Turin Brakes) – Pass It On (The Coral) – Personal Jesus (Johnny Cash) – Pineapple Head (Crowded House) – Poor Misguided Fool (Starsailor) – Road Rage (Catatonia) – Seen The Light (Supergrass) – Seven Nation Army (The White Stripes) – Shine On (The House Of Love) – Silence Is Easy (Starsailor) – Sk8ter Boi (Avril Lavigne) – Stay Away From Me (The Star Spangles) – There There (Radiohead) – Thinking About Tomorrow (Beth Orton) – This Is How It Feels (Inspiral Carpets) – Wake Up Boo! (The Boo Radleys) – Words (Doves) – Yoshimi Battles The Pink Robots (Flaming Lips) – You're So Pretty – We're So Pretty (The Charlatans) – You've Got Her In Your Pocket (The White Stripes)

Essential Acoustic Playlist

9701A VC ISBN: 1-84328-207-0

All The Small Things (Blink 182) – All You Good Good People (Embrace) – Angie (The Rolling Stones) – Any Day Now (Elbow) – Bittersweet Symphony (The Verve) – Buddy (Lemonheads) – Burning Down The House (Talking Heads) – Central Reservation (Beth Orton) – Come Together (Primal Scream) – Cryin' (Aerosmith) – Don't Dream It's Over (Crowded House) – The Drugs Don't Work (The Verve) – Empty At The End (Electric Soft Parade) – Everybody Hurts (R.E.M.) – Everyday Is Like Sunday (Morrissey) – Fast Car (Tracey Chapman) – Fat Lip (Sum 41) – Fell In Love With A Girl (The White Stripes) – Fireworks (Embrace) – Fly Away (Lenny Kravitz) – Future Boy (Turin Brakes) – Going Places (Teenage Fanclub) – Good Riddance (Green Day) – Heaven Knows I'm Miserable Now (The Smiths) – Hotel California (The Eagles) – Hotel Yorba (The White Stripes) – Hunter (Dido) – It's A Shame About Ray (Lemonheads) – Karma Police (Radiohead) – Kiss Me (Sixpence None The Richer) – Losing My Religion (R.E.M.) – Love Burns (Black Rebel Motorcycle Club) – The Man Who Told Everything (Doves) – Mansize Rooster (Supergrass) – Mellow Doubt (Teenage Fanclub) – Movin' On Up (Primal Scream) – Moving (Supergrass) – Mr. Jones (Counting Crows) – Next Year (Foo Fighters) – Novocaine For The Soul (Eels) – Over The Rainbow (Eva Cassidy) – Panic (The Smiths) – Porcelain (Moby) – Pounding (Doves) – Powder Blue (Elbow) – Rhythm & Blues Alibi (Gomez) – Save Tonight (Eagle Eye Cherry) – Silent Sigh (Badly Drawn Boy) – Secret Smile (Semisonic) – Shot Shot (Gomez) – Silent To The Dark (Electric Soft Parade) – Slight Return (The Bluetones) – Soak Up The Sun (Sheryl Crow) – Something In My Eye (Ed Harcourt) – Something To Talk About (Badly Drawn Boy) – Song 2 (Blur) – Song For The Lovers (Richard Ashcroft) – Standing Still (Jewel) – Street Spirit (Fade Out) (Radiohead) – Teenage Dirtbag (Wheatus) – Tender (Blur) – There Goes The Fear (Doves) – Time In A Bottle (Jim Croce) – Underdog (Save Me) (Turin Brakes) – Walking After You (Foo Fighters) – Warning (Green Day) – Waterloo Sunset (The Kinks) – Weather With You (Crowded House) – Wicked Game (Chris Isaak) – Wild Wood (Paul Weller)

Classic Acoustic Playlist

9806A VC ISBN: 1-84328-332-8

Ain't No Sunshine (Bill Withers) – All Tomorrow's Parties (The Velvet Underground) – Alone Again Or (Love) – Another Brick In The Wall Part II (Pink Floyd) – Bad Moon Rising (Creedence Clearwater Revival) – Black Magic Woman (Fleetwood Mac) – Both Sides Now (Joni Mitchell) – Brain Damage/Eclipse (Pink Floyd) – Break On Through (The Doors) – California Dreamin' (The Mamas & The Papas) – Cocaine (Eric Clapton) – Cosmic Dancer (T. Rex) – Crazy Little Thing Called Love (Queen) – Daydream Believer (The Monkees) – Days (The Kinks) – Desperado (The Eagles) – Eight Miles High (The Byrds) – Everybody's Talkin' (Harry Nilsson) – Five Years (David Bowie) – For What It's Worth (Buffalo Springfield) – Fortunate Son (Creedence Clearwater Revival) – Get It On (T. Rex) – Handbags & Gladrags (Rod Stewart) – Happy (The Rolling Stones) – He Ain't Heavy, He's My Brother (The Hollies) – Heroin (The Velvet Underground) – A Horse With No Name (America) – I Feel The Earth Move (Carole King) – It's Only Rock And Roll (The Rolling Stones) – It's Too Late (Carole King) – Itchycoo Park (The Small Faces) – Layla (Eric Clapton) – Leaving On A Jet Plane (John Denver) – Life On Mars (David Bowie) – Light My Fire (The Doors) – London Calling (The Clash) – Long Time Gone (Crosby, Stills & Nash) – Long Train Runnin' (The Doobie Brothers) – The Look Of Love (Dusty Springfield) – Lust For Life (Iggy Pop) – Maggie May (Rod Stewart) – Make Me Smile (Come Up And See Me) (Steve Harley & Cockney Rebel) – Miss You (The Rolling Stones) – Moondance (Van Morrison) – More Than A Feeling (Boston) – Mustang Sally (Wilson Pickett) – New Kid In Town (The Eagles) – Oliver's Army (Elvis Costello) – Pale Blue Eyes (The Velvet Underground) – Perfect Day (Lou Reed) – Silence Is Golden (The Tremeloes) – Sloop John B (The Beach Boys) – Smoke On The Water (Deep Purple) – Space Oddity (David Bowie) – Start Me Up (The Rolling Stones) – Strange Kind Of Woman (Deep Purple) – Stuck In The Middle With You (Stealers Wheel) – Summer In The City (Lovin' Spoonful) – Sunny Afternoon (The Kinks) – Suzanne (Leonard Cohen) – Sweet Home Alabama (Lynyrd Skynyrd) – Tempted (The Squeeze) – Tequila Sunrise (The Eagles) – Turn Turn Turn (The Byrds) – Venus In Furs (The Velvet Underground) – We Gotta Get Out Of This Place (The Animals) – Whiter Shade Of Pale (Procol Harum) – Wuthering Heights (Kate Bush) – You're My Best Friend (Queen) - You've Got A Friend (James Taylor)

Essential Acoustic Strumalong

9808A BK/CD ISBN: 1-84328-335-2

All You Good Good People (Embrace) - American English (Idlewild) – The Drugs Don't Work (The Verve) – Grace (Supergrass) – Handbags And Gladrags (Stereophonics) – Hotel Yorba (The White Stripes) – Karma Police (Radiohead) – Love Burns (Black Rebel Motorcycle Club) – Poor Misguided Fool (Starsailor) – Powder Blue (Elbow) – Silent Sigh (Badly Drawn Boy) – Silent To The Dark (The Electric Soft Parade) – Tender (Blur) – There Goes The Fear (Doves) – Underdog (Save Me) (Turin Brakes)

Classic Acoustic Strumalong

9844A BK/CD ISBN: 1-84328-397-2

Alone Again Or (Love) – Another Brick In The Wall Part II (Pink Floyd) – Cocaine (Eric Clapton) – Get It On (T. Rex) – Handbags And Gladrags (Rod Stewart) – London Calling (The Clash) – Lust For Life (Iggy Pop) – Make Me Smile (Come Up And See Me) (Steve Harley & Cockney Rebel) – Mustang Sally (Wilson Pickett) – Perfect Day (Lou Reed) – Start Me Up (The Rolling Stones) – Stuck In The Middle With You (Stealers Wheel) – Sunny Afternoon (The Kinks) – Venus In Furs (Velvet Underground) – Whiter Shade Of Pale (Procol Harum)

Available now in all good music shops